MW00639348

MUSICAL CHAIRS

A True, Forgotten Tale of
Love, Music, and Furniture

By Ruth Anfinson Bures

WAGONBRIDGE PUBLISHING

2024

First edition, paperback
ISBN: 978-1-953444-13-4

*Disclaimer: This is a work of historical fiction. Facts about the lives of real people
and events are presented along with literary embellishments, such as invented
dialogue, fabricated events, and fictionalized scenes. The reader should not
consider this book anything other than a work of literature.*

Wagonbridge Publishing
661 East Howard St.
Winona, MN 55987

FOREWORD

When researching the history of the Winona Municipal Band for its 2015 centennial celebration (1915-2015) I came across a group of very interesting people. The director from 1920 until 1940 was O. W. (Orville) Reese. Reading through articles archived in the Winona Newspaper Database, I discovered information about Orville's wife, Babette Heyer Reese, her sister, Freda Heyer Christensen, and Freda's husband, Walter W. Christensen, all talented musicians. I learned that they had formed a vaudeville act in the early part of the 20th century called *The Musical Reeses* and toured in Canada, the Midwest, and central plains states. In the years before coming to Winona, they lived in Chicago, Illinois and South Bend, Elkhart, and Peru, Indiana. In 1918 they all moved to Winona and bought a furniture store. I was able to make contact with Heyer and Christensen descendants who provided me with information about this group's years before coming to Winona. Their lives took many interesting twists and turns. I hope you enjoy following them.

CHAPTER ONE

THE EARLY YEARS: 1901 – 1910

from the private collection of Sue Thurman

BABETTE HEYER

Oh, Mama, look at this!

Eleven-year-old Betty (Babette) Heyer waved the newspaper in front of her mother's face as they were sitting on the sofa in their Chicago home. It was an early summer afternoon in 1901. Her baby brother, Frederick, was napping, and her sister, Freda, eight, was playing outside in the yard with her five-year-old brother, Herbert.

Susanna Heyer held up a finger in warning. "Just a minute, please. I want to finish the story I'm reading."

Betty hovered nearby, impatiently twisting her curls until her mother put the book down and said, "Now what's this all about?"

"It's an advertisement in the newspaper for the Chicago Musical College. See?" Betty pointed at a place in the corner. "I would so love to study music there. It's where my piano teacher, Miss Clark, was trained. She said it was a wonderful experience. That must be why she is so good."

"Yes," agreed Susanna. "She is a very skilled pianist."

"Remember the recital with Hans Von Schiller's piano performance last year? Miss Clark told us we should go to hear him. I never knew anyone's fingers could move that fast."

Susanna smiled. "I remember. His skill was most impressive." She took the ad Betty waved in front of her and read it more closely. "This school has been around a long time, since 1867. And Dr. Florenz Zeigfeld is still the president."

Betty leaned over her mother's shoulder. "Oh, look here, Mama. Mr. Von Schiller is on the board of directors."

"It certainly has some well-known names associated with it," said Susanna as she looked over the faculty list. "It says it's the only school like it in the country. This is its 36th season. They must be good at what they do. And the building is quite impressive."

© *Minneapolis Journal*

"Oh, my goodness!" Betty said, pointing at the ad. "It looks like a castle."

Susanna read a little more. "They say their courses are based on the system they've developed over 35 years."

Betty twirled away, too excited to sit still. "That must be why they turn out such great musicians."

Susanna read on. "Hmm. Their tuition is low compared to the quality of instruction. I'm sure it would be an inspiring place to study. But even with low tuition how in the world could we afford it?"

Betty perched on the chair next to Susanna and tapped her finger on the ad. "It says right here that they will give 37 free and 150 partial scholarships. They are taking applications for this coming fall. The deadline is August 10."

Susanna nodded thoughtfully. "Maybe we should look into this. I know how much you love playing piano. Maybe you could get a scholarship. You have made so much progress. Do they take students your age?"

"If we ask, they will send a free, illustrated catalogue. Maybe that will answer our questions," Betty said.

"It would be helpful. Let's get one to see if you qualify to apply for a scholarship. I will write tomorrow."

"Oh, thank you, Mama. It would be a dream come true for me!" Betty threw her arms around Susanna and gave her a big hug.

"Let's not count our chickens before they're hatched," Susanna cautioned, as she went to the desk to get paper and a pen. "They have to accept you before we can celebrate."

"I won't," Betty assured her, "but I'm sure I can do this!"

A week later the catalogue arrived. Susanna and Betty thumbed through it. It was close to 100 pages with a table of contents so they could easily find the information they needed. Betty searched for the one piece of information she really wanted to know. "Look here!" She pointed to a paragraph in the catalogue. "They do have a preparatory department for 6th and 7th grade students!"

"That's wonderful. Let's look at the details," Susanna said.

They scanned descriptions of the courses taught at the College and lists of what instruments students could study. "I would love to learn to play the saxophone," Betty announced. This instrument, invented in the 1840's, had captivated the ears of many composers and listeners.

Susanna turned to the page that discussed scholarship policies. "Here they explain their plan of free scholarships. They have been offering them for over thirty years."

Betty read a bit more. "Look, Mama. They say that scholarship students win prizes and medals more often than paying students. And they believe that all students should have a chance to learn music, whether or not they can pay. The whole idea is phil . . . an . . . throp . . . ical." She sounded out the big word. "I'm not sure what that means."

Susanna smiled. "It is a way they are offering qualified students an opportunity they couldn't afford otherwise."

Betty twirled away again. "So maybe that means I can go."

"You must have a letter of recommendation from a pastor, a school principal, or another reliable person who knows you deserve to apply," said Susanna.

Betty furrowed her brow. "Do you think our pastor will write a recommendation for me?"

Susanna nodded. "He certainly has heard you play in church often enough. He knows how good you are. And he is well acquainted with our financial situation. I do think he'd be happy to help."

Throwing her arms around her mother, Betty squealed. "Oh, thank you, Mama. This is so exciting."

Susanna laughed. "Don't thank me yet. Let's find out what else needs to be done to apply for a scholarship. And we'll have to talk to your father."

Together Susanna and Betty learned that all scholarships would be awarded after an examination in August. Susanna pored over the admission and scholarship application form while Betty read through the audition requirements. Betty had never auditioned before, but she was confident her skills were adequate.

She said, "Oh, this won't be too hard. Miss Clark has taught me the scales and arpeggios, and there are at least three pieces I can play from memory. I am pretty good at sight-reading too."

"I think there's a likelihood they would accept you, then. You have worked very hard, and your skills have really improved," responded Susanna. "These application forms aren't too complicated. I'll get started on them now. I think we can convince Papa this is a good idea."

That evening the children all sat at the dinner table with Mama and Papa. Betty was bubbling with excitement. She wiggled on her seat, but didn't say a word, even when Freda raised both eyebrows, questioning her. Herbert pushed peas around his plate, and baby Frederick Jr. sat in his highchair, smashing potatoes with his hands.

Susanna said, "Boys, stop playing with your food and finish eating like gentlemen."

The boys obeyed for a few minutes. They went back to their antics when the subject changed.

"Fred," she said, turning to Papa. "Betty has a question to ask you."

Fred paused, a forkful of peas halfway between his plate and his mouth. "What could that be?"

"Oh Papa, I'm so excited," Betty gushed.

Freda giggled and said, "It doesn't take much to make her excited. Like the time she got to play piano for the church program. She could hardly sit still to practice."

Betty resisted the urge to stick out her tongue at her sister. She tried to ignore Freda and kept her eyes on Papa. "Have you ever heard of the Chicago Musical College?"

"Why yes. It has a very good reputation around here for educating excellent musicians," Papa answered.

"Mama and I were reading the newspaper, and we saw an advertisement for it. We sent for their free catalogue. It says they have full scholarships available for this fall, and they are accepting applications until August 10. They also have a preparatory program for younger students my age. We only have to fill out the form and submit the scholarship request, and, and, and. . . ." She stumbled over her words.

"Wait a minute, Babette. Calm down," cautioned Papa. "I understand why you are so worked up. Music is very important to you, I know. And when I listen to you play the piano, I can hear that you play very well. But this is an important choice you're making."

Betty responded breathlessly, "Thank you, Papa. I enjoy playing so much. I know it's a big decision, but I really want to try. Music is everything to me."

Fred thought a minute, then replied, "Well, if you could win a scholarship, that would take care of one problem. But going to this school would be a pretty big step for an 11-year-old girl. Are you sure music is what you want to do with your life? Don't you want to get married and have a family?"

"Oh, Papa. I've dreamed about becoming a great pianist for so long. I will have to play an audition, but I think I'm prepared for that. And Mama already started filling out the application."

Fred looked at Susanna with raised eyebrows. "Really? Let's not move too quickly here. If you become a great pianist, how will you make a living?"

Betty thought a moment. "Well, I can teach lessons like Miss Clark or accompany other musicians. They pay people to do that, you know. I could even play for a vaudeville show."

Papa slapped his hand down on the table so hard that the silverware shook. "Over my dead body! Those show business types are not always the best characters."

"Oh please, Papa. Let me try this. I can change my mind later if I don't like it. And I don't have to play for vaudeville."

"I think vaudeville sounds fun," Freda paused, her fork halfway to her mouth. "What's wrong with vaudeville?"

Papa frowned at her, then turned his attention back to Betty. "I know you love playing the piano and you're getting to be very good at it. I guess I know what your mother thinks," he said, looking at Susanna. "But is this really a good idea for our daughter?" he asked.

Susanna said, "Well, I can see that studying at the Chicago Musical College would be a great opportunity for her to hone her skills if she is set on a musical life. As she said, she could still change her mind later."

Fred sighed. "You seem very determined to do this. It wouldn't be my first choice for your future, but I guess it wouldn't hurt to try for a scholarship. Go ahead and send your application."

"Oh Papa, thank you." Betty stood and threw her arms around him. "You have made me so happy!"

Fred smiled half-heartedly. "I really hope this works out for you."

A letter from the Chicago Musical College arrived after about a week, which seemed to Betty an eternity. It congratulated Babette Heyer on being chosen to audition for a scholarship and listed three dates and times she could come to play for the faculty. Susanna quickly selected a date and sent her reply off by return mail.

Betty had been practicing like mad, rehearsing all her scales and arpeggios, and playing the music her teacher picked out for her, until Freda said to Susanna (out of her sister's hearing), "If I hear that one more time, I think I'll scream!"

Susanna whispered back, "If you need to do that, please go outside. Betty is determined to do her best, and we have to do our best to help her."

Freda stomped outside to toss a ball to Herbert while little Freddie dug a hole in the dirt with great gusto.

On audition day, a neighbor agreed to watch Freda, Herbert, and Freddie while Susanna and Babette were gone. Their house on Division Street was a short walk from busy Milwaukee Ave, which went directly to downtown Chicago. They climbed aboard the steam cable car and rode to the Loop where they quickly found the impressive Chicago Musical College building.

"Oh, Mama, it does look like a castle." Betty gasped. "A castle of music!"

They entered the building and found the receptionist. She smiled at them. "Are you here for an audition?"

Susanna nodded and the receptionist told them how to get to the recital hall. They ascended to the second floor. Since they had arrived a little early, they seated themselves on some chairs in the hallway.

Betty squirmed on the hard seat. After a minute she stood, straightened her skirt, and sat back down. But after another minute she jumped up again.

Susanna took her hand and pulled her back to her seat. "Are you nervous?" she asked.

"Maybe a little, Mama. What if I forget how to finger a scale? What if I hit a wrong note in my audition piece? What if I fall off the piano bench?"

Susanna chuckled and put her arm around Babette, giving her a gentle squeeze. "None of those things will happen, you know. You are very well prepared and simply need to stay calm. Keep your mind on the music and play with all your heart. You will be fine."

Betty relaxed a little. "Thank you, Mama. I'll try my best."

The audition room door eventually opened, and a booming voice asked them to please come in. They entered a medium-sized room with a big piano on the stage in front, surrounded by seats in a semi-circle.

The man sitting in the middle of the circle stood. "Welcome. I am Dr. Florenz Ziegfeld, President of the Chicago Musical College. You must be Babette Heyer."

Betty nodded, a bit intimidated by his powerful presence.

Dr. Ziegfeld turned to Susanna. "I presume you are her mother, Mrs. Heyer."

Susanna said, "Yes."

Dr. Ziegfeld looked at Betty. "Miss Heyer, we have been looking forward to hearing you play. We have read your recommendation and the list of pieces and exercises you have studied."

Betty blushed. "Thank you, Dr. Ziegfeld. I am honored that you invited me to audition."

He introduced the panel of faculty members. Betty recognized Hans von Schiller and Walter Knaupfer, two of the piano instructors. Dr. Ziegfeld invited Betty and her mother to be seated.

Susanna took a seat on one of the chairs at the back, and Betty walked onto the stage and sat down on the piano bench.

"Would you like to play some chords to get a feel for the instrument?" Mr. Knaupfer asked.

"Yes, sir." She played chords in a few keys.

Mr. von Schiller asked her to play three octaves of the major scale in the key of E, ascending and descending, followed by its relative minor scale in the same pattern. Thankfully, Miss Clark had prepared her, and she knew what to do. She played the scales flawlessly.

Dr. Ziegfeld then asked what piece she had prepared to play for them.

"*Für Elise*, by Ludwig von Beethoven," she replied. She began to play from memory. Again, she played with all her heart like Mama had told her, and with no mistakes.

"Well done!" Dr. Ziegfeld exclaimed when she finished. The other teachers looked impressed and applauded. Betty stood up with a smile and curtsied like Miss Clark had taught her, saying, "Thank you."

Dr. Ziegfeld said, "Thank **you**, Miss Heyer. You will hear from us in a week or two. We have some other students who are going to audition, and we need to give them a chance."

Susanna thanked them as well, as she and Betty left the room.

"Oh, Mama, how did I do?" Babette asked when they were out of the building.

"You played as well as I've ever heard you play!" answered Susanna as they walked toward the cable car stop.

"I know I put my heart into it, just like you said. It felt good. Did it really sound good, Mama? I wanted them to understand how much studying here would mean to me."

Susanna hugged her daughter. "I think they all appreciated your performance. Now we have to wait until they notify us of their decision."

The cable car stopped, and they climbed on for the ride home. They found a spot to sit. Betty sighed, "Yes. That will be the hard part."

Every day Betty anxiously checked the mail. Finally, after many long days, an impressive looking envelope arrived from the Chicago Musical College. "Mama, look what came in the mail!" Betty burst into the house with the day's postal offerings, her curls bouncing as she ran.

"What is it?" Susanna reached for the envelope.

"It's a letter from the Chicago Musical College. Oh, I hope it brings good news."

"Well, let's open it and see. Now where is that letter opener? I just used it yesterday. Oh, there!" Susanna snatched it from the desk. She slit the envelope open and slowly slid out a very official looking piece of paper.

Betty bounced on her toes. "Can I read it? I'm so excited I'm just shaking!" Her mother handed her the unfolded letter and after a few seconds, Betty squealed, "Oh Mama, they are offering me a full scholarship to study music there! I can learn composition, theory, and harmony. I could even learn to play another instrument. And I will keep getting better at the piano!"

"That is fantastic. We can share it with the rest of the family at dinner," said Susanna.

Papa returned home from work rather late, so dinner was ready to be set on the table. Betty could hardly wait to tell everyone. They took their seats and Papa said grace.

Everyone started eating and after a few moments Susanna looked over and saw Herbert and Freddie making rivers of gravy through their mashed potatoes. Susanna said, "Boys, stop playing with your food and eat like gentlemen." Again, the boys obeyed for a few minutes. Susanna turned to her husband and said, "Fred, Betty has some news for you."

The boys resumed landscaping their food.

Fred looked up from his plate. "Don't keep me in suspense, Betty. What news?"

"You remember, Papa, when I told you about the Chicago Musical College scholarships? And you agreed that I should go ahead and apply? And how Mama and I went downtown for the audition?"

Fred answered, "Yes, of course. The idea of you studying music at that school didn't thrill me, but I could see you had your heart set on trying out. Your mother told me that you played very well."

Betty glanced at Mama with appreciation and continued, "I thought I played as well as I could. And the judges must have agreed because they are offering me a full scholarship to study music there this fall! Her voice rose as she talked until Herby plugged his ears and Freda made a face.

"Well, congratulations, young lady!" said Papa. "That is quite an accomplishment. Although I still have some doubts about a future in music, I am very proud of you."

Freda told Betty she was proud of her too. Little Freddie just smiled. Then Herby began to frown.

"What's wrong, Herby?" asked Susanna.

"Will Betty have to live somewhere else? I would really miss her."

Freda added aloud, "I'd miss her too." In her mind she was thinking, "But I won't miss hearing her practice."

"Don't worry," said Betty. "I can still live here with you. But I'll spend most of my days at the college. So, you won't hear me practicing all the time."

"Thank goodness," thought Freda.

To Freda's dismay, Herby said, "But I really like hearing you play. Will you still play our piano?"

"I'm sure I will, especially if I am preparing for a performance. But that means you, and Freda, and eventually Freddy, will have more time to practice your own piano lessons."

"Now for some practical considerations, Betty. How will you get there each day?" asked Papa.

"Mama and I took the cable car on Milwaukee when I went to audition. I'm sure I could do it alone now that I know the way."

"Yes, that would be safe. The cable cars run often. And it's not that expensive," Papa said thoughtfully.

Mama added, "It was no trouble at all. I'm sure Betty could handle that. She is quite a grown-up young lady."

"I am certain the instructors will keep her very busy with lots of music to practice, and music theory, composition, and history to learn. She won't have much time for mischief," concluded Papa.

Babette entered the Chicago Musical College that year. She studied and practiced very hard.

She played exercises, scales, and arpeggios, along with masterpieces by Beethoven, Brahms, Schumann and many others she didn't know as well. She played very musically and soon was asked to accompany singers and instrumentalists.

She made good friends with many of the students and was always willing to help them when they had trouble with their music theory. Sometimes other piano students came to her in tears when their teachers were unhappy with their progress. She helped them work out complicated fingerings and articulation details. She seemed to have a knack for figuring out their musical problems and even some of their personal ones.

Betty and the other scholarship recipients were occasionally subjected to condescending attitudes and remarks from the wealthier students. Children of moneyed families were recruited vigorously by Dr. Ziegfeld and his son, Flo Jr., because their families made great donors. They had to have some talent to be accepted at the CMC, but they often weren't as motivated or interested as the scholarship students.

Betty and her friends banded together. They told stories they'd heard about some very snooty students who didn't practice and received loud lectures from their instructors at their lessons that could be heard in the hallways. They enjoyed thinking up silly ways to distract the students they didn't like at recitals and giggled at their revenge plans. But they never really did anything. They mostly outdid them in musical skills and academics, and that was satisfying enough.

By 1903, thirteen-year-old Betty was already a sought-after accompanist for the Chicago theaters. One day she had a message asking if she could play for a show on December 30, over the holiday break. She would play piano with the theater orchestra for Mr. Bluebeard, a musical starring Eddie Foy.

It was to be presented at the Iroquois Theater, a brand-new venue for musicals and vaudeville shows. The Iroquois had been called the most beautiful theater in Chicago and declared to be absolutely fireproof. Betty was excited for the opportunity because she wanted to see the new theater and had heard it was a great show.

But Susanna and Freda had come down with fevers, terrible coughs, and congestion. Pneumonia, diphtheria, measles and tuberculosis were common diseases in those years. Everybody knew someone who had died or had debilitating health problems from them. People was terrified of these contagions.

Fred came to Betty a couple of days before the performance and said, "I am so concerned about your mother and your sister. They are very sick, and I am not able to tend to them because of work. Your brothers want to help, but they are too young to do much."

"Oh, I know, Papa. I am worried about them too. And, as much as I'd like to see the show and play for it, I know you need my help. I'll see if one of the other pianists can substitute for me. If not, I'm sure the orchestra musicians will hardly miss the piano," she responded.

No one was available to substitute for her because so many of her friends had gone home for the holiday break. The music leader assured her that the orchestra could cover all the piano parts.

The audience was sold out for the matinee that day with 1,700 attendees. Many of them were families with children still in a festive holiday mood. As the second act began, a light sparked a fire backstage. The stagehands tried valiantly to contain it, but the area was full of flammable props and materials, and it spread rapidly. It was soon clear they could not stop it.

The audience could see the smoke and flames and began to panic. Mr. Foy went onstage pleading for calm, still believing the theater was fireproof. Many of the musicians had already fled, but some remained after Mr. Foy asked them to keep playing to reassure people. Flames continued to spread. People screamed and rushed to the exits, but many of the doors were locked. When the double bass and cello caught fire, the last musicians quit playing and found their way out through a bathroom window. 602 people did not escape. The well-publicized "fireproof Iroquois Theater" was, in reality, a firetrap.

© *Chicago Tribune*

The next day, Betty read the news with horror and fled to her room crying. Susanna, who was recovering from her illness, followed her and asked her what was wrong. Through her tears, Betty sobbed, "All those people were killed at the theater fire! And I might have been too. Or one of my friends. It's too awful to think about."

"Yes, I heard about that. You are right," said Susanna, quietly. "It is so tragic. Thank goodness you stayed home to take care of us."

"Oh, Mama, I'm not glad you and Freda were sick. But I am glad I wasn't there. All those poor people." Betty wiped away her tears and held on to Mama for a long time.

The summer before Betty returned to the Chicago Musical College for her final year, Fred announced that he'd received an excellent job offer in Elkhart, Indiana, near Xenia, Ohio, where they used to live. He explained, "This position pays more money and allows me the opportunity to do what I like best, invent things." He'd been working for the telephone company in Chicago and made many improvements in how calls were connected. One project he helped with was the new rotary dial.

He went on, "I have many more ideas, and I really like that area. Chicago is too big and busy. I also miss our friends in Xenia. We'd be closer to them in Elkhart." Elkhart was making itself known to musicians as the home of the C.G. Conn Instrument company, so this idea was welcomed by his musical family.

Freda said, "Is Xenia where I was born?"

"Yes," said Susanna. "You and Betty and Herbert were all born there."

"I kind of remember it," recalled Betty, smiling. "We had a lot of friends to play with. They all lived nearby."

Freda said, "I remember the big house we lived in. At least it seemed big to me."

Susanna looked at Freda, "You were about five when we moved to Chicago. It was hard for both of you to leave your friends. Betty, you would have been eight and Herby was only three."

"How old was I?" piped up Freddy. "Why don't I remember Xenia?"

Freda answered, "Because you weren't born yet, silly."

Freddy pouted.

"That's right," said Susanna. "You were born when we lived in Chicago."

Betty was worried about school. She asked, "Papa, what about me finishing my studies at the CMC?"

Fred said, "I know this is your last year there. I won't ask you to leave because it is important for you to graduate, after all your work. But we will have to find someplace else for you to live. It has to be a safe one."

"Oh, Papa, I have many friends who live in Chicago. Some live closer to the school than we do. I would miss all of you terribly, but I'm sure I can find someone who will let me stay with them for this year. I can easily take the train to Elkhart to see you when we have vacation."

"I suppose that could work out," said Papa, "but we will need to meet the family and make sure you will be safe."

They did find a suitable family who knew Betty and was willing to have her stay with them. Their daughter was Betty's friend. The family packed their belongings and readied themselves for the move.

Before leaving Chicago, Fred, Susanna, and the siblings hugged Betty with tearful goodbyes.

Betty said, "I will miss you all so much,"

Susanna gently wiped Betty's eyes. "We will all miss you, too. Try to be as helpful as you can this year. You know how to cook and clean, and you can help with the younger children. You can take the train to Elkhart for Thanksgiving and Christmas."

Betty's last year at the Chicago Musical College passed in a whirl. There was a lot to learn and practice, but there still were parties and fun events she shared with her friends. Most of her classmates were young women, so there was little opportunity for romantic interests.

At Thanksgiving, she bought a train ticket for Elkhart and joined her family for the big dinner. "What fun to be together again," she thought. She had much to be thankful for. Her little brothers were sad when she had to leave on Sunday, but she told them, "You know, I will be home for Christmas in just a few weeks. I will find some special things to bring you from Chicago."

Back at school, she continued practicing and preparing for graduation. She found time to shop at the nice Chicago stores for Christmas gifts she could bring to Elkhart. She found a fancy pen for Papa, a pretty scarf for Mama, a necklace with a little heart for Freda, and toys for her little brothers. Plus, candy for everyone – especially her brothers. What a great gift exchange they had when she returned home for the holiday.

As part of their preparation for the graduation competitions, she had been invited to perform in January for a recital at Music Hall in Chicago with two other pianists and three vocalists. She excitedly showed her family an article about the upcoming January recital from the *Chicago Daily News*. "Imagine." she exclaimed. "My name is in a Chicago newspaper!"

Freda was impressed and asked her parents if they could go hear the program.

Papa said, "No, I don't think so. I am working on a new gadget as your mother says, and that will be taking most of my time."

Freda and her brothers were disappointed. Freda was especially unhappy because she loved shopping in Chicago. Betty told them she would perform her piece for them at home. After all, she wouldn't be the only performer on the January program.

Freda really looked forward to hearing it and said truthfully, "I would love that." She missed her sister.

Betty said, "I can play it right now. I have already memorized it."

They all listened as she played her new piece.

When she finished, Freda said, "That was amazing. I loved it."

"It was really beautiful, Betty," said Herbert.

Freddy, who was only six, had not listened as carefully, but he chimed in. "You sure can play a lot of notes."

Betty smiled and ruffled his hair. "Thank you, Freddy."

Mama and Papa were impressed. "You have improved so much. We are very proud of you," Susanna said.

Papa added, "The decision to send you to the Chicago Musical College was the right one. You play like a professional."

They all assured her that she would do very well in January, and they would be thinking of her. Betty thanked them and reminded them that they would be coming to Chicago to see her graduate in the spring.

Betty spent the winter months working on her piano piece for the final competition among the graduating students. For the graduates of the CMC, there were prizes given in various categories such as piano, violin, voice, and scholarship, among others. The winner received a diamond medal and two runners-up, gold medals. This year there were 180 other students in the piano competition.

Betty was confident her professor had prepared her very well. Her Schumann piece was technically difficult and expressed a lot of emotion. Betty told her friends she felt that her teacher had taught her how to make the most of it. But in spite of all her practice and preparation, Betty also was concerned that a few of the older students had a lot more experience than she had.

"Oh Betty, you worry too much," one of her friends said.

Another added, "You know you are one of the best pianists here."

A third chimed in. "You play as well as any of them."

With her confidence shored up, she went in for her turn to play. She made no mistakes. She remembered Mama's words from many years ago, "Play with all your heart." So, she did. A few days after her performance, the results were posted. The list revealed that her score had tied with two older students, Rhea and Linnie, for first place.

The three high scorers were asked to play again. Betty knew she had played well before, but this rematch made her very nervous. "I wish I didn't have to do this. I feel like I played better than both of them the first time," she said to her friends. They reassured her that she could do it again, but she protested, "They both have so much more experience than I do."

Her nerves were on edge as she went to her seat at the piano for the tie-breaking performance. Her piano professor, who was one of the judges, smiled encouragement, and she began playing.

All went well until she missed a few notes and had to start a passage over. When she was done, she smiled and curtsied, but was very upset with herself.

The judges awarded the diamond medal to Rhea. She and Linnie were awarded gold medals, which was still a significant accomplishment. She knew that her piece was harder than their selections and she thought she had played as well as they had, except for her one mistake. She told herself that her nervousness affected her performance, but she was proud of her gold medal anyway.

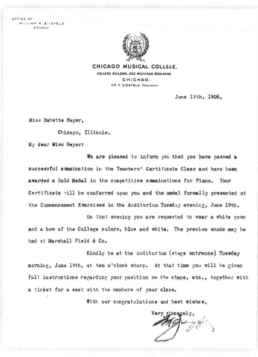

from the private collection of Sue Thurman

The graduation ceremony was held a few days after the competition, allowing enough time for the programs to be printed with the medal winners' names. It was in the big hall. Her family had taken the train to Chicago to be there. Herb and Freddy had all they could do to sit still as the long list of graduates and award winners was read. Susanna and Freda did their best to keep them quiet.

Finally, Freda leaned over to them and said, "You won't get any cookies or punch at the reception unless you behave." That kept them still for a while.

Everyone had been asked to be quiet as the graduates' names were read. But when Betty was announced as a gold medal winner, young Freddy couldn't keep himself from squealing with pride, and the rest of the family smiled happily. Afterwards, Betty bid tearful farewells to her classmates and promised to keep in touch. Her trunk was ready, so she could return with her family to their new Elkhart home.

FOUNDED 1867

Chicago Musical College
COLLEGE BUILDING, 202 MICHIGAN BOULEVARD

DR. F. ZIEGFELD, President

FORTIETH ANNUAL
COMMENCEMENT EXERCISES

AUDITORIUM
Tuesday Evening, June 19, 1906
EIGHT O'CLOCK

CHICAGO MUSICAL COLLEGE

Palmam Qui Meruit Ferat
The following is the List of Awards in the Different Classes, 1905-1906.

Post Graduating Class
Piano

Diamond Medal	Miss Edith M. Corette, Wilmette, Ill.
Gold Medal	Miss Prudence Neff, Nebraska City, Neb.
Gold Medal	Miss Madeline Williamson, Chicago.

Violin

Diamond Medal	Miss Wally Heymar, Warsaw, Poland

Vocal

Alexander H. Revell Diamond Medal	Miss Anna C. Jensen, Chicago

For Excellence in Composition

Gold Medal	Miss Wally Heymar, Warsaw, Poland

Elocution

Diamond Medal	Miss Cora Lynn Piggott, Chicago

Graduating Class
Piano

The W. W. Kimball Diamond Medal	Miss Nellie Ruby Nelson, Chicago
Gold Medal	Miss Marcia Melissa Manley, Roscoe, Ill.
Gold Medal	Miss Charlotte A. Andrus, Chicago.

Violin

The Studebaker Diamond Medal	Miss Margaret Prentiss Austin, Toledo, Ohio.
Gold Medal	Mr. Ellis Levey, Chicago.
Gold Medal	Miss Garli Hazneh, Stockholm, Sweden

Vocal

Rev. Dr. H. W. Thomas Diamond Medal	Miss Ada Dorsey, Grand Rapids, Mich.
Gold Medal	Mr. Johann H. K. Berthelsen, Manitowoc, Wis.
Gold Medal	Miss Clara E. Johannen, Chicago.

For Best Average of Scholarship

Diamond Medal	Miss Marcia Melissa Manley, Roscoe, Ill.

For Excellence in Composition

Gold Medal	Miss Virginia Graham, San Francisco, Cal.

For Excellence in Harmony

Gold Medal	Miss Isabel Lee Sleight, Ironwood, Mich.

Elocution

Diamond Medal	Miss Genevieve M. Rahig, Chicago.

Teachers Certificate Class
Piano

Dr. F. Ziegfeld Diamond Medal	Miss Rhea Watson, Lima, Ohio.
Gold Medal	Miss Babette Susanna Heyer, Elkhart, Ind.
Gold Medal	Miss Linnie Sutherland, New Castle, Colo.

Violin

Edwin A. Potter Diamond Medal	Mr. Will Prior, Chicago.
Gold Medal	Miss Gail Watson, Lima, Ohio.
Gold Medal	Miss Florence Bryant, Chicago.

Teachers Certificate Class

Piano

Dr. F. Ziegfeld Diamond Medal	Miss Rhea Watson, Lima, Ohio.
Gold Medal	Miss Babette Susanna Heyer, Elkhart, Ind.
Gold Medal	Miss Linnie Sutherland, New Castle, Colo.

Violin

Edwin A. Potter Diamond Medal	Mr. Will Prior, Chicago.
Gold Medal	Miss Gail Watson, Lima, Ohio.
Gold Medal	Miss Florence Bryant, Chicago.

Betty began unpacking her clothes in the room she and Freda would share. She shook out her dresses and hung them. As Betty tucked things in drawers, she noticed the walls were covered with newspaper articles about famous actors and actresses, and posters from the latest plays and performances. Freda had pinned them to ribbons and tacked them on every inch of space.

Betty called Freda into the room. "Those must have taken hours to collect. Do you want to be an actress yourself?"

Freda answered, "Oh yes. Yes, I do. It would be such a glamourous life! Being on stage and hearing all that applause. I really enjoyed my part in the Christmas play that you saw when you were home."

"Yes," said Betty. "You were a beautiful angel. But these stage actresses have to spend hours practicing and learning their lines. Besides, Papa would never let you do that. He really doesn't like show business types."

"I know that, for sure. He told me I should get a respectable job at a bank, since I am good with numbers. But numbers aren't nearly as fun as being on stage. I remember when he wasn't very happy about you going to school to study music. And I don't know how actresses get their start unless people in their families are in the theater. I've thought about running away, but I never could do that. That would break Papa's heart. Maybe Mama's too."

"Yes, it would be hard for both of them, especially for him. He wasn't overjoyed when I went to the Chicago Musical College. But I think he got used to the idea."

Freda plopped down on her bed. "Well, playing the piano is not as exciting as acting." She followed Betty's gaze around the room. "I would really like to be on stage with them." She sighed and sat up. "What are you going to do now that you are done with school?"

"I might try to find some piano students to teach or some accompanying to do," Betty replied.

Freda said, "I suppose you could do that, but I sure wouldn't enjoy trying to teach lessons. All students do is forget to practice and make excuses for their mistakes."

"I'm sure some of them will do that," countered Betty. "Maybe that's what some people in this family do at their lessons. What a waste of their parents' money." She tsked.

Freda blushed and shuffled her feet. "There are some things I like doing better than playing piano."

"Yes, that's quite obvious." Betty folded another blouse and put it in the bureau. "As soon as I finish putting things away here, I am going to find out how to put a little ad in the newspaper. And maybe I'll make some posters to put up at church and some of the schools."

In June, *The Elkhart Weekly Review* ran a nice article about Babette Heyer noting that she was a marvelous performer on the piano and planned to start a class to teach piano. It described her training and experience at the Chicago Musical College at length.

A few weeks later at the dinner table, Betty was very quiet. She had not gotten any calls.

Susanna asked, "Are you not feeling well, dear?"

"Oh, I'm feeling ok. But I'm not happy that I haven't found any piano students yet. And no one at church has asked me to accompany them."

Fred spoke up. "Elkhart has more than its share of musicians. So many of the people who work at the C. G. Conn Instrument Company are performers. And so are their wives and children and other family members."

Susanna added, "The Conn Instrument Company used to sponsor a music conservatory that attracted lots of instrumentalists and other musicians. Many of them settled permanently in Elkhart. There is a lot of competition for music students. And it limits opportunities for accompanying bands and soloists. So even with your outstanding recommendations and experience, it is hard to get started here."

Betty needed to come up with another plan. She had a friend, Anna, who was a few years older. They had met each other when Anna and she were taking piano lessons with Miss Clark. Anna had married her schoolmate, Joe. They had two young children and still lived in South Bend. She was now the organist at the Indiana Avenue Christian Church, and she taught piano lessons.

Betty sent Anna a note asking about teaching in South Bend, explaining that in Elkhart she hadn't been able to attract any piano students, and the jobs accompanying performers and groups all seemed to be filled.

Anna responded right away, writing that she had more students than she could handle. She invited Betty to come for a visit. She promised to introduce Betty to the choir director, who had noted that they needed another piano teacher. With the interurban connection, South Bend was only an hour away from Elkhart so Betty could continue to live with her own family. Anna added that if the weather was bad, Betty could stay in Anna's extra bedroom. Betty could also easily travel from South Bend to Chicago for work as an accompanist.

The interurban train connected several towns along the south shore of Lake Michigan all the way to Chicago. These long-distance streetcars, usually one car long and painted bright orange, ran several times per day. Since they were electric, they could also navigate the streets of South Bend on the existing city streetcar tracks. Unlike Elkhart, South Bend had no special interurban station, so people would just signal from street corners if they wanted to hop on.

The more Betty thought about Anna's suggestions, the better this idea seemed. She wrote a note to Anna and arranged a visit.

Betty met the choir director. After they chatted a bit, he said, "I have a list of young people who want to take piano lessons, and Anna's schedule is full. You would have several students to start with, without even advertising. You can use one of the Sunday School classrooms that has a piano and a closet to store your music. Does that interest you? By the way, Anna recommends you highly."

"Oh yes!" Betty said, thrilled with the idea of teaching in South Bend. "When can I start?"

Betty's first student appeared after school on a Monday. Smiling she said, "Hello, Tom. My name is Miss Heyer. Tell me a little about yourself."

"I'm eight years old and starting third grade." He seemed a little nervous, so she asked him about his family. He said, "I have two older sisters. My father is a banker, and my mother takes care of us. We have a dog and a big yard."

"That's nice," she said. "I love dogs. My family has one too. I have one sister and two brothers. Now tell me, do you really want to learn to play the piano?"

He answered hesitantly, "I guess so. It's kind of my mother's idea. She thinks it would be good for me. It might be fun to be able play for people, but I don't like to sit still very long."

Betty smiled. "Playing for other people is very fun. But you need to practice, and sometimes that part is more work than fun. Well, let's get started. We will try to have some fun. Have a seat in the middle of the bench. What do you notice about the keys?"

Tommy gazed at the keyboard. "Some are black, and some are white." He studied them a little longer. "The black ones are bunched in twos and threes," he answered.

"Excellent!" Betty clapped her hands together. "Now spread your arms out toward the two ends. Is a group of twos or threes closest to your nose?"

"A group of two," he said, giggling.

"Now find the white key that is to the left of the left black key."

Tom examined the keys carefully and pointed to the correct white key.

"Very good!" Babette said. "All the keys have names but that one is very important. It's called middle C."

They were off to a great start.

At first Betty made the round-trip ride from Elkhart to South Bend every day she taught. But after a few months she found that the trip back and forth between the towns took a lot of time that she would rather spend teaching. She asked Anna, who lived in a fairly large house, if she could stay in her extra room in exchange for watching Anna's young children when needed. She could also help with meals and cleaning.

Anna and her husband, Joe, talked it over. Anna said, "With our little ones, Betty could be a great help."

Joe agreed, saying, "I'm sure you will appreciate the help and the company."

Betty hadn't been there very long before she added some pupils. After she had been teaching a while, she decided she could teach more students, so she placed an ad in the *South Bend Tribune*. By 1907 she had a thriving studio.

from the private collection of Sue Thurman

ORVILLE REESE

When Babette Heyer was gaining her education and developing a career teaching, Orville Reese was gaining a reputation in the South Bend area as a musician and band leader, while working in sales at local dry goods stores. He was born in 1876 and had grown up in Kansas and Nebraska. When he was seven years old, his mother, Eva, died after a long illness. His father, Reuben, had to continue working, so he enrolled Orville in a military boarding school. Young Orville participated in band and took cornet lessons. Reuben arranged for his son to spend the summers in Michigan, where many of the Reese family still lived.

After Orville finished school, he had worked in sales, ending up at the Blak Flag dry goods store in Hastings, Nebraska. There he was promoted to head salesman because of his ability to market their wares effectively. In 1898 Orville enlisted to serve in the Spanish-American war as a band musician. He enjoyed this position very much and still was able to keep his Blak Flag job.

That same year Reuben moved from Nebraska to Benton Harbor, Michigan, a small town of fewer than 10,000 people. The original Reese family farm, where Orville had spent many summers, was located not far from Benton Harbor, near Eau Claire, Michigan. Orville stayed in touch with his father and was glad that Reuben seemed to be happy in Michigan. In 1899, Orville received a letter from his father. It said, "I have met a lovely widow, Josephine. I want you to meet her. I should let you know that I plan to marry her on June 30. I would love to have you here for the wedding. I also wonder if you would consider leaving Nebraska to live somewhere closer to us."

Orville was not too surprised, as Reuben had mentioned Josephine in other letters. Orville missed his father and had no other close family in Nebraska, so he agreed to move. He resigned his sales position and relocated to Michigan mid-June. He had always enjoyed his summers there and looked forward to being near his father, cousins, aunts, and uncles again. He also transferred his military service to Michigan's band units, and actively served 16 years in regimental musical activities.

Reuben and Josephine's wedding was lovely. Having lost their first partners, the older bride and groom seemed well suited to each other. Reuben had plans to expand the crops and animals they raised at the family farm, which his brother, Chauncey, still operated.

Reuben was hoping that Orville would stay and help on the farm, so he asked him, "What are your plans? Would you want to stay and help us with the farming? We could use another hand."

Orville agreed to stay for a while to help Reuben with his farming business. He really liked Josephine and enjoyed being with other family members. But after a couple of years, he realized that farming was not what he wanted from life. He had other ambitions.

He told Josephine, "I don't want to disappoint Father, but I don't love farming the way he does. I want to get back into music, and I'm sure I could find a job in sales. I have valuable experience."

Josephine listened and said, "I think Reuben already knows that you aren't as enthusiastic as he about farming. He also knows how you love music. It would probably be best to just tell him."

One evening Orville told Reuben, "Father, I really don't feel that I am cut out for farming. I am very good at sales, and I think I could find a job at some store in a larger town." He added, "A bigger community would provide much more opportunity both for a sales job and my music. I even have thought about starting my own band. South Bend, Indiana is not far away and is a good size. It would be perfect."

Reuben realized that Orville was right. He had noticed that Orville had little real interest in farming. Every time that Reuben talked excitedly about planting a different crop or experimenting with chickens, Orville responded with a nod, then retired to his room to practice. He was far too wrapped up in music to give it up. Farming was a 24-hour, year-round responsibility, busiest in the summer months.

Reuben said, "Well, son, if you think sales or music is your future, I won't stand in your way. Music is not a lucrative field, although it is very enjoyable. I'm glad you know that you will need an income of some kind. Your knack for sales could bring you a good income and still give you time for music." Besides, he thought to himself, if his son found work in South Bend, he would be close enough to see regularly.

Orville took the train to South Bend and quickly found a room in a boarding house. He asked the landlady for permission to practice his cornet in his room.

She agreed but put him in a corner room where he wouldn't bother anyone. She told him sternly, "No playing after ten o'clock at night or before nine o'clock in the morning."

By 1901 he landed a sales job at McLane, Baird and Co's store and by 1903 had taken a better position at the Economy Store. With an income and very few expenses, he began saving money.

Opportunities in music were also available. He continued playing in military bands and joined one of the local bands where his talent soon became obvious. He found other performing jobs, and, after he was asked to step in to substitute for the regular director, his ability as a conductor was observed and acknowledged.

Band entertainment was very popular everywhere. Orville soon found himself busy directing a number of organizations, since almost every town had its own band or bands. Businesses had bands, some schools had bands, and private groups formed bands. He kept up his cornet playing and developed saxophone skills. Orville knew that the saxophone was becoming a very popular instrument and was aware of its appeal. The nearby Elkhart C. G. Conn Instrument company had begun manufacturing them, along with their many fine brass horns, so he was close enough to find a good instrument, reasonably priced.

Other directing jobs came his way. He led the Twentieth Century Limited Band, which, according to the *South Bend Tribune*, featured many "colored musicians." He also led the Boys' Marine Band and, for a while, was engaged in Elkhart with the C.G. Conn Band. He was hired to lead the Brown Commercial Car Band of Indianapolis, the Ford Band, and the Peru, Indiana City Band. Fortunately, they rehearsed on different schedules.

Finally, he felt he had enough of a following among musicians and confided his plans to start his own band to a friend. "I believe I know enough musicians that I could recruit," he said.

His friend responded, "Well, the musicians I know think highly of you."

Reassured, Orville made announcements at rehearsals of the other bands he directed. "I am searching for good musicians to participate in a new musical enterprise I am going to start, the Reese Concert Band of South Bend. Participation in one band does not preclude you from joining the new band. But you must have skill and dedication to be allowed to join. I will have auditions to choose the best players for this band." He found enough competent instrumentalists to create his new band. They organized and rehearsed and soon this new band was giving popular concerts for big audiences.

Orville was always trying to figure out how to attract more attention and recognition. His bands had several very competent sax players, so one day in early 1907, he asked them to stay after their rehearsal. He told them, "I've been asked to provide music for the YMCA speakers' series in March. It will be at the First Methodist Episcopal church so there isn't room for a whole band. But I think they would enjoy a saxophone group. Would you like to get together to form a saxophone quartet? I should think we would have many other opportunities to play come along."

Three of his players were willing to put in the extra effort, so they formed a saxophone quartet with Orville that was, according to the *South Bend Tribune*, "the only musical organization of its kind in this part of the state." They performed for the YMCA meeting and were well received. They soon were engaged for many other occasions. Orville was making a name for himself.

Meanwhile, Betty was also making a name for herself in South Bend. She kept attracting more students to her busy studio. Under her tutelage, their skills improved quickly, and she soon became a very popular teacher.

In February she decided that seven of her students were playing well enough to perform in public. She decided to organize a musicale featuring them at the Indiana Avenue Christian Church. She would play two pieces also. It would be on a Tuesday evening in April, and she would bake a cake and make punch to enjoy afterwards. She wrote up a short article about it for the newspaper.

The event attracted a good audience, some coming over from Elkhart, including her mother and Freda. Orville Reese was in the audience too. He had read and heard about this talented and lovely young lady and decided he should get to know her.

Following the performance, Mama and Freda came up to her. Freda said, "You must really inspire your students. I actually enjoyed listening to them play."

Mama said, "Your pieces were lovely, Betty. You play so beautifully."

Others came up to tell her how they enjoyed her program. Then Orville approached her and introduced himself. "Hello, Miss Heyer. My name is Orville Reese. I have read about you in the newspaper and wanted to hear you play for myself. You play at a professional level. It is a pleasure to meet you."

Smiling, Betty blushed and answered, "Thank you, Mr. Reese. I have worked very hard. I am happy to meet you as well." Mama and Freda were still standing nearby. Betty introduced them.

Orville bowed his head and said, "Pleased to meet you, Mrs. Heyer and Freda."

They shook Orville's hand and exchanged pleasantries.

Susanna said to Betty, "We will help you finish up here, and then we can catch the interurban back to Elkhart." She and Freda busied themselves with cleaning up the plates and cups left around.

Betty continued her conversation with Orville. "The local papers have written often about your bands. You must be very busy with so many responsibilities."

"Yes, I guess I am," he replied with a hint of pride. "I founded the Reese Concert Band, and I continue to direct the Twentieth Century Band and the Marine Boys' Band. I've had to give up some of my other obligations, unfortunately. There just aren't enough hours in the day! I also need to keep up my cornet and saxophone practice. I teach a few students too."

"I would love to hear one of your bands play," said Betty. "I've only recently moved to South Bend and have been really busy here with my teaching." She gestured at the church. "I haven't had much opportunity to get to know the musical community."

Orville said, "Well, we could remedy that easily enough. My Twentieth Century Band is giving a concert at the end of this month. There will be some pieces featuring the entire band plus some small group numbers. I will be performing a saxophone duet early in the program and a cornet duet later."

"Oh, that would be delightful to attend," Betty said eagerly. "Where will the concert be held?"

"We will be playing at the Mt. Olivet Church on West Monroe Street. It's really not that far from here. I would be happy to escort you there if you would like to come. You could be my special guest," he added with a smile. "I do need to get there a bit early to tune the musicians and make sure everyone knows when they are performing."

Betty considered the offer. She was concerned that her church friends would think she was a little rash if she agreed to have him escort her there, especially after just meeting the man. She said, "That's very nice of you, but I'm sure you will need some time to get everything in order for the concert. My last lesson is rather late that day. I will come with a friend."

Susanna and Freda hugged Babette goodbye and returned to South Bend on the interurban. Freda said her mother, "What did you think of Mr. Reese?" They had both watched with curiosity as Betty and Orville talked.

Susanna said evenly, "He seemed very polite," and dropped the subject.

Babette went home the following weekend, after her last lesson on Friday. She rode the interurban to the Elkhart station, where Susanna and Freda were waiting for her.

They walked home conversing about the Tuesday musicale. Babette talked about some of the students who had played that evening and were progressing well.

Before they came to the house, Susanna queried, "Can you tell us more about Mr. Reese?"

Betty answered, "Orville Reese is a very well-known band director in South Bend. He's a good musician too, I've read. He plays cornet and saxophone and probably other instruments. He said he had seen newspaper articles about me and wanted to hear me play. He was very complimentary about my playing."

"Did you like him?" asked Freda.

"Honestly, Freda. I just met him. But the answer is yes. He seemed very pleasant. He invited me to come to hear his Twentieth Century Band in a couple of weeks."

"It looked to me like he's already sweet on you!" Freda said dramatically.

Betty frowned. "Don't be silly, Freda! You see romance everywhere."

"Now, Betty, maybe you should think about this," said Susanna. "He seems quite a bit older than you."

"Oh Mama," responded Babette, with a bit of indignation. "I have no intentions of finding a beau. He offered to escort me to the concert, but I told him I would come with a friend."

Susanna was relieved.

Herby, Freddy and Papa were happy to have Betty stay for the weekend. She played the piano for them all and some games with her brothers. Her siblings all performed their latest piano pieces for her, and she praised their progress. Sunday evening, they accompanied her to the interurban station and waved until she was out of sight. Everyone was sad when she left. No mention of Orville Reese was made whole weekend.

The day of the Twentieth Century Band Concert came quickly. Betty had invited Anna to accompany her. Anna asked if her niece, Mary, could come too. "You know how Mary loves music."

Mary, age seven, was one of Babette's younger piano students and quite precocious. Betty said, "Of course! She will enjoy it!"

They rode the streetcar to the Mt. Olivet Church and joined the crowd inside. The program was impressive. Mr. Reese's Band played several marches that had young Mary tapping her toes and a waltz in a lively tempo that made it hard for her to sit still. Between their numbers were solos and smaller groups. Babette was especially interested in the saxophone duet that Mr. Reese played with Miss Krick. She noted that he had a beautiful tone and played masterfully. There were other vocal solos and groups. Toward the end of the program, Mr. Reese and George Williams played a cornet duet called, *Like the Rose, You're the Fairest Flower.* As the two men took their bows, Orville looked right at Betty and smiled. She blushed and smiled back.

Betty, Anna, and little Mary stayed to congratulate the musicians and their leader on the enjoyable performance. Betty introduced Anna as a fellow musician and her niece, Mary, as one of her best students. Mary smiled at the compliment and described her favorite numbers in the concert. She said, "I loved the *University of Pennsylvania March*. It made me feel like marching up and down the aisles, and the waltz made me want to dance. But the Rose duet was the best!"

Orville glanced at Betty, who smiled and blushed. He said "Thank you all so much for coming. I'm glad you enjoyed it. Miss Heyer. I hope we meet again soon."

Reddening a little more, Betty replied, "So do I." Her heart skipped a beat.

On the way home, Betty asked Anna what she thought of Orville. Anna responded, "He certainly is a fine musician. He plays well, and even though his band is fairly new, they did a very respectable job with their music. He must know how to prepare them. Why do you ask?"

Betty answered, "I guess I like him, and I think he likes me. He is a remarkable musician. And, he has such a cute dimple in his chin!"

"He does have a youthful appearance," Anna said smiling. She had noticed his dimple too. "But he does seem older than you," she added with a tone of caution.

Betty looked thoughtful.

Orville called Betty before the week ended. "Miss Heyer, would you be pleased to attend a vaudeville show with me?"

"Mr. Reese," she began, smiling a little at his gallant wording.

"You must call me Orville," he interrupted. "And will you allow me to call you Babette?"

She laughed. "Of course, Orville. I would like that."

Before long they were seeing one another frequently, going to concerts, and taking walks together. They discussed music, of course, and many other topics. They also discussed the difference in their ages, almost 14 years. Orville told her, "Babette, I can barely believe you are not even 18. You seem so mature."

She responded, "Well, Orville, you seem very youthful and full of energy!"

One warm late August evening they took a walk and chatted about music for a bit, as usual. But when they reached a secluded area, he took her by the hand, saying, "Babette." He paused, looking into her eyes. "I care for you, deeply. I've never met anyone who had so much musical ability and could converse intelligently on so many different topics. I feel very happy being with you. I have never felt this way about any other girl before. I would really like to have you meet my family." He pulled her close and kissed her.

Betty was a little surprised but enjoyed her first real kiss. She realized how fond she had become of Orville. She answered, "I like you very much too. You know so much about music, and we have a great deal in common. I would enjoy meeting your family. The only reservation I have is that I am still so young. I do need to talk it over with my family."

Betty went home to Elkhart over the long Labor Day weekend. She was happy to see her family again. The boys were growing so fast. When she and Freda were getting ready for bed on Saturday, she confessed that she really liked Orville Reese and that he liked her. Freda was not too surprised, but she had concerns. "You know he's almost as old as Papa? Papa is 44. Orville just turned 31. That means Papa is only about 13 years older than Orville. And Orville is almost 14 years older than you!

Betty replied indignantly, "Our age difference is more like 13 ¾ years. But I do know how I feel and how well we get along. And I like him. So, we'll see." But she was worried if her parents could accept the idea of her being with someone so much older. After all, she'd been so busy studying, practicing and teaching, she hadn't had time for boyfriends before.

Freda went on, "You know you will have to talk about this with our parents. I don't think Papa will be too thrilled with the idea that you like an older man, especially after all your education."

"You're right," Betty admitted. "But I'm sure he'll like Orville when he gets to know him. There will be time for that. After all, so far, we're just friends."

Freda looked skeptical. It sounded a bit more serious than that. She kept her thoughts to herself.

They didn't talk about it again that weekend. Sunday after church, they visited a few friends and relatives and on Monday, Betty and Freda helped Mama pack a big picnic hamper of chicken and ham sandwiches, lemonade, and fruit for a picnic in the city park, where the city band was giving a concert. They were all a little sad when it was time for her to take the train back to South Bend.

Through the fall, Orville and Betty saw each other often. They discovered that they had the same tastes in music, liked the same composers (although Orville had a higher opinion of John Phillip Sousa than Betty did), and held themselves to the same high standards of musical performance.

In October, when the harvest was done, Orville invited Betty to Michigan to meet his Berrien County family. She felt she was ready and agreed to come. They took the train to Benton Harbor, where Reuben and Josephine met them with their buggy and drove them to their farm. They were delighted to meet Babette. Orville's other relatives were also friendly and welcoming. Betty soon felt at ease.

At one gathering Orville told them, "You know, Babette is a marvelous pianist. She received a full scholarship to the Chicago Musical College when she was only 11 years old!"

Everyone was impressed and murmured their approval.

"She graduated with a gold medal performance at the age of 16."

More murmurs of approval.

"Now she is teaching piano in South Bend where I attended a lovely musicale that she presented with some of her students."

Reuben said, "It would be a treat if you would play for us. Would you be willing to do that?"

"Of course," Betty said.

Reuben continued, "Wonderful. There is a piano in the parlor at the family farmhouse near Eau Claire. We just had it tuned."

"If you would like, I will be happy to invite our relatives and neighbors for a shared meal tomorrow. They will be thrilled to hear you play for them," Josephine added.

Betty agreed, saying, "It would be an honor."

The word was spread to family and friends that tomorrow they were invited to come for a share-a-dish meal, followed by a performance by Orville's friend, Babette Heyer.

The next evening, the old homestead was filled with people enjoying food and conversation. When folks were finally eating their deserts, Orville announced that the music would soon begin. Everyone took their last bites and quieted down, finding places to sit on the sofas and chairs and even on the parlor floor. Some lined up along the wall. Betty was happy to see such a friendly audience. She played some of her favorite classical pieces, announcing each before she started. Everyone listened intently. Then, as a surprise, Orville took out his cornet and the two played a few popular songs they had rehearsed beforehand. People sang along with the tunes they knew like *In My Merry Oldsmobile*, *School Days*, and popular songs from well-known operettas. Everyone had fun. They clapped and cheered when Betty finally stood up and bowed her head in appreciation. Orville thanked them for coming.

Orville and she talked together after the crowd had gone home. "I think everyone enjoyed themselves tonight. You were a great hit!" he told her.

"I'm glad we practiced beforehand, and you could join in too. Your father looked so proud." Betty said. "I had a wonderful time. It's amazing and almost magical when people make music together."

"They all seem to think you're pretty amazing too, Babette. My father and Josephine included. So do I," he added, smiling at her. "I think we make a good team! We could have a great future together!"

Betty looked at him seriously. "Do you really think so? Oh, I hope so. I'm only 17 and I am afraid of what my parents will think because you are so much older. But that shouldn't matter if we really care for each other, should it?"

Since everyone was in the kitchen and they were still in the parlor, he gave her a hug and lightly kissed her hair. "No, it shouldn't. I think we will be able to work everything out,"

Soon it was Thanksgiving. Betty as usual, planned to go to Elkhart to spend the holiday with her family. But this time her joy was tempered by worry. She would be happy to see them all, but she was planning to tell her parents, and maybe Freda, that she was falling in love with Orville Reese. She was fairly sure her parents would not be happy.

Thanksgiving Day went well. Betty and Freda were up early to help Mama stuff a big turkey and put it in the new gas oven they bought when they moved to Elkhart. They all worked to get the potatoes mashed, rolls cut and buttered, green beans boiled, and sweet potatoes baked. Mama had already made the pumpkin pie. Freda chattered about school and the latest vaudeville shows she and her friends had seen. Betty described her students, the good ones and the ones that made all kinds of excuses for not practicing. The boys played with their toys while Papa read the newspaper, exclaiming how hungry they were and how the aroma coming from the kitchen wasn't helping.

Finally, it was time to eat. Father gave thanks for all their blessings and began to carve the turkey. The boys behaved themselves, and they had a lovely meal together. They ate until they nearly burst, but they still found room for Mama's pie.

After they cleared and cleaned all the dishes and put away the leftovers, everyone was sleepy. Papa napped on the couch, Mama dozed in her chair and the young folks nodded over books they were reading. Betty decided this was not a good day to tell her parents about Orville.

On Friday, Papa had to go in to work, and the boys and Freda had cleaning chores around the house. Betty pitched in as they dusted, swept, and scrubbed floors and sinks and the bathroom. Afterwards, they all found projects to keep them busy until dinner, which was a lot of Thanksgiving leftovers. Betty decided that this wasn't a good day to talk about Orville either.

On Saturday everybody wanted to get outside. It had snowed just enough to make a snowman, which occupied them for a while. The boys soon turned that into a neighborhood snowball fight until Freddy got hit in the face and started crying. He cheered up when Papa offered to take them all ice skating. The local pond had already frozen, so everyone found their skates, even Mama, and off they went. Betty decided that this still wasn't a good day to talk about Orville.

Sunday, Betty knew it was her last chance to tell her parents about Orville. After church and dinner, Fred and Susanna sat down in their customary chairs to read the newspaper. The boys went outside, and Freda went up to her room to read about the latest romances among the actors and actresses she admired. Betty seated herself in an empty chair and cleared her throat. "Mama and Papa, there is something I would like to discuss with you."

Papa seemed surprised and Mama looked uneasy. They lowered their papers. Papa said, "The last time I heard you sound this serious was when you had to convince me to let you attend the Chicago Music College. What is it now?"

"Chicago **Musical** College, Papa," Betty gently corrected him. She took a breath and went on, "I have met a wonderful man."

Susanna narrowed her eyes.

"His name is Orville Reese. He is a great musician. He directs many bands and plays cornet and saxophone very well. We have a lot in common."

Fred said, "I think I remember that your mother mentioned meeting him when she and Freda came back from your musicale last April."

"Hmm," Susanna said, recollecting the look in her daughter's eyes that day. "Isn't he a good deal older than you?" she asked.

Betty replied, "Yes, Orville is older. But he has so much musical experience. And," she added hastily, "he is a good businessman too. He works in sales and his own band, the Reese Concert Band. He is organizing a large expo for South Bend food merchants and manufacturers to showcase their wares. It is going to happen next year at the end of February."

"My goodness, Betty, you are only 17. There is a lot of time for you to meet other eligible gentlemen," said Susanna. "Your father and I were 22 when we were married."

"Exactly how old is this Orville?" Fred furrowed his brows.

"He turned 31 in August," replied Betty quietly, steeling herself for what she feared he would say next.

"THIRTY-ONE!" he thundered. Upstairs, Freda heard Papa's raised voice and crept out in the hallway to listen in. "He's closer to my age than yours!"

Betty didn't argue, but simply said, "He's very kind to me, and I love him very much. He loves me too and we have talked about marriage. He took me to meet his family in Michigan, and they were very welcoming to me. I played a little concert for them. It was great fun . . . "

Fred cut her off. "There is NO way I will ever consent to you marrying a man this old. I will not discuss it further!" He stomped out of the room.

Betty was near tears.

Susanna said, "Your father is right, Betty. Orville is too old to be a suitable husband for you. I hope you will change your mind."

"Oh Mama," she said softly, "I've never felt this way before. We are so happy together . . . "

Susanna interrupted, "You haven't had much experience with boys or men. How can you be so certain you love him? Men, especially older men, can take advantage of a pretty young girl's naivete."

"Orville would never do that. He feels we have a great future together since we are both good musicians and think so much alike," Betty said defensively.

"We shall see. In the meantime, I had better calm your father down." Susanna left the room.

Betty went upstairs to pack her things. Freda had turned her attention back to her magazine but finally looked up and said, "Betty, I couldn't help but overhear your conversation with Mama and Papa. Are you really in love with him?"

"Oh Freda, he is so kind to me, and we have such fun together. We like the same music and he has so many ambitions. I know we would be happy together. But I'm not sure what to do about Papa. Orville wants to meet him and ask for my hand. I don't think that would go well."

"Probably not, but you are almost an adult," Freda noted with a knowing look. "You won't need Papa's consent when you turn 18."

"But I would want it," Betty replied sadly.

Susanna and Freda accompanied her to the train station without much conversation. The boys were busy with a game and Papa was too upset to come.

Monday Betty spent the day crying, thinking, and practicing. She dried her tears and taught several students in the afternoon. Orville was going to meet her after dinner to talk about an idea he had for the upcoming Expo.

He knocked on the door and Betty opened it. "What is wrong, Babette?" he asked, noting her red and puffy eyes. "Did something bad happen when you were home?"

"Oh, Orville, my father had a fit when I told him about you. He said he'd never consent to me marrying someone as old as you even when I told him how many things we share and how much we both love music. My mother said I was way too young to know my feelings. But I DO know."

"I can understand them wanting to protect you, but we both know that I would take care of you," he said, putting his arms around her.

Betty leaned onto his chest and cried some more. "I so wanted them to approve of you."

"Maybe they will with time. We just need to keep our chins up and move forward." He tipped her chin up and gave her a quick kiss, since no one else was around.

She dabbed at her eyes, smiled weakly, and said, "What is this big idea you want to tell me about?"

"You know about the Pure Food and Manufacturer's Exposition that the Reese Band is sponsoring?" he asked.

Betty nodded.

"It will start in the last week of February and last for two weeks. We have lots of exhibitors signed up because it is a great opportunity for them to be introduced to new customers. I was thinking that it might also be an opportunity for local musicians to showcase their talents!"

"How would that work?" asked Betty, skeptically. "I really don't see much connection between food, manufacturing, and music."

Orville answered, "Musicians need a way to become known more widely.

We would invite interested music teachers and performers to participate in a contest during the exposition. They could perform each day, if they are willing. People would vote on who they like best. It would be a good way for them to decide who should teach their children or perform for their events. The music they play would provide entertainment for everyone too."

"Oh Orville, that sounds like a grand idea." Betty brightened a little. "It is hard to attract students except by recommendations from current students." Recalling her experience at the Chicago Musical College competition, her expression turned serious again. She explained. "I am a little nervous about competitions though."

"You have nothing to fret about, my dear. There is no one in South Bend who plays as well as you," Orville assured her.

Betty agreed to participate.

Betty went to Elkhart for Christmas, which fell on a Wednesday in 1907. Her family exchanged gifts as they always had, and she enjoyed watching Freda and her brothers open their packages. She had bought new gloves for her mother and a book for her father.

Conversations with her parents were strained, but she had good times with Freda, Herby, and Freddy. Susanna kept hoping Betty would tell them she had changed her mind about Orville, but his name was never spoken over the holiday.

Betty told Susanna that she would not be staying there very long after Christmas. She needed to return to South Bend because she had agreed to play the organ for the church service between Christmas and New Year's.

On Friday she packed her things and asked Freda to walk with her to catch the interurban back to South Bend. She knew her parents were still quite upset.

As they walked along, Freda asked, "Now, what are you going to do?"

Betty answered, "I will play for the church service, like I told Mama and Papa."

Freda said, "I know that. I meant what are you going to do about Orville? Are you going to marry him when you turn 18 in May?"

"I haven't completely made up my mind about that yet. Orville says we have splendid musical opportunities ahead of us. I don't know exactly what he has in mind, but it sounds exciting. More exciting than teaching piano lessons every day. I really don't mind that, though. But if I do decide to marry him, I guess I won't need Papa's permission after I turn 18."

"Part of me thinks it's a very romantic idea," exclaimed Freda. She went on in a quieter voice, "But another part makes me sad that the next time I see you, you might be a married woman."

"If you and Mama and the boys can come to Orville's exposition in February, you can see me before my birthday. Maybe you can convince Papa to come. He can meet Orville and find out what a very nice man he is," Betty suggested.

Freda looked at her knowingly. "It sounds like you have made up your mind." She shrugged her shoulders. "I will mention it to Papa when the holidays are over. I'm afraid he wouldn't want to give the impression that he approves of Orville."

"Probably not," agreed Betty. They arrived at the interurban station and waited for the bright orange car to arrive. Betty hugged Freda goodbye, boarded, paid the conductor for her ticket, and took her seat. She thought a lot about how much she loved her parents and siblings and how bad she would feel if they were hurt. But she loved Orville too.

Back in South Bend she played for the Sunday service at her church, then took the train to Benton Harbor where Orville met her. They celebrated the New Year, 1908, with his family.

On the train ride back to South Bend, Orville talked excitedly about the exposition. "We have so many exhibitors who have signed up to rent display tables." He listed several of them.

Betty was impressed. "That sounds very interesting. How many musicians have registered for the contest besides me?"

"The last time I counted there were eight men and seven women. We have boxes for collecting the votes, one for the men and one for the women," he responded. "And you have one of the largest studios of students, so you should get a lot of votes."

"The idea still makes me a little nervous, but I guess I've had more experience now. Who will you vote for?" she teased him with a smile.

"I think you know," he answered tenderly.

January and February kept Orville busy arranging the exposition. Betty helped as much as she could, moving tables and chairs and setting up signs. She wrote a note to her mother describing the exposition and saying she hoped they would come for the opening day, but she would understand if they couldn't. Susanna replied that they would try to be there, but Papa probably would stay home. Work was keeping him busy, she added. Betty guessed the real reason.

Opening day finally arrived. All the exhibitors had set up their tables and displays. A large crowd gathered, and Betty was thrilled to see Mama, Freda, Herby, and Freddy there. She ran toward them and hugged them all. Susanna was a little stiff but returned her embrace.

Betty said, "I'm so glad you came. This is such an exciting day. I would like to introduce you to Orville who planned all of this." Betty pointed to where the stage was set up.

Orville saw them and came over, smiling.

Susanna recalled, "Freda and I met you last spring at Betty's musicale. But I don't think you've met her brothers, Herbert and Frederick."

The boys shook hands with Orville.

Orville said, "I hope you enjoy the exhibits. There are some samples of food and some small toys they are giving away."

The boys wiggled with excitement. "Oh, we will have a good time!" Herby exclaimed eyeing the candy and other goodies.

The mayor gave a speech, welcomed everyone, and praised Orville for putting together such an interesting show. He concluded his remarks saying, "Business in South Bend is good and events like this will make it even better." Then the Reese Concert Band played a Sousa March, the mayor cut the entrance tape, and the crowd flooded in.

A piano had been provided by the local music store. Betty was the first to play. She performed both of the pieces from her musicale along with some other pieces. When she finished, a fairly large crowd, including her family, surrounded the stage. They cheered and clapped enthusiastically.

She stepped down from the stage and the other contestants took their turns playing.

Before they left to catch the interurban back to Elkhart, Susanna took Betty aside. "It seems like you are determined to marry Orville. Am I right?"

Betty nodded and again listed all the things she loved about him. "Besides all that, he is truly supportive of me and has exciting plans for our future. I know you and Papa think I'm too young, but I know how I feel. And this feels right."

Susanna continued in a serious tone, "I do hope you know what you're doing. Your Papa will be disappointed. But you will be old enough to make your own choices, good or bad, after your next birthday." She hugged Betty tightly and gave her a kiss. "I wish you the best with all my heart."

She turned to go, calling to Freda and the boys "Hurry or we'll miss our train." Betty felt a lump in her throat as tears filled her eyes. She wasn't able to see that Susanna's eyes were as moist as her own.

At the end of the first week, votes for the most popular lady and gentleman musicians were counted and published. The newspaper item about this "Interesting Contest" reported that Babette Heyer was leading the lady musicians with 490 votes while her closest competitor had 242.

"Oh look, Orville!" Betty waved the newspaper at him. "I have twice as many votes as Miss Schaffer. She has been in South Bend for years. And the two of us are way ahead of the others."

"What did I tell you? I was sure you would do well," Orville said knowingly.

At the end of the exhibition's two weeks there was a closing gathering. Several of the merchants got up to thank Orville and the Reese Concert Band for their efforts. The band played a final march. The *South Bend Tribune* declared it a "pronounced success . . . from a financial standpoint," and named the winners of the most popular musicians' contest: Mr. Davis in the gentleman musician category with 1,252 votes, and Babette Heyer in the lady's category with 5,364. Mr. Davis's prize was a Gentleman's Morris Chair, and Babette's was a piano scarf and brooch. She was delighted.

PURE FOOD SHOW CLOSES

Miss Heyer and Bruce Davis Win Popular Musician Contest.

South Bend's first annual pure food show and manufacturers' exposition closed Saturday night after a two weeks' run at the Market rink on South Main street. The exposition was held under the auspices of Reese's band and was a pronounced success. From a financial standpoint the show was more than satisfactory to the promoters.

Throughout he show a contest to decide the two most popular musicians was held. Miss Heyer, with a total of 5,3664 votes, was declared to be the most popular lady musician and received a piano scarf and brooch as a prize. Bruce Davis was found to be the most popular gentleman musician and received a gentleman's Morris chair. He received 1,252 votes.

© *The South Bend Tribune* - March 9, 1908

Orville and Betty talked over their marriage plans. They both knew they wouldn't be able to have the customary ceremony in her parents' home. Orville felt bad that her father was so opposed to their union. He proposed that they travel to his family's home to say their vows. Orville's father, Reuben, knew the Justice of the Peace for the area and agreed to set up a time on May 10, for their marriage.

On Betty's 18th birthday, May 9, 1908, the two made sure they had her birth certificate and other documents they might need and boarded the train to Benton Harbor, where Josephine and Reuben met them. They celebrated her birthday with a family dinner that evening that included a special cake Josephine had baked. Betty was touched by their reception and grew a little quiet as they wished her Happy Birthday, missing her own family. She did ask Josephine for the cake recipe, which she hoped to bake in the future. Josephine was touched.

May 10 dawned a beautiful, sunny spring day. Betty saw that as a good sign. Reuben took them to Benton Harbor where they pledged themselves to each other in marriage.

Reuben and Josephine had prepared their downstairs bedroom for the new couple to give them some privacy. At bedtime, Betty and Orville retired to the room and shut the door. They hugged and kissed each other. Orville gently began to caress her in ways that frightened but also excited her. He undressed her slowly and removed his own clothes. They stood regarding each other for a moment, embraced again, and tumbled to the bed. Orville softly kissed her body and before she realized it, they had consummated their union.

The next morning, she pinched herself to check if this was all a dream. She was Babette Reese now, with a talented husband and an exciting future. She sent her parents a letter, telling them that she had married Orville. She hoped they would accept him and even like him. She asked if they could visit before school started in the fall.

Frederick told Susanna, "I know she is married now, and I'm still not happy about that. I kept hoping she would change her mind. But I suppose, now that it's done, I should get to know this fellow."

Susanna wrote back, inviting them to come over Labor Day. Fred would have Monday off and they could take a picnic to the city park, just like they used to. Freda was excited to see her sister again and find out how this marriage thing was going. Herby and Freddy were happy to hear that Betty and her new husband would be visiting. Maybe he would bring them more candy.

On the train trip to Elkhart, Betty felt apprehensive. She hoped Papa would like Orville and realize that he was taking good care of her. When they arrived, she saw her parents standing at the platform. She and Orville stepped down from the train and cautiously approached them.

Betty went to her father and hugged him. He hugged her back and she turned to her mother. After Susanna embraced her, Betty said, "Papa, I would like you to meet my husband, Orville."

Orville stepped forward and offered his hand to Fred, saying, "It is nice to meet you, Mr. Heyer. Babette has told me many things about you and your inventions."

Fred warmed a little, shook Orville's hand, and responded, "I am glad to meet the man who swept my daughter off her feet. According to her you are quite a musician."

Orville replied, "Yes, music is very important to me, as it is to Babette. But I also enjoy business and have worked in retail most of my adult life. I plan to provide her with a good life."

"According to Susanna, Betty seems very happy in the letters she's written," Fred continued.

"We are both happy, Mr. Heyer. Your daughter is a lovely person besides being a great musician," Orville said.

They collected their luggage and walked toward the Heyer home.

Over the weekend, Orville completely captivated Herb and Freddy, now 13 and 8. He played catch with them and helped them with their baseball swings. Babette watched them through the window and said, "Well, Orville has a couple of new fans in this family."

Freda, who was standing nearby added, "I like him too. He is very nice to all of us."

By the time the new couple boarded the train back to South Bend, the Heyer parents had warmed to Orville quite a bit, although Fred still thought his daughter was too young to be married.

After the exhibition, Babette acquired several new students who wanted to take lessons from her. She continued teaching at the church. She had packed up the few belongings she had at Anna's home, and moved into the small apartment Orville was renting. Her schedule was quite full, but she continued to advertise for more students. Orville kept working at the Economy Store where he was promoted and given an increase in salary. His band was engaged for several dances and events, and he was hired to direct other groups too.

Orville was very frugal and had already saved quite a bit of money over the years. His income plus Babette's earnings from teaching added to their nest egg. Of course, Orville let her keep some cash for new clothes and other necessities. He always told her, "We need to save up for the right time." She wasn't sure what that meant, but it sounded reasonable.

Sunday afternoons were about the only time they could spend time with each other since their schedules were so different. Orville worked at the store every weekday. In the evenings he was often busy rehearsing bands.

He had many performing engagements over the weekends. Babette spent the days practicing and preparing for her students. Saturdays and weekday afternoons and many evenings she was busy with teaching. Occasionally they were able to go to vaudeville shows or concerts together in the evenings.

One weekend in February of 1909, Orville told Babette that he had an idea he wanted to discuss with her. As they sat together in the small drawing room of their apartment, Babette said, "Tell me about this idea you have."

Orville began with a serious tone. "You know, we have seen many vaudeville shows. Most of them are farcical comedies with silly plots, pratfalls, acrobatics, magic, and low-quality musical acts. People laugh and clap. But I think many of them would appreciate something classier. You and I are both accomplished musicians, and it seems as though we could put together a high-quality act that would be very entertaining."

Babette's hands trembled, nearly spilling her tea. She remembered her father's reaction when she told him she could make a living accompanying vaudeville acts. He wouldn't like this idea at all, but she had a husband to listen to now. "I think that's a good idea," she said hesitantly, "but Papa doesn't have a very high opinion of show business types."

Orville stated emphatically, "You are a married woman now. There's no danger for you being in vaudeville. He has nothing to worry about. I would see to it that no one would bother you."

"But how could we make playing piano and cornet and saxophone entertaining enough to attract attention?" Babette wondered aloud.

Orville explained, "We might need to expand the instruments we play. I think you could easily learn to play the xylophone. It has wooden bars in the same pattern as a piano, but you hit them with hammers to make sound."

"That sounds like fun. I have seen xylophones before, but I have never tried to play one. They have really become popular since I was at the Chicago Musical College. I would be willing to try to learn. Can we afford to buy one?" Babette asked. "And what would you play besides cornet and saxophone? Where on earth would we keep so many instruments? We certainly don't have room here," she said looking around their small quarters.

"Those are good questions, Babette. I have enough money saved to buy a xylophone, and I think I have a solution for where to keep it. The church has room to store it where you teach your lessons. You can talk to Anna about that and the pastor if necessary. You can practice before and after your lessons. I'm sure you will figure it out very quickly," Orville said confidently. "I have been thinking about buying an instrument they call the aluminum bars or harp. It's very beautiful to see, but it takes a lot of room too. I could keep it with the Reese Band percussion instruments and practice it around our band rehearsals. There are books that can instruct us on developing the techniques we need."

"Oh, Orville, I think this is a swell idea. You do remember that I learned to play the saxophone at school, don't you? I haven't played very much since then, but I am sure I would remember if I had one to use. Could we afford to buy one?"

from the private collection of Sue Thurman

"Yes, I think so," he replied. "I have friends who work at the Conn factory, and I'm sure they could find an affordable instrument for you."

Through the spring of 1909, Orville and Babette spent hours working on their new instruments, while saving every penny they earned. Before long, Babette had polished her saxophone skills and become proficient on the xylophone between teaching piano lessons and accompanying jobs. Orville had many evenings taken up with rehearsals and performances but managed to perfect his technique on the aluminum bars.

They learned well-known songs from popular radio shows and current light operettas and prepared some of the beloved melodies from grand operas. Orville arranged many of them for their various instrument combinations. His band experience came in handy. He decided to call their act the *Musical Reeses*.

from the private collection of Sue Thurman

They worked very hard through the summer and fall too. They talked about what songs to play in what combinations and in what order. That was crucial to keeping the audience engaged. They knew their listeners liked novelty and surprise. Orville's aluminum bars would be new to most of them, so that would be intriguing.

One day Orville came up with another idea. "Babette, you play the xylophone so well. Could you play it with the bars covered with a thin cloth?"

Babette said, "I've never seen anybody do that before, Orville, have you?"

He shook his head and said, "That would be very impressive, indeed." He looked at her, "Maybe you could wear a blindfold, too."

Babette said, "Now that would be a challenge. But I have always liked musical challenges. I will give it a try."

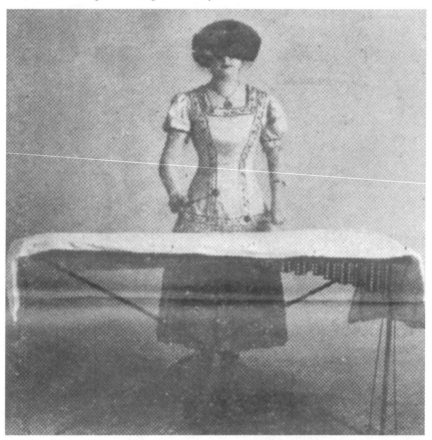

from the private collection of Sue Thurman

The next time she practiced, she covered the bars with a thin white satin cloth. Within a few weeks she mastered playing the music she had been working on without watching her mallets.

Next, she tried playing the pieces with her eyes closed until she had a good sense of how the music "felt" when she could not see her hands move. Finally, she tried doing both at the same time and found it surprisingly easy. She demonstrated her new skill to Orville and said, "Well, what do you think?"

Orville listened but seemed a little distracted. He answered her rather quietly, "That was excellent. Now you can do something that is unique."

Babette sensed that Orville was upset. Thinking there must be something wrong with her playing, she asked, "Do you think I need more practice?"

"No, it's nothing about your playing. That was amazing. It's that I just heard all the vaudeville orchestras in our area are going to lower their tuning pitch. I'm not sure why, but I think the East Coast musicians are tuning that way. So, our music will sound really unpleasant if the other musicians play with us."

"Oh, dear. That will be a problem," Babette said.

Orville went on, "Yes, the theater pianos will all be changed to the new tuning. It won't be such a problem for our saxophones or my cornet. We can lower their pitches by adjusting different things. But the xylophone and the aluminum bars can't be changed like that. We will have to replace them."

"Can we afford to do that? Those are expensive instruments." Babette looked at him apprehensively.

"I don't think we can afford not to. We can't make our debut on such a sour note." Orville chuckled a little at his own joke. "I do have enough money saved up to get replacements, and we can probably sell the other instruments to someone who doesn't need to be so picky." Orville smiled at Babette and added, "I didn't mean to make you feel bad. You have done a great job mastering this challenge. I think you will be our act's outstanding feature along with my aluminum harp."

They felt hopeful that their act would be a big hit.

By 1910 Fred Heyer had warmed up considerably to Orville and even to the idea of his daughter performing in a vaudeville act. They reassured him that there was nothing questionable or risqué about the *Musical Reeses'* act.

In January it was announced that the Star Theater of South Bend was for sale. Knowing that Babette and Orville were preparing for their vaudeville debut, Fred discussed buying the building with Susanna. He told Susanna that he had enough money put aside from his invention royalties to pay for half of the asking price. He said, "I think it's a great opportunity. I know the building needs some work, but we can find folks to do those repairs."

Susanna asked, "But where will you find the rest of the money? I wouldn't mind moving to South Bend to be closer to Betty and Orville."

"My friend, Robert Snoke, has always enjoyed show business," Fred said thoughtfully. "I bet he would like this idea. And he certainly has the means. I'll talk it over with him."

Fred found that Robert was interested. Before long they were the proud new owners of the Star Theater. The Heyer family moved to South Bend and settled in a house on Pennsylvania Avenue, not far from Orville and Babette's apartment. They engaged workers to make the needed improvements to the theater.

Fred asked Orville if he would consider acting as theater manager, for a small salary of course. Orville was elated. There would be space in the building to hold his band rehearsals and store their act's instruments. The best part for Orville was that there would be a real stage to practice on when the theatre wasn't being used. The Star Theater re-opening was announced in the South Bend News.

Through 1910, the *Musical Reeses'* act began coming together nicely. They knew that a vaudeville act needed to last a maximum of 20 minutes, so they had to time their pieces exactly and arrange them in an order that moved quickly and smoothly from one part to the next.

"I wonder if I should be billed as Betty or Babette. My family still calls me Betty," she said as they wrote the copy for their ads.

Orville said, "I like the sound of Babette. I think for our act, we should call you Babette. It sounds professional and impressive. It might intrigue people."

She decided, "I guess I can answer to both Babette and Betty."

CHAPTER TWO

VAUDEVILLE: 1910 - 1911

from the private collection of Sue Thurman

FREDA HEYER

Freda visited Orville and Babette fairly often and was intrigued by their plans to create a vaudeville act. She loved the idea of being on stage and had been working regularly at the Star Theater which her father partially owned, and Orville managed. She confided to her sister, "I wish I could join your act. You know I am a good singer and I've sung lots of solos in church. I think I could learn to play the saxophone too."

Babette said, "It would be nice to have three performers. There's so much more we could do with the harmony. We'd need to figure out how you would fit in, but it would be easier to keep things going with three of us. Do you think Papa would let you? You know what he said about show business types."

"Yes, I do know. But I'm already 16. You were only 17 when you decided to marry Orville. And Father knows I would be with you and Orville. Papa likes Orville now and would trust him to watch out for me."

Babette said, "You would add a lot to our act. Let's propose it to Orville and see what he thinks."

Freda looked delighted.

Orville liked the idea. He had heard Freda sing and play the piano at the Star Theater and recognized that she was very talented too. He said, "I will need to ask your father's permission. After all, he is my boss." He thought a moment, then asked, "Do you think you could learn to play the saxophone?"

"Oh, yes. I have tried Betty's. But I don't own one to practice on. And who would teach me? I don't have money for lessons." She frowned as her excitement turned to dismay.

Orville said, "You could practice on Babette's for now. And I could teach you to play. I could rearrange our duets into trios."

"I would love that, and I would work very hard. When can we start?" Freda asked, her disappointment disappearing.

"Probably next week. I think Thursday afternoons would be ideal. Yes," Orville said. "Let's meet at two at Babette's church."

Fred gave his permission. Freda could join their musical act. "After all," he said later to Susanna, "I think Freda already had her heart set on this."

"Yes," agreed Susanna. "Freda has been stage struck for a long time." She thought about all the posters and pictures of performers Freda had pinned to her walls in Elkhart. They now adorned her room in South Bend.

Freda was a quick study, and Orville began working on new trio arrangements that the three of them could play together. Freda could sing many of the popular songs that she had learned when working at the Star Theater, so these were added to the act, with Babette playing the piano. They adjusted their name to the *Three Musical Reeses*.

Through his musical experience Orville had made the acquaintance of Charles J. Parraent, the leader of South Bend's Oliver Opera house and Auditorium Theater orchestras. Professor Parraent's orchestras had accompanied many vaudeville acts, so he had observed what audiences liked and wanted. Orville came to him for some advice. Parraent was aware of Orville's musical accomplishments, so he offered to assist them in developing a high class vaudeville act. Orville was happy to accept his help.

Parraent advised them on the "classy" costumes they should consider wearing. He suggested that they all dress in pure white satin material to create a wholesome image. Freda and Babette showed him some dress designs they had copied from a magazine. He agreed they would be appropriate.

Susanna had taught her daughters how to sew, and she even bought a new electric sewing machine they could use. They made themselves similar stylish dresses with slightly puffed sleeves, fitted bodices, and full skirts. They set the hems about midcalf, which was rather short for the 1910's.

Orville's outfit was a military style white jacket with crisply pressed white pants, a little longer than they needed to be.

Freda and Babette's shoes were similar, also white, with fashionably pointed toes and a tight fit. Small, narrow feet were desirable for women at that time. Ladies tried to push their feet into the smallest size possible.

The professor taught them how to walk on stage, saying, "Walk confidently. Take medium sized steps, with no mincing or stomping." He helped them plan the sequence of music that called for the least amount of moving their musical equipment around stage and utilized all the time they were allowed. They learned how to bow properly, maintaining the dignified look of the serious musician when done performing. They could only smile at the very end of the act. They had some professional photographs taken to use for publicity, highlighting the various instruments they played and their novelty features.

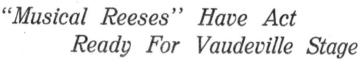

from the private collection of Sue Thurman

By the beginning of 1911 they finally were ready to try their act in front of a live audience. They invited some friends and family to watch their dress rehearsal at Robert and Fred's Star Theater. They performed with polish, remembering Professor Parraent's instructions. All the friendly spectators reacted with delight and amazement.

One of them said, "You are certainly as good as any vaudeville show I've ever seen! You are ready to go on the road." The word started to spread, at least around South Bend.

The sisters were giddy with excitement. "They really seemed to like our show." Freda said. "But my feet are killing me!"

Babette said, "Me too. My toes would like some more room. It did look like our audience enjoyed our performance. I wish I hadn't missed that note in the first piece. I've practiced it so many times. I guess I'll need to work on it some more."

Orville said, "Don't be so hard on yourself. You are probably the only one who knows you missed it, besides me and Freda. I'm sure you won't make the same mistake again."

Orville prepared some flyers with photographs describing *The Three Musical Reeses's* act and distributed them to area theaters. They were hired for a week of shows in mid-February by Thomas Moss, who owned the Majestic Theater in Elkhart, Indiana. Moss was a friend of Professor Parraent, who had been raving about the Reese's classy act as he coached them.

They were elated to have their first paying job. From their South Bend homes, it would be easy getting to Elkhart and back with the interurban connection.

Their premiere performance elicited a glowing review. Susanna saw it first and exclaimed to Fred, "Listen to what the newspaper reviewer wrote about their performance! 'MUSICAL REESES ARE MAKING EMPHATIC HIT. The Majestic crowds are larger than they have been during the weekdays, and much of the increase is attributed to the Reeses.'" She cut it out of the paper and put it on the desk.

➤ THE MUSICAL REESES ➤

HIGH CLASS NOVELTY MUSICAL ACT

Featuring Miss Babette in the GREATEST XYLOPHONE NOVELTY of the day. She performs on the instrument with the keys completely covered with a cloth and herself blindfolded.

MISS BABETTE

The following are a few of the many press notices of the Musical Reeses:

The Musical Reeses are doing a novelty musical act that for cleverness beats anything of the kind seen here before. Miss Babette performs on the Xylophone with the keys completely covered with a cloth and herself blindfolded. This feat is little short of marvelous and has served to stamp her as one of the GREATEST NOVELTY MUSICIANS of the day. — WICHITA BEACON, Wichita, Kansas.

The Musical Reeses offer what is easily one of the best instrumental musical acts ever seen here. Both members are artists and all the features of their act are highly pleasing. ESCANABA MIRROR, Escanaba, Mich.

The Musical Reeses with numbers on a variety of instruments made an instantaneous hit. Their act has melody and goes with a dash, which makes it very popular. — DIXON NEWS, Dixon, Ill.

O. W. REESE

from the private collection of Sue Thurman

Fred responded, "It sounds like they made a great impression."

Mr. Moss invited them to return to the Majestic in March. They were also booked to perform at the Lyric in South Bend and other theaters in nearby towns. They seemed to be off to a great start.

Professor Parraent thought it was crucial for the Reeses to get their act on a vaudeville circuit. These circuits determined an act's success by setting up a schedule of consecutive performances in their associated theaters. The circuits owned or had arrangements with multiple theaters in other towns, where they would schedule the acts they hired for appearances.

Parraent knew people in Chicago associated with the more successful vaudeville circuits. He had bragged to several of his contacts about the Reese's unique "classy" act.

Thomas Moss told the Reeses that he really liked their act and wanted to help them out. He said, "I know Charles has already put the word out about the *Musical Reeses*. I personally know several of the Chicago booking agents. If I can make arrangements, could you come to Chicago to present your act there next week when you are done here?"

Orville had already arranged some future bookings on his own, but he knew this would be an important opportunity, so he said, "Of course. That would be work very well."

"That is good news. I can be in Chicago to introduce you around, and I'll be in touch about more details," said Mr. Moss.

Later, Orville told Babette and Freda, "Mr. Moss has asked us to perform for some of the Chicago vaudeville circuit managers next week. We would have much more security if we could sign up with one of them." He didn't tell them he'd already agreed, but Babette and Freda sensed it could be a crucial chance, so they made sure they were free.

When they wrapped up their week at the Majestic, they packed up their costumes and instruments and went to Orville's father's home in Eau Claire late Saturday evening. Reuben and Josephine were very proud of the *Three Musical Reeses* and had invited a number of friends to their home to meet them Sunday afternoon.

The trio presented a shortened version of their act which delighted the audience of about 40 neighbors, relatives, and friends. Josephine served delicious cake and lemonade. According to the local newspaper article, the guests "showered the charming entertainers with compliments and well wishes for their future."

Monday, Babette, Orville, and Freda packed their things into Reuben's car and bumped along the rutted roads to the nearby train station. They bought tickets for Chicago and loaded themselves and their gear on board.

Arriving in midtown Chicago on Monday, they found a boarding house that had two rooms available, and extra space for them to store their instruments. They fell asleep, exhausted.

At breakfast on Tuesday Freda said, "I don't think I've ever been so nervous. This is our big chance to impress them."

Babette, who was nibbling some toast, said, "I can hardly eat anything. I hope we perform our best."

"Well, we'd better be awake and on our toes if we want to join one of the important circuits. There is a lot of competition out there. We have to really make a splash," Orville added.

Thomas Moss had scheduled them to perform a partial week in Chicago. Moss came to pick them up and help transport their instruments to one of the smaller theaters he helped manage. He had publicized the Reese's performance so there would be an audience and had also invited several agents to attend.

They quickly set things up for their opening. The audience was full and very enthusiastic. Orville, Babette, and Freda did the best they had ever done, and the audience rewarded them with appreciative applause and a standing ovation.

One of the agents approached them following their act and introduced himself as Mr. Keith. "That was very enjoyable, and you got a great reception from the audience. I wish we could offer you bookings in the big markets. Unfortunately, our calendar is quite full for the rest of the year." Holding the introductory material Orville had prepared, he went on, "I do see that you are already booked to do another week at the Majestic and a split week, April 20 through 23 in Escanaba, Michigan."

Orville nodded. "Yes, our opening week in Elkhart was a big success. We received rave reviews there and filled their theater. They invited us back later in March." Orville pointed to the newspaper clippings he had attached. "We know some folks in Escanaba, and they booked us for those shows. My father lives in southern Michigan near Eau Claire, and he helped us arrange a private performance at his home."

"Very good." The agent quickly scanned the reviews. "You have ambition and are using your connections. That's a good sign. I could offer you some performances in Canada in June. There are theaters in Sudbury and Cobalt that need some acts to fill out their schedules. Why don't we meet at my office about two o'clock to talk over the details? It's in the building across the street, office 507."

They stored their instruments and prepared to return to the boarding house. Thomas Moss approached them and said, "Congratulations. Your performance was outstanding. Mr. Keith represents one of the smaller circuits but that will be a start. He calls his business the Keith Circuit, but it's not as well-known as the Orpheum or Pantages circuits."

Orville said, "Thank you for letting us know, Tom. We have a meeting with him this afternoon. He said something about bookings in Canada. Do you know anything about the towns called Cobalt or Sudbury?"

"Sudbury was settled when The Canadian Pacific Railway expanded their track westward. It began as a rail worker's camp, but it wasn't long before someone discovered the area has a lot of valuable mineral deposits. Cobalt is a booming mining town, too. They found silver there and, you guessed it, cobalt. They are both kind of rough places, but the local folks love to be entertained. Keep an eye on your ladies though." Tom gestured toward Freda and Babette. "Both towns have grown a great deal. These jobs should be a good beginning for you."

Betty and Freda smiled and said goodbye, giving each other questioning looks as Tom walked away.

When Tom was out of earshot, Orville said, "I know this wasn't what we were hoping for, but we have to start somewhere."

They stopped at a diner for a quick lunch and had a discussion about appearing in Canada. Freda was clearly disappointed they wouldn't be playing in a bigger city, saying, "Who ever heard of Cobalt or Sudbury, Canada?"

Babette thought it might be wise to ask for a booking in a larger town, but Orville noted that the more they practiced, the better they would get. Everyone agreed on that point. They set off for Mr. Keith's Office.

The elevator took them to the fifth floor and 507 was right across the hall. Orville knocked on the door and the secretary opened it saying, "You must be here to see Mr. Keith. He is expecting you."

They stepped into the well-appointed office and looked at the fine furniture and the walls covered with photos of famous vaudeville acts. Freda couldn't help imagining their picture added to the gallery. "Maybe this could lead to better things," she mused to herself.

The secretary walked toward the inner door, opened it, and announced their arrival.

Puffing on a cigar, Mr. Keith stood up and invited them to come in and sit down. He shook Orville's hand, then smiled at the ladies. "Are you interested in the Canadian bookings?"

Orville, acting as the group's spokesman, replied, "Yes. I think it would be good to go there. We may be able to try a few new things. We need to keep our act fresh."

Mr. Keith agreed and continued, "If you decide to sign with us, we will copy your promotional material and send it to the places you are engaged. We have relationships with the newspapers so you will get very good publicity." He paused a moment, then continued, "You will need to arrange your own transport to those towns. There are good train connections. And you also must find your own accommodations. Staying with friends or relatives is ideal, but there are many reasonable boarding houses that cater to traveling entertainers. They usually charge somewhere between $5 and $10 per week and you will only need two rooms. I can give you some phone numbers to call. Your act will earn . . . " he paused to consult some papers. "I think we can pay your group $150 per week, even though you are a new act."

Babette raised her eyebrows at Freda, who softly, but audibly, drew in her breath. They clearly wondered if Orville should consider these terms after all he had invested in their instruments, costumes, and preparation so far.

"These jobs are coming up the first and second weeks of May. Is that enough time to make arrangements?" Mr. Keith asked, glancing at the calendar on the wall. "It's now the beginning of March. You have yourselves scheduled to return to the Majestic in Elkhart at the end of March, and then appear in Escanaba, Michigan, in April."

Orville refused to acknowledge Babette and Freda's concerned looks. He replied, "Yes, I'm sure we can make it to Canada in time. Trains run there every few hours. We will do our March return engagements in Elkhart and our April dates in Escanaba. We will then pack up and ride the train to Canada."

"Hmmm," mused Mr. Keith, still looking at the calendar. "There is an opening in Detroit, Michigan, at the Wayne Roof Gardens in mid-June and the possibility of doing some shows in Buffalo, New York, later in June. There may be some other opportunities in the area in July, too, but I need to work out the details. How does that sound?"

Orville said, "I think it all would be acceptable." Finally, he glanced at his wife and Freda for their approval. Freda looked down. Babette frowned. "Yes," continued Orville, forging ahead even though he could see they were troubled. "I'm sure we won't disappoint anyone."

"Excellent," said Mr. Keith. "I will write up a contract for these dates. Of course, should other opportunities come up, we can make changes. And a bit of advice for you. I know you are aware of the need to have a variety of material in your acts. Before you return to Elkhart, be sure to try to come up with different costumes and songs. I know you don't have much time, but once people have seen an act, they want something different."

"I understand," said Orville. "I am sure we can do that. We already have more music than we use in an act, so we can change things in and out. The ladies will be more than happy to have new costumes!"

Freda and Babette didn't object, but they exchanged uncertain looks.

Orville went on, "I have another question for you. Would it be possible to schedule some appearances in the southern central states during August and September? I lived in Kansas and Nebraska when I was a child and would like to see that area again."

Mr. Keith drummed his fingers on his desk. "I think appearing there would be an excellent idea." He consulted his calendar again. "You do need to make yourselves more widely known. There are some openings in Wichita and Hutchinson as well as Joplin, Missouri, and maybe Oklahoma City."

"Perfect," responded Orville. "I would like my wife and her sister to see where I grew up."

"Let me draw up the contract then, so you can be on your way." Mr. Keith opened a drawer, took out some papers, filled in some blanks and handed them to Orville.

Orville carefully looked over the contract, asked for a pen, and signed with a flourish. "Thank you, Mr. Keith. We will give these performances our very best."

Mr. Keith stood up, shook their hands and gestured toward the door, which the secretary opened as if on cue. They took their leave.

Back at their boarding house, Babette finally spoke up. "Do you think that was the best offer we could get? How will we make enough to pay for all of our food, travel, and housing expenses? And buy new costumes too?"

Freda added, "We certainly won't have time to make them ourselves with all these performances. We don't even have a sewing machine to use anymore."

Orville answered, "I guess you will need to find a dressmaker. For right now it will have to do. We didn't get any other offers, you remember. I do have money saved up to supplement the meager pay and cover the extra things. But this contract," he pointed to his copy, "will give us a chance to make a name for ourselves."

Freda, who wanted the act to succeed, voiced her agreement. "After all, I suppose a bird in the hand is worth two in the bush," she concluded.

Babette, not totally convinced, gave a small shrug.

They did two more shows in Chicago but didn't receive any other offers. The word was out that they were under contract.

from the private collection of Sue Thurman

WALTER CHRISTENSEN

Young Walter Christensen was making himself known in South Bend around the same time as the *Three Musical Reeses* began to appear in public. Tall and lanky, he looked older than his years. He had just finished formal schooling and was in love with show business. He found employment in local theaters, primarily the Oliver, where Charles Parreant directed the music. Gifted with a beautiful baritone voice, he was frequently hired to do illustrated songs, a type of entertainment that involved singing a popular song while hand painted glass slides were shown to illustrate the lyrics. His talents were much in demand. He had also learned how to manage operating the multi-reel silent films now being circulated. He was busy with work in area theaters, churches, and choruses.

© *South Bend Tribune* - December 30, 1910

During the last week of March, 1911, he was scheduled to appear at the Majestic Theater. His role was to present illustrated songs between the acts "in one" as they said. That meant he would sing in front of the curtain while scenery, props and equipment were being changed behind it. On the same bill were the *Three Musical Reeses*, there for their return engagement. They were playing 'in two' meaning they used the whole stage. The entire bill was hired for the week starting on Monday, March 27, giving two shows per day, an afternoon matinee and an evening performance.

Orville, Babette, and Freda took the interurban from South Bend to Elkhart early Monday and got their equipment to the Majestic. That morning was the first run through of all of the acts to work out the timing and scene changes, without makeup or costumes.

Freda glanced at the names on the bill as they were waiting. She gave a little squeal when she read that Walter Christensen would be performing. She pointed his name out to Babette and said, "I went to a show with a friend last fall in South Bend and heard him doing illustrated songs. He is so handsome and has such a gorgeous voice. I wanted to marry him right then."

Babette said, "Settle down, Freda. Maybe you will have a chance to meet him this week. You get so worked up over romantic notions. Remember, you are only 17."

"The same age you were when you met Orville," Freda retorted.

As the acts appeared, other performers could watch, but needed to be ready when their time came up. Since Walter appeared in between each act, he observed the others from the front row so he could listen for his cue. When the *Three Musical Reeses* came on, he was intrigued by the xylophone and the aluminum bars and thoroughly enjoyed the saxophones. But he found himself staring at Freda, who sang beautifully and looked lovely even without her makeup and costume.

He was quite smitten and decided to find her backstage. When they were finished getting their instruments to a safe place, Orville and Babette went back to their dressing rooms to make sure their costumes and makeup items were in order. The dressing rooms were nothing but crowded closets with hardly enough space to turn around. Freda and Babette had to share one, so they took turns. Freda waited in the hall while Babette organized her things.

"Hello, Miss Heyer," came a voice from behind.

Freda, surprised, turned and saw Walter standing there.

"My name is Walter Christensen. I am performing between acts here this week. Your act is fascinating. So many unique instruments and combinations." He smiled shyly and added, "And your singing is beautiful."

Freda, her heart pounding, said modestly, "Thank you very much. How did you know my name?"

Walter said, with a twinkle in his eye, "I have my ways."

She smiled at him. "And I know who you are. A friend and I went to one of your illustrated songs shows in South Bend. We liked it very much. You have a beautiful voice. I must say I saw your name on the bill here and remembered you. I was hoping to meet you."

"Well, now you have," said Walter, smiling back. "I would like very much to get to know you better. Is there a chance we could meet before the matinee to take a walk? Maybe we could find a place to eat something together?"

"I will ask my sister, Betty. She is very protective of me. I can't afford a fancy restaurant. Maybe we could find a lunch counter somewhere. I will let you know what she says."

Walter walked away to his dressing room with a spring in his step.

When Babette came out, Freda said breathlessly, "I just met Walter Christensen. He seems as nice as he looks! He said he would like to get to know me better and wants to take a walk with me before the matinee performance. We might stop to get something to eat, too."

Babette wasn't too keen on the idea, but she consulted Orville. He thought it would be all right, since it would be daylight, and they both needed to get back for the afternoon show.

Babette told Freda, "I have some reservations but just be sure you are back in time for the performance. And Freda, be careful. You don't know much about Walter."

Walter guessed Babette's answer was "yes" when he saw Freda coming toward him in her coat. He put on his jacket, and they walked to a variety store lunch counter. They talked about many subjects and discovered they had much in common. They were both aiming for careers in show business. They both enjoyed music and singing. They learned that they liked the same types of music, songs, movies, and vaudeville acts.

"Oh," said Freda, looking at her watch. "Where did the time go? We'd better get back to the theater." They paid for their food and walked back to the Majestic.

When they reached the theater, Walter said, "I would really like to get together with you again after we're done tonight."

Freda responded, "I'm not sure I can do that. You see we live in South Bend, so we need to catch the interurban back."

Walter said, "That's a coincidence. I live in South Bend, too. Maybe we could sit together."

"I would like that." Freda smiled at him and turned to go to the dressing room.

"Well," said Betty as Freda approached, "I was beginning to worry that you'd be late."

"Here I am," Freda responded. "And there is still plenty of time to get ready."

Babette looked at her with a little concern. "You certainly look like you enjoyed yourself."

"Oh, I did." Freda sighed. "He's as nice as I thought he would be. I think he is the one for me."

Babette scolded, "Freda, you are always falling for handsome men."

Freda knew that was true. She had crushes on most of the actors whose pictures had been pinned to her wall.

"I think you should get to know him a little better," Babette continued.

They were standing in the doorway to their dressing room. Orville overheard them and said, "It looks like you'll have this whole week to get to know him."

Freda told them that Walter lived in South Bend too. After the evening show, they hoped to sit together on the train so they could get to know each other better. "Would you object?" she asked. "You and Orville will be in the same car."

Babette said, "I do think we should meet him first. You know we promised Papa we would take care of you."

Orville agreed. "That seems wise. I heard him sing this morning too. He is very good looking and has a fine voice. I wonder if he plays the saxophone?" he said half to himself.

"You can't be thinking of him joining our act?" questioned Babette.

"Actually, that wouldn't be a bad idea," said Orville. "He's a good musician."

Freda smiled at the thought, but Babette raised her eyebrows.

Walter passed through the hall about then. He nodded at them.

Orville spoke first. "You must be Walter Christensen. Freda was just telling us about you."

"That's my name. We're one and the same," he quipped. "Freda and I had a great conversation on our walk. She is utterly charming. And I was very impressed with her singing this morning in your act."

Freda blushed and smiled coyly at Walter.

Walter continued, "She said she had heard me perform in South Bend. I am appearing here this week. I am mostly a singer, and I do illustrated songs."

"Yes, we heard you this morning, too. You are a very good singer," said Orville.

"Thank you," said Walter. "And I was quite impressed with your entire act. I really enjoyed the saxophone trios. I used play saxophone in school."

Orville perked up and said, "Yes, the saxophone is very popular. The audience enjoys our trios."

Babette said, "I think I have read your name in newspaper ads. You seem to have many engagements."

"I keep busy," answered Walter. "I also know how to run the reels for movies, so that occupies the rest of my time. I earn enough to cover my needs."

"Freda told us that you also live in South Bend. She said she wants to sit with you on the train back tonight," said Orville.

"I did suggest that. It seems like a good chance to get to know each other."

Orville and Babette looked at each other. Orville said, "I think that would be acceptable. Do you agree, Babette? We'll be in the same car."

She nodded.

Walter and Freda smiled at each other.

The matinee went well, except that one of the wheels of the aluminum bars wouldn't turn.

Walter came by and suggested oiling it. He knew where some oil was stored and brought it. That fixed the problem wheel, so it moved easily.

They thanked him and he said, "I was happy to help."

When Walter walked away, Orville said to Babette, "He does seem like a nice guy."

Babette didn't respond.

Between shows, Walter and Freda found a quiet corner backstage and talked. They continued their earlier conversation, learning more about each other, their families, their schooling, their work, actors and actresses they liked, their favorite songs and movies. They were surprised at how similar their tastes were.

Suddenly it was time for the evening performance.

After Monday's evening show, they all walked to the interurban station together. The car was crowded and noisy. Walter and Freda found a seat toward the back. The car bumped and jolted along the track, stopping at almost every corner.

Orville and Babette seated themselves toward the front and talked over how their act had gone and what they could improve or maybe change. The subject turned to Walter Christensen. Babette agreed, a bit reluctantly, that he seemed like a good fellow, a very talented guy.

"You know," said Orville, "I thought it before and I'll say it now, our act could really benefit from another performer of his caliber. If he's any good at the saxophone, we could present an impressive quartet. And he has a sense of humor too. It is something to consider. It would add more variety to our act. We have to keep the public's interest."

"Really, Orville, is that all you think about?" asked Babette, glancing around to make sure they couldn't be heard. Freda and Walter were absorbed in their own conversation.

"He would be a great addition," said Orville.

Babette knitted her brows. "I'm not sure we are ready for that. It would complicate our touring because we would have to reserve separate rooms for Freda and Walter. Even that would raise eyebrows."

Orville agreed. "Unless they decide they like each other well enough to get married," he suggested.

Babette gasped. "It's far too soon to think about that! They just met. Papa would never give her permission to marry. She is only 17. She won't be 18 until next November."

"You remember our wedding. You were 17 when we met. We waited until the day after your 18th birthday to get married because your father wouldn't grant his permission. And then the official never asked for proof of your age." Orville said.

"That's right. I had my birth certificate along, but no one asked to see it." Babette thought a minute. "I have reservations about Freda and Walter, though. I don't know how she could be ready for marriage. She has always seemed to like someone new every day. They really don't know each other. You and I knew each other for several months before we got married."

Orville said, "Well, I'm fairly sure your parents wouldn't approve. They sure didn't approve of me."

Babette agreed. "Freda does have a flair for the dramatic, and she can be impulsive, not to mention strong willed. But this might be a little too much even for her. I'm not sure she is mature enough for marriage."

"I think Freda is old enough to make her own decisions. You were," said Orville.

Babette frowned. "It seems like you are in favor of this for our act's sake, not for Freda's." She turned toward the window, ending the exchange.

Walter and Freda sat in the back, chatting about their show business experiences. They talked over their appearance at the Majestic and what went right, what they could do better, and how the audience reacted. She chuckled when she related how one young boy came up to her after the show and asked her to marry him. "I had to explain to him, kindly of course, that he was way too young to get married. I asked him to please wait a few years."

Walter told about some of the funny things young women in his audiences had done after he sang, sending him their perfumed hankies and such. "And I never knew who gave them to me so I couldn't thank them." He laughed. "They don't pay as much attention to me when I am in the operator's booth."

They shared stories of embarrassing moments performing. Walter said, "Once I forgot the lyrics and had to hum the tune. It was awkward, but I don't think the audience noticed because they were so busy watching the pictures."

Freda described the time she forgot that she was supposed to perform next. "I was sitting off stage watching the stagehands move things, and Babette had to come and push me onstage. She scolded me for not paying attention." They laughed at these and other mistakes they'd made and silly things they'd observed in other performers.

By the time they arrived in South Bend, Walter and Freda were sitting close to each other and making plans to get together Tuesday. Orville and Babette got off at the stop near their apartment. They waved good night at the new couple and started toward their apartment.

Walter and Freda went a few blocks further to a stop closer to the Heyer home. They walked toward her parent's house. She decided she was not ready to introduce him to her parents. She had clear memories of Fred's response to Babette's announcement that she was in love with Orville and did not want to hear a repeat of that exchange.

Freda asked Walter where he lived. He answered, "I still live at home with my mother, Christina, my older sister, Tillie, and my brother, John. Mother worked for many years as a secretary. Tillie has a pretty good job as a stenographer and helps our mother with expenses. John is studying to be a plumber. Our father died when I was quite young."

"Oh, I'm so sorry. That must have been very hard. You know, Orville's mother died when he was just a boy. I can't imagine losing a parent," she said with sympathy.

"It was difficult. I was quite young, so I don't remember much, but I have heard the stories. Someday I will tell you more. My mother and sister have worked very hard to provide opportunities for John and me."

They stopped about a block away in the shadow of some overgrown lilac bushes. Walter pulled her close and kissed her. Freda's heart pounded as they embraced.

She said, "I'm so glad you've played the saxophone!" Walter looked a bit bemused, shook his head, then walked away toward his home, whistling.

Riding the train Tuesday morning to Elkhart, Orville and the two sisters sat near each other. Walter had gone earlier.

With somewhat thinly veiled intent, Babette turned to Freda and commented, "It seems like you and Walter are getting along famously."

Freda looked at Babette innocently and answered, "Oh, yes. He is such a gentleman. And we really enjoy each other."

Babette glanced at Orville, who was engrossed in a newspaper. "I get the impression that you seriously think you are in love. Am I right?" she quietly asked Freda, realizing she sounded a lot like her own mother a few years ago.

Freda didn't answer.

Babette went on, still sounding like Susanna, "You do know that there are many other things to consider before selecting a husband. Like how would he support you? Do you value the same things? You are such a romantic and have always had crushes on handsome men. You need to be practical."

"I don't think there's anything practical about being in love." Freda sighed. "Anyway, I am sure we would get along as well as you and Orville. And, of course, we both value music and performing." Freda was silent for a minute before asking, "How could you tell you were in love with Orville?"

Babette thought a little and said, "At first, I felt my heart race every time he was near. And there was some magic in our first kisses! Like you, we had our love of music to connect us. Since we've been married, he has been supportive of my playing and encouraged me to continue. He is always gentle, even in our intimate moments."

Freda looked surprised.

Babette blushed a little. "I have really enjoyed getting to know his family. They are so welcoming. It was hard that Papa was disappointed in me, but I am glad he finally is getting to know and like Orville."

Freda considered Babette's words. "Walter did kiss me last night!" she whispered, "and it was heavenly."

Babette raised her eyebrows. "Freda, you have known him only one day! You need to think of your future. I hope Mama and Papa didn't see you kissing. You know how Papa would react."

"Yes, I do," said Freda, "but we were around the corner by those bushes. Oh, his kiss made me feel like I had butterflies in my stomach. I do want to marry him." Freda went on, "He is so interesting and knows so much about the theater world. He lives with his mother, sister, and brother since his father died a while ago. He told me all about the movies he's shown. I think he's seen everything ever filmed. Of course, he can see them for free. And you know how much I admire those movie stars."

"I certainly do," answered Babette recalling the clippings pinned to Freda's walls.

Freda continued, "I am thinking ahead. You heard that he plays saxophone. He could make our act more interesting."

"That would not be the best reason to marry him," said Babette. "You still need some time to learn more about Walter. There are things that aren't apparent about a person at first."

"Like what?" Freda asked.

Babette glanced at Orville to make sure he was still engrossed in the newspaper then explained softly, "Orville is always kind to me. But he is very prudent with our money. Some might call him stingy. I have to spend very carefully because he is always talking about future plans. He is very busy with his job at the store and the bands he directs. Between my teaching and his commitments, we haven't been able to spend much time together. In the early days, I hardly ever saw him except on Sunday afternoons. That continued until recently when we started practicing our act. Thank goodness he has dropped some of his responsibilities to concentrate on the Musical Reeses. We've been together more in the last few months than we were in the two—almost three—years we've been married."

Freda asked, "Do you think it was a mistake to get married so young?"

"No, I don't. Some things have been harder than I thought, but I am enjoying this vaudeville act. I hope we get lots of bookings."

The train arrived in Elkhart, and they prepared for their shows. The matinee went well. As on Monday, people responded to them exuberantly, oohing at Orville's performance on the aluminum bars, which was a real novelty for them. The saxophone trios were well received, and Freda's singing was perfect. Everyone gasped at their last segment when Babette rolled out the covered xylophone and Freda attached a blindfold over Babette's eyes. She played with such ease and skill that the audience clapped loudly and stood for an ovation when she finished.

It was another mild day, so Freda told Orville and Babette that she and Walter were going to spend some time in the city park between shows. Orville looked at Babette, and they both gave their approval.

Babette said, "Just be sure you're back in plenty of time for our evening entrance."

As they walked in the park. Walter put his arm around Freda's shoulders and said, "I've never met anyone like you, Freda. You are so smart and lively. Not to mention funny and lovely. The thought of being with you makes me very happy."

Freda stopped and turned to him. "I feel the same way, Walter. Well, not the lovely part, I guess."

Walter chuckled. "I suppose not."

Freda said, "The first time I saw you in South Bend, I thought we could be a couple. Now I know that's true. Do you think this could be love?"

"I'm not sure, but from what I've seen in the movies, it's pretty close." Walter squeezed her shoulders. Since no one was around to see them, he hugged her tightly to him. "I think I would like to marry you."

"Walter, are you proposing?" asked Freda.

"I guess I am. I know people will say we haven't known each other long enough. Even our families don't know about us, except for Babette and Orville. It feels strange that we haven't met each other's families. But I am sure of what I am feeling. Will you marry me?"

"My answer is yes," said Freda, returning his hug. We'll have to work around my commitments to The *Three Musical Reeses*. I think it's a great idea. I won't be 18 until fall, but I do look older, don't you think?"

"You look marvelous," Walter said. "If you're willing, I'm sure we can make this happen."

"I also hope you will become part of our act. But I do wonder what people will think about us marrying," she continued.

"I don't know. I imagine my family will not be happy, nor your parents either, since we are both so young," Walter said.

"How old are you?" Freda asked Walter, amazed that she didn't know the answer.

Walter drew himself up to his full six feet. "I'm 17 too, but I'm told l look a lot older. I could say I'm 21."

Freda looked at him carefully. "Yes, you could certainly pass for 21."

"I hope everyone will eventually come to accept the idea and be happy for us. As for joining the Musical Reeses, I would love to be part of your classy act. I think I could add quite a bit! And we shouldn't care what other people think!" Walter stamped his foot for emphasis.

"You're right," said Freda, stamping her foot too. "This is about us!"

Walter smiled.

Freda continued, "I don't think they require proof of age for a marriage license. I can just say I'm 18 or 19. Babette said they didn't ask for her birth certificate."

Walter nodded.

Freda said, "If we don't tell anyone except Orville and Babette, no one can stop us. I do think Babette will come around, since she was 17 when she met Orville. And Orville likes you. But we'd better get married right away if you are going to join our tour. I suppose there is still time to get a marriage license today. The government building is a couple blocks that way." She pointed down the street. "If we get our marriage license today here in Elkhart, no one in South Bend will know about it until the deed is done Thursday. We'd better hurry so we are back in time for the evening performance."

"Indeed!" Walter took Freda's hand, and they headed off toward the government building.

Babette took Freda aside when they returned to the theater and said, "Freda we need to talk. Are you in love with Walter? Or are you just infatuated?"

"I am sure I am in love with him. I told you we like all the same things, the same music, the same actors, the same songs, the same movies . . ."

Babette interrupted her, "Oh, Freda, Mama said you were sweet on someone new almost every day. How can you be sure this will last?" asked Babette.

"I just know it." Freda tossed her head. "I have a big surprise for you." She showed her the license to marry she and Walter had gotten.

"My goodness!" Babette exclaimed. "When are you planning this?"

"Thursday," said Freda, breathlessly.

Babette looked flabbergasted and said, "That is awfully fast. Not even four full days after meeting him. Are you sure you know what you're doing?" she asked, knowing she was again echoing Susanna's words when she wanted to marry Orville.

"I think so. We really love each other, and Walter wants very much to join the Musical Reeses," Freda answered.

Babette decided not to tell Orville before the evening show. She didn't want him to be distracted. She was flustered enough for both of them.

Babette managed to keep herself focused on the music, so the Tuesday evening performance went even better than the matinee. Afterwards, they met their audience and signed autographs until the line of people ended.

Freda whispered to Babette, "I've always dreamed of this." She smiled and signed her name on the playbills.

The sisters put away the act's smaller items, and Walter helped Orville stow the big instruments and prepare things for Wednesday. They went to the dressing rooms to change out of their stage clothes. When the two sisters were ready, they stood in the doorway, speaking to each other in low voices.

Walter and Orville came down the hall. "What on earth are you two discussing? Are you conspiring together?" asked Orville,

Freda said, "I wouldn't call it conspiring exactly." She showed him the marriage license.

He looked at Freda and Walter seriously. "Well, that is a surprise. Your marrying does seem a little hurried as these things go. But it probably is a good idea if we want Walter included in the Musical Reeses." As an afterthought he asked, "Do you really like, er, love each other?"

At the same time, both Freda and Walter said, "Yes." They laughed and clasped hands as they walked toward the door.

Babette and Orville followed at a little distance. Babette asked Orville quietly, "Is our act the most important thing in your life? Aren't you concerned about Freda's well-being?"

"Oh, I think Freda will do very well to marry Walter. I've inquired a bit about him, and everyone seems to think highly of him."

Babette looked a bit skeptical. "I'm just not sure they know enough about themselves or each other for marriage."

"From what I've observed, they seem to be taken with each other." Orville turned away, concluding the conversation.

The group boarded the train back to South Bend. This time the couples sat near each other.

Orville asked in a low voice, "When are you actually going to get married?"

"We are planning it for this Thursday morning," answered Freda.

"Will you tell your families? Orville asked. "Your parents might raise some objections."

Freda said, "We know they will. That's why we aren't telling anyone but you and Betty right now. We have arranged for a Justice named Aaron Work to perform the ceremony Thursday morning. We have asked him to keep it a secret." She paused, then added, "We would like both of you to be there with us."

Babette said, "If you think this is the right thing to do, I suppose I shouldn't stand in your way."

"I think we can take care of everything," Freda said. "They have to publish the license in the Elkhart paper soon after, but no one in South Bend will know until we're married!"

Orville said, "I hope this works out well for you both. You do seem to like each other a lot."

Babette asked, "Are you doing this for our act or because you think you are right for each other?"

"I suppose the answer is both. We love each other, and we love the idea of being on stage together," answered Freda.

Babette said, "I'm sure Mama and Papa won't be overjoyed. Freda, you are still only 17."

"I will be 18 in November," she said defending herself. "You were nearly as young when you got married. Besides, I would really enjoy having Walter in our act. After all, you have Orville."

"It sounds like you're not going to tell our parents, are you?" Babette accused.

"Of course we will. After we're married. And you should talk. You went against Papa's wishes when you married Orville. Remember how Papa accepted that!" Freda replied indignantly.

Orville tried to calm everyone, saying, "I actually think this a good idea. Congratulations, Walter. I think you and Freda will be happy together. This is a good step for everyone." He put his arm around Babette. "You know, these sisters are pretty amazing."

Walter, who was beginning to feel uncomfortable, smiled and said, "Without a doubt. Thank you. I appreciate your encouragement."

They remained wrapped in their own thoughts for the rest of the ride to South Bend.

Walter accompanied Freda on her way to the Heyer house. Again, he held her close and kissed her beneath the lilacs before they parted ways. "I can't wait until Thursday," he said.

Freda said, "Two days is a long time. I'll see you tomorrow. Then it's only one day we have to wait!" She blew him a kiss and walked toward home.

Wednesday, Walter and Freda took an early train to Elkhart to check on some wedding details. They needed to purchase rings, pick out a pretty bouquet, and order a cake to be sent to The Majestic on Thursday afternoon.

Orville and Babette came a bit later allowing enough time to arrange for flowers for the celebration. Babette gave Freda a necklace that her grandmother had passed down, and unclasped her own bracelet for Freda to wear, which covered the "something old" and "something borrowed" bridal requirements. Freda bought a blue handkerchief to take care of the "new and blue" tradition.

Once all their errands were completed, they walked to the theater in plenty of time to prepare for their shows.

The matinee went as well as Tuesday's performance, with an enthusiastic and receptive audience. People once more lined up for their autographs.

During the break, Orville found an empty room and asked Walter to show him what he remembered about playing the saxophone and motioned toward his own instrument.

"You don't mind if I use your saxophone?" Walter asked.

"Not at all. Go ahead and try a few scales or whatever suits you." Orville rummaged through their music for something Walter could sight-read.

After a couple of honks and squawks, Walter remembered how to get a clear tone and played some scales he recalled.

"Hmm. Not a bad sound. Can you read this?" Orville showed him a sheet of music.

Walter played it and only missed two notes.

Orville said, "Excellent! I think we can work out some arrangements for you to join us for our next engagement. Would you be willing to sing duets with Freda?"

"Of course. She will be my wife."

The evening show was also successful. They were all in high spirits when they boarded the interurban.

After arriving in South Bend, Walter walked Freda home. They talked about their upcoming wedding and made a list for Thursday. They discussed how they would keep things secret and what they should say in notes they left explaining why they weren't going to be home Thursday night. They kissed and parted.

Fred and Susanna were still up when Freda arrived home. Monday and Tuesday, she had had stories from the shows to share with them while she ate some of their supper leftovers. But this time she just said, "Good night" and went upstairs to her room. Lying on her bed, she turned the recent and coming events over in her mind, and wondered if she was doing the right thing marrying Walter. It all seemed so logical and romantic, but she had to admit, it was rushed.

At the Christensen house, Walter's mother and sister had waited for him, too. John was out. Christina asked, "How did the shows go tonight? By the way, there is some leftover stew for you."

Walter said, "Thanks but I'm not very hungry. I think we did a good job. The audience was very receptive." He didn't feel like conversation, afraid he might give something away, so he didn't elaborate.

Tillie asked, "Is anything wrong, Walter? You're usually so talkative after your shows. Tonight, you seem a little distracted."

Walter answered, "I guess I am just thinking about the new song they asked me to sing tomorrow." He looked the other way so she couldn't see his expression. As soon as he could, he went to his room, where he, too, lay awake wondering if he was doing the right thing. He knew that he was ready for a change and a new challenge.

Thursday dawned, and Walter got up and dressed in his best and only suit. He looked around his bedroom where his brother was still asleep, grabbed a few things and quietly put them in his satchel. He quickly scratched a note to leave on his pillow saying, "I will not be coming home tonight. I will explain later." He tiptoed downstairs, grabbed a chunk of bread and walked away, chewing and wondering what his brother, sister, and mother would make of his note. He went directly to the streetcorner on the interurban route to catch an early car to Elkhart.

Freda too was awake early. She dressed in her fanciest frock, making sure she had her "somethings" with her. She put a few extra things in the oversized drawstring bag she had sewn for carrying things to and from the theater. She sat at her desk to write a note to her family telling them not to expect her home that night, and that she loved them all very much. She came downstairs for breakfast and managed to tease her brothers as she did every morning. She left earlier than usual, explaining that she had to take care of a few things in Elkhart before the shows. She hugged Mama and Papa, holding each one an extra moment. Then, without looking back, she walked to Orville and Babette's apartment.

Following the tradition of grooms not glimpsing their brides before the wedding, they had decided that Walter would take an earlier train, and Babette, Orville, and Freda would come a little later. They needed to stop for Freda's bouquet before they would meet at the office of Justice Work at 10 a.m.

Walter stopped at a local hotel to reserve a room for two nights. He was at the government building first and paced back and forth outside Mr. Work's office. There were few people in the hallways at that hour on a Thursday. Around five minutes before 10 o'clock he finally heard the squeaky hinges of the building's main door open. He listened to the echoing sounds of footsteps ascending the staircase. After what seemed an eternity he saw Orville, Babette, and Freda round the corner. The bride, holding her small bouquet of chrysanthemums, and the groom smiled broadly at each other, as they entered the office to say their vows. The justice declared them man and wife, and the bride and groom kissed. Then tears, hugs, and congratulations filled the room.

It was close to 11 a.m. when the ceremony and document signings were done. The two couples treated themselves to a lunch at one of the better Elkhart restaurants. Afterward, Orville and Babette went to the theater while the new Mr. and Mrs. Christensen walked to the telegraph office to send telegrams to their families. They didn't want them to worry about their safety. They then went to the theater to get ready for the matinee performance.

Freda showed off her ring to the other players and said, "Walter and I just got married! We will celebrate here between the shows with a cake and punch. We hope you will join us."

The other performers clapped and cheered. A few of them had guessed what was going on between Walter and Freda, and the rest were happy to finally understand their mysterious behavior over the past two days.

After the matinee, the cake was delivered. Babette handed out pieces on napkins, and Orville poured punch. The other performers offered congratulatory toasts. Someone sat at the piano and played dance tunes. Walter and Freda and several others whirled around until someone suggested they save their energy for the next show.

When the evening show was over, autographs had been signed and equipment was stowed, Orville and Babette got ready to return to South Bend. Freda filled two boxes with cake and asked Babette to deliver them to the Heyer and Christensen families. Freda asked her to tell them they would come soon and explain everything.

Babette lingered to hug her sister goodbye. Freda whispered, "Do you have any advice for me?"

"Now you want my advice?" Babette smiled. "I think you will figure it out."

Walter said to Freda, "It's time to go to our hotel to check in."

Freda gathered up her things. Walter helped her put on her coat and held the door open for her. She glanced back at Babette with a look that said, "See what a gentleman he is?" She put her arm in Walter's.

In their hotel room, they took off their coats and embraced. They began unbuttoning each other's clothes as their senses filled with new sights and feelings. Then Walter took Freda in his arms and gently moved her toward the bed. Their adolescent passions took over and they explored each other until they fell into exhausted sleep.

The Friday morning sun shining in the window woke Freda. Their wedding day had been cloudy and drizzly. She opened her eyes and exclaimed, "A sunny day. That's a good sign!"

She looked over at Walter who was watching her. "My goodness," she exclaimed. "What a marvelous night! What time is it?"

Walter smiled and kissed her, saying, "It's already 10:00."

"Let's get something to eat and go to The Majestic," Freda suggested.

Walter agreed. "I hope our families enjoyed the cake. I'm sure your brothers did. I know our parents will be upset. Our mothers must have asked Babette to explain things. She had to tell them more of our story."

"My parents would have asked plenty of questions," said Freda.

Walter said, "Mother does know I can take care of myself, but I really don't want to hurt her. We must go back to South Bend tomorrow morning before our last shows. Then we'll hurry back here for the matinee. We will stay here tonight, but where will we stay Saturday night? I share a room with my brother so staying there would be impossible."

Freda got up and started getting dressed. "I think we should visit your family first, then mine. After we talk to my parents, I am going to ask them if we can stay in my room tomorrow night. I'm quite sure they will agree though I'm not expecting they will be happy. Goodness, I'm hungry."

"When the Saturday evening show is over, I'll help Orville with the big instruments. You and Babette can take care of the smaller ones. We can store them in their apartment until we leave for Chicago on Sunday. We'll need to transport it all on the interurban. The cars shouldn't be too full on a Saturday night." Walter got up and began dressing.

They stopped in the hotel dining room for a late breakfast and went on to The Majestic, where Babette and Orville were just arriving. Freda asked, "How did Walter's family react?"

Orville said, "Your mother was very pleasant to us. She was surprised by your wedding news, and obviously disappointed to not have been there. Your sister had suspected something was up because you had been so quiet the night before. She didn't seem as happy. Your brother just smiled. They were all relieved to get your telegram. I'm sure they will want to talk to you soon!"

"Yes, we are going there tomorrow morning to talk to both of our families before our last shows," said Freda.

Walter asked Babette, "How did your parents react?"

She answered, "They were shocked. Mama cried. Papa looked like he might explode. But Mama put on a brave face and calmed him down a bit. I'm sure they want to hear your explanation. By the way, Herb and Fred loved the cake."

Freda smiled and said, "I expected that." Her expression changed as she added, "And I also anticipated Mama and Papa's reactions. I hope we can reassure them when we go there tomorrow."

Babette looked at Freda with sympathy and said, "Yes, you need to do that. I don't envy you the task ahead."

Freda looked at Walter and sighed. He put his arm around her shoulders.

Their Friday shows went well, and the audiences were filled with appreciative attendees. They signed lots of autographs, then put away their instruments and costumes.

Orville and Babette returned to their South Bend apartment. Freda and Walter went back to their hotel, where they had the privacy to explore new ways of pleasing each other.

Saturday morning, Walter and Freda got up early, packed their things and checked out. They had a quick bite in the hotel dining room and boarded the interurban for South Bend.

They first walked to Walter's home and knocked at the door. Tillie opened it and said, with a sharp tone, "Well, there you are." She opened the door further and stepped back to let them through. "And I assume this is your new wife?" she said looking directly at Freda.

Walter answered, "Yes, this is my wife, Freda."

"Mother has been so anxious about you. I have too. When the telegram came, she stopped worrying so much but we've all been upset," said Tillie.

Christina looked as if she had been crying. She began crying again as Walter walked over to her. He lifted her from her chair and hugged her.

"Freda and I met this week in Elkhart, where the *Three Musical Reeses* and I were on the same bill. We fell in love at first sight, as they say. Their touring schedule is very busy so it made sense to get married as soon as we could," explained Walter. "Now I can join them for some shows."

"But Walter, you are so young," Christina said.

Walter answered, "I think I am old enough to know my own mind. Lots of people get married at my age."

"We were glad to meet Freda's sister and brother-in-law last night. They told us about the *Three Musical Reeses*. They did seem like nice people, although we weren't overjoyed with their news." Christina dabbed at a tear.

John, who was upstairs, heard their voices and came down the stairs. "What is going on here?" he asked.

Walter introduced Freda to him and repeated the story of their marriage.

Tillie directed her gaze accusingly at them saying, "And you didn't have the decency to tell your family?"

Walter continued, "We didn't tell Freda's family either, except Babette and Orville, who perform with her. Freda is an exceptional musician and has a beautiful voice. I know it's only been a few days, but we realized right away we were meant for each other."

Tillie eyed him skeptically. "You really didn't have much time to get to know one another, did you?"

"Tillie, don't always assume the worst. Freda and I have a great deal in common. Orville invited me to join their act when I don't have commitments here in South Bend. He has written music that I can play in their saxophone group, and there are songs that I can sing with Freda. They will call the act the Musical Reeses since there can be either three or four of us now. Orville wants to sign on with one of the bigger vaudeville circuits so we can tour the country. We are going go to Chicago tomorrow where we can make more connections."

"Isn't that grand?" huffed Tillie with a hint of sarcasm. "My little brother, a vaudeville star."

"You know that I have always enjoyed show business. But I wasn't getting very far with my jobs around here. This is a great opportunity for me. The Musical Reeses have appearances scheduled through the summer."

John, who had been listening, said, "Walter, you are full of surprises. I, for one, wish you success. I'm not sure who will make more people happy, you as a performer or me as a plumber. At least I know I will always have work," he added in jest.

Walter and Freda smiled. Walter said, "Thanks, John. I appreciate that."

He turned back to his mother. "We can't stay long because tomorrow we leave for Chicago, and we still have to visit Freda's parents. And then get back to Elkhart for our last shows."

"Tomorrow!" Christina gasped. "This all has happened so fast."

"You know what they say," Walter went on. "You have to strike while the iron's hot."

Walter went to the bedroom to gather some of his things. Freda stood by the door under Tillie's icy gaze. Christina and John asked her some questions about herself, and Freda felt slightly more comfortable.

Walter soon came down the stairs. "Thank goodness he didn't take long," thought Freda.

As they prepared to leave, Christina wiped her eyes and said, "Walter, I know you have a lot of talent. And I hope this goes well for you." She smiled weakly at Freda. "And you too, Freda. Take care of my boy."

"I will," answered Freda. "He is a very kind gentleman, and I care deeply for him."

To Walter, Christina said, "I will miss you. Please let us know how things are going."

"I will miss you and John and Tillie too, Mother. We will keep you informed."

He hugged his mother and brother before they hurried out the door. Tillie had left the room.

On the walk to the Heyer's Freda and Walter talked about his family's reaction. Walter said, "I'm sure Mother and John will learn to like you."

"Your mother and brother seem very sweet, and I think they could like me. I'm not so sure about your sister, though," Freda said.

"Tillie has strong opinions about everything. And she has always been very protective of me. She might see this as sort of a betrayal."

"She certainly didn't seem very friendly."

Walter put his arm around her and said confidently, "She will warm up when she gets to know you."

Freda wasn't that sure.

The reaction at the Heyer household was not much different. When they arrived, Susanna opened the door. "Come in," she said without much warmth. Her eyes were red from crying.

Fred came in from tinkering in his workshop and looked at Freda first, then Walter.

"Hello, Mama and Papa," Freda nervously twisted the ring on her finger. "I would like to introduce Walter. You have heard that we got married yesterday."

Susanna said, "Let's sit down." She was determined to be pleasant. "Betty told us the basics last night, but we would like to hear your version."

Fred paced the room, refusing to sit. "What on earth are you thinking? You haven't even known each other a week. And Freda, you have never even had a beau, just schoolgirl crushes. How can you think you are ready to be married?" His voice had an edge. "I don't understand how this could be. You are only 17 and I hear Walter is young too."

Though expected, it wasn't the welcome Freda had been hoping for, and she took Walter's hand, afraid of what he was thinking. "Oh, Papa, please don't be so upset. I have known of Walter for a while. I saw him perform last fall. And yes, I did have a crush on him, even back then. But when I met him in person and learned what a gentleman he is and how much we have in common, I guess I lost my head along with my heart." She borrowed Walter's words. "It was love at first sight."

Fred was not convinced. "How will you support her?" he asked Walter.

Walter answered, "I have a lot of experience performing illustrated songs and running movies. I plan to join the Musical Reeses and perform with them when my other commitments allow."

"Betty and Orville think he will be a great addition to our act. He has a beautiful voice," Freda added. "Betty gave me many things to think about, but in the end, she agreed with our plan. I've seen how things have worked out for them."

Fred was not having any of it. "You are both too young to know what you are doing. What if your act doesn't succeed? You certainly haven't thought things through very carefully. What will you do then? I am too upset to discuss this any further. But what's done is done, I suppose." With that he stomped off to his workroom, muttering about both his daughters making rash choices.

Susanna looked at them both a bit sadly. "You really are so young, even younger than Babette was. I'm sorry Fred was so harsh. It will take some time for him to get used to having both our daughters married. But I do wish you had waited a year or at least a few months."

"I know, Mama, but I'm almost 18. And this way Walter can tour with us. I'm sure Papa will like Walter as much as he likes Orville when he gets to know him."

"Walter," Mama said, "you do look like a nice young man. I've seen your name in the newspaper ads for illustrated songs in South Bend."

"Oh, Mama," Freda gushed. "I can't wait for him to join our act. He plays the saxophone, so we have a quartet now. You must have seen the reviews we got in the Elkhart newspaper for our weeks at the Majestic."

"Yes, I did. It sounded like you were well received," Susanna said. "I know appearing on stage has been your dream for a long time, Freda."

"Yes, it has. I am so excited."

"That's all hopeful, Freda. But show business can be very difficult."

"I have heard that, but so far, I have really enjoyed it."

"I suppose I should say congratulations, but I admit I have some misgivings."

Walter looked at his watch and said, "It's almost 11 o'clock, Freda. We need to get back to Elkhart for our last shows."

"Where are you staying tonight when you are done at The Majestic? Would you like to stay here in your room?" Susanna asked.

"That will be very helpful." Freda answered, happy she didn't have to ask. "Tomorrow the four of us are going to Chicago where we might make more connections. Then we appear in Escanaba just north of Chicago later in April. We have other shows booked as well, so I guess we'll be on the road."

"So soon? I was hoping we'd have some time to get to know Walter." Susanna frowned, then glanced at the mantel clock. "You had better leave so you won't be late for your shows."

Young Herb and Fred had been playing in their room, but they stopped to eavesdrop on the conversation downstairs.

Fred turned to Herb and said, "I'm glad there will be five men and three women in our family. I hope Walter is as nice as Orville."

"Freda has always been a great sister, and I hope she will be happy," added Herb, turning back toward their bedroom.

Freda and Walter arrived in Elkhart just in time to get ready for the last matinee. The Saturday shows had the biggest crowds of the week. The *Musical*

Reeses got their usual reception and spent quite a while signing autographs for each show. Then they packed up their instruments and other gear, said goodbye to the other performers, and wheeled their boxes to the station. In South Bend, they got it all safely to Babette and Orville's apartment. Walter and Freda said good night and walked to the Heyer home.

Sunday morning Susanna prepared breakfast. When Freda introduced her brothers to Walter, she told them that Walter ran movie reels and knew about all the latest equipment. They pestered him with questions about the latest developments. Fred Senior mostly listened but gradually grew impressed with Walter's expertise on the mechanics of running films. He was considerably calmer than the night before as he learned more about Walter, although he did not go so far as being friendly. He soon excused himself and went to his workshop.

After breakfast they said their farewells. Susanna said, "Before you go, I want to give you this." She handed Freda an envelope.

"What is it?" asked Freda.

Susanna answered, "These are all the articles I've clipped from the newspapers about your appearances at the Majestic. I think it would be a good idea to keep as many of them as you can. Then you can remember these days."

Freda hugged her mother and said, "I love you. Please tell Papa I love him too."

Susanna said, "We love you, too and we both hope you do well."

"Thank you for letting us stay here and feeding us such a great breakfast," Walter added.

Freda and Walter left for Babette and Orville's to help move all their instruments and equipment to a corner where the streetcar to Chicago stopped. They hoisted everything onto the car and rumbled off, bound for Chicago.

"Whew, I feel like we've been in a whirlwind, and everything has been rushed," Freda said as they took their seats.

"Kind of like everything else this week," said Walter, winking at Freda.

In Chicago, they found rooms in the boarding house where Orville,

Babette and Freda had stayed earlier. They attended several shows and became acquainted with many performers and managers. They practiced some new things, and Freda and Walter had time to enjoy each other and their new marital status.

One day Freda got a letter from Susanna containing a clipping about their wedding story. A friend who lived in Indianapolis had read it in the newspaper and cut it out.

Freda exclaimed, "Look Walter! Our wedding story was written up in the *Indianapolis News*!" She handed the clipping to Walter.

He scanned it and said with a bit of irritation. "I wish they could spell my last name correctly! Now it's your last name too."

"I still think it's exciting. I'll put it in the envelope Mama gave me. We're almost famous!" she exclaimed.

"Almost," Walter emphasized. "I'd be happier if they spelled my name right for a change. It does make a pretty good story." He handed the clipping back to Freda.

CUPID AS A "BILLTOPPER."

Takes Hand In Rearranging Vaudeville Program at South Bend.

[Special to The Indianapolis News.]

SOUTH BEND, Ind., April 7.—Romance, on its sentimental side, as well as on the practical phase, worked out happily, and in short order, on the vaudeville stage here this week. Walter Christianson and Miss Freda Heyer met for the first time behind the scenes Monday. Miss Heyer is one of the "Musical Reeses." Christianson was on the bill, but was in another act. Monday's acquaintance, Tuesday's flame, Wednesday's betrothal, and Thursday's wedding, at Elkhart, forms a record made to fit the vaudeville player's plan of town-to-town living. A place has been made for Christianson as a "Musical Reese," and he and Mrs. Christianson in future will appear in the same "turn."

© *The Indianapolis News* - April 7, 1911

Since Walter had already committed himself to performing illustrated songs and running movie reels in South Bend over the summer, they created a flexible schedule that would include him when he was available. Orville worked out several duets that Walter and Freda could sing together when he joined them, or she could sing by herself. He also wrote saxophone parts that could be added to their trio arrangements. This way Walter could be one of the *Musical Reeses* whenever he was free. The publicity Mr. Keith's office sent out still referred to them as the *Three Musical Reeses*, but whenever Walter joined them, he was introduced as a special surprise.

All four of them went to Escanaba for their scheduled appearance April 20 to 23. They were happy to be paid since they found themselves running short of money. They drew record crowds and adding Walter as a special surprise worked well.

Walter had committed himself to a few May dates working in South Bend. Orville decided that just the *Three Musical Reeses* would appear for the engagements in Canada.

Freda and Walter bid each other a tearful farewell.

"Good heavens," grumbled Orville. "They will only be apart a couple of weeks."

Babette smiled. "That's typical Freda!"

When they got off the train in Cobalt, Ontario, they were happy to see Mr. Keith had kept his word. There were pink posters everywhere advertising the *Three Musical Reeses*. Freda read one out loud as they walked by. "LYRIC, WEEK OF MAY 1, Three Reeses Novelty Musical Act, Some Music, Some Swell Lookers, Classy Wardrobe, Winners of the Gold Medal"

Babette chuckled as she repeated, "Swell lookers. I never really thought of myself that way."

"I suppose we have Orville to thank for the 'Classy Wardrobe,'" said Freda, laughing.

In Sudbury, Ontario, articles in the local newspaper touted their May 8, 9, and 10 performances as an "Exceptional Opportunity at the Grand Opera House." The sisters laughed as they read the words 'Swell Lookers' and 'Classy Wardrobe' again.

Freda said, "Orville does look impressive in this picture of him with the aluminum harp."

from the private collection of Sue Thurman

At the shows in both towns, they had good, loud, and appreciative audiences. Freda found copies of the papers and clipped more articles for her envelope. When their engagements were over, she collected one of the posters they had laughed about.

During the last part of May they played in Dixon, Illinois, where Walter was able to join them as a special feature. He convinced his mother and siblings to come see a Saturday matinee. In early June the Three Reeses appeared in Sault St. Marie, Michigan. Then Orville and Babette returned to Chicago.

Freda went on to South Bend to be with Walter. He had been staying at his mother's home, and she joined him there. Mrs. Christensen was friendly and tried to make her comfortable. Freda did what she could to help out and not be a burden, but Tillie was not overjoyed at her presence and made Freda well aware of it. When Walter was working, Freda frequently visited her parent's home where she felt welcomed by her mother and brothers. She usually left before her father returned from work.

Back in Chicago, Orville received word that the job Keith had mentioned in Detroit, Michigan was available if they could get there. "Of course, we can," said Orville, confidently.

Saturday, Babette sent a telegram to Freda, instructing her to meet them in Niles, Michigan, on Monday, June 19, and buy a ticket to Detroit. She and Orville would be coming through Niles from Chicago. The three would play at the Wayne Hotel Roof Gardens in Detroit that evening.

Freda tried to talk Walter into joining them and said, "Oh, Walter this could be our big break! You could cancel a day or two and join us."

"I don't think that would be wise," Walter answered. "We need my income." As usual, he was engaged at another South Bend theater. "What is it that you always say? 'A bird in the hand is worth two in the bush.' I think I'd better keep my obligations and not risk being replaced by someone else. I will try to join you if I can." He knew there were always new applicants for his jobs.

Freda hurriedly packed what she needed and got ready to go. Walter's mother came into the room and apologized that Tillie had not been very friendly. She said, "I have seen how happy Walter is with you and I am glad for him. Tillie worries so about me, but I am happy that Walter found you. I am sorry Tillie has been unwelcoming."

Freda hugged her and said, "Thank you, Mrs. Christensen. You have tried to make me feel at home here and I appreciate that."

NIGHT LETTER.

Form

THE WESTERN UNION TELEGRAPH COMPAN

INCORPORATED

25,000 OFFICES IN AMERICA   CABLE SERVICE TO ALL THE WORLD

This Company TRANSMITS and DELIVERS messages only on conditions limiting its liability, which have been assented to by the sender of the following I Errors can be guarded against only by repeating a message back to the sending station for comparison, and the Company will not hold itself liable for erro transmission or delivery of Unrepeated Night Letters, sent at reduced rates, beyond a sum equal to ten times the amount paid for transmission; nor in any case b of Fifty Dollars, at which, unless otherwise stated below, this message has been valued by the sender thereof, nor in any case where the claim is not presented in sixty days after the message is filed with the Company for transmission.
This is an UNREPEATED NIGHT LETTER, and is delivered by request of the sender, under the conditions named above.

THEO. N. VAIL, PRESIDENT   BELVIDERE BROOKS, GENERAL

RECEIVED AT

189 CH DC CA   49 Paid NL.

NC Chicago June 17th. 1911.

Mrs. Fred I. Christensen,

1010 Fuerbringer St., SouthBend, Ind.

We play Wayne Roof Garden Detroit Mich. Monday Will leave Chicago

905 Monday morning and go through Niles Meet us at Niles Buy ticket

from Niles to Detroit Be sure and have a little money with you Answer

at once 1644 North Clark St.

                    Betty.   907PM

from the private collection of Sue Thurman

They smiled at each other, and Christina said, "I was very impressed by your show in Illinois. You all are very good musicians. I wish you well in Detroit."

Freda thanked her and brought her things to the door. She had to travel to Niles by herself before joining Babette and Orville for the rest of the trip. She was excited. Detroit was a big city.

Freda's collection of programs, posters and articles grew. Their shows went well as did subsequent ones in Buffalo, New York, and some smaller towns. Their appearances drew big and welcoming audiences, but they did not bring offers of future bookings.

Orville and Babette returned to Chicago and Freda to South Bend to await their August and September bookings in Kansas, Missouri, and Oklahoma.

Orville hoped performing for different audiences might connect them with other circuits. The Orpheum Circuit out of California had a number of theater connections in the central states. He hoped an agent would be interested in signing their act.

Freda, Orville, and Babette were eager to start their big west central states tour. They got their instruments and baggage to the train station on Saturday morning, August 5, 1911. As exciting as the trip was, they weren't especially looking forward to the two-day train ride to Kansas.

They approached the ticket window and asked for three tickets to Hutchinson, Kansas. The ticket master said, "That will be $213, please."

Orville pulled out his wallet and peeled off the bills.

"My goodness." Freda couldn't keep the surprise from her voice. "That is a lot of money!"

Babette said, "Yes, it certainly is. More than we make for a week of shows."

Orville looked a bit unhappy but said, "I heard someone say once that in order to make money you need to spend some. I know we are taking a chance, but I am hoping it will pay off for us."

They slept as well as they could in their seats on the train since they hadn't wanted to spend the extra for sleeping quarters. On their arrival in Hutchinson, they unloaded their things and brought them to the theater in Riverside Park.

Again, they saw evidence that Mr. Keith had promoted their appearance adequately. Freda, Babette, and Orville eagerly read the reviews that appeared in the local papers after their shows. Orville said, "This is a good one. 'The Three Reeses do a variety of musical numbers on different instruments that show considerable skill and taste in the way they render them.' That's quite a statement, 'considerable skill and taste.'"

Freda said, "Well, we do put on a high-class act. Hear this. 'Their work can be classed as considerably better than the McLarsons who were liked so well while here several weeks ago.'" They all appreciated that statement and felt that maybe they were getting somewhere.

On Sunday they boarded the train for their next engagement at Wonderland Park, in Wichita, Kansas, August 13. Again, they saw flyers and posters promoting their appearance. Unfortunately, Freda was not feeling well, so she did not participate in all of the shows. In spite of her absence, their reviews were positive. Orville read from the *Wichita Beacon*, "It says the *Musical Reeses* offer what is easily one of best instrumental musical acts ever seen here. Both members are artists, and all the features of their act are highly pleasing. One of the best." He smiled at the compliment. Freda added all of these to her envelope.

Orville spent a morning composing a letter to the Eau Claire, Michigan, newspaper about their travel experiences. He felt that it couldn't hurt to keep their names in front of people back home while they were gone. Plus, most of the people from Michigan had never seen these parts. He wrote, "August 15. We are now in the land of grasshoppers; one has to actually kick them out of the way to keep from stepping on them. Our first stop was at Hutchinson, Kansas, a pretty little town of 31,000 population and it and the surrounding country is directly over a bed of rock salt. The bed is 300 feet deep and covers an area of over 40 square miles, consequently all the water in the vicinity has a salty taste. The drinking water for the city is furnished from springs . . .and sold at 25 cents per can for the largest size. I tell you Michigan residents ought to appreciate their supply of fresh water for it is the best water there is; my mouth is watering now for a good drink from the Eau Claire town pump." He described the different crops he had seen while riding the train and noted that "the weather has been unmercifully hot, being from 100° to 110° in the shade." Reuben saved that newspaper to show them when they returned.

Their next engagement was August 20 at Electric Park, Kansas City, Missouri, followed by an appearance the week of August 27 at another

Wonderland Park in Joplin, Missouri. Their shows were all received warmly, and the reviews were added to Freda's collection. However, they did not lead to offers of further engagements.

Somewhat discouraged, they finished with a week starting September third at the New Lyric Theater in Oklahoma City. Walter was done with his summer engagements so he telegraphed Orville that he could make the three-day train trip from Chicago to join them there.

Orville and Babette were happy to add him to their act as they were all getting a little tired of each other. Of course, Freda was ecstatic to see Walter and flew to his arms when they met him at the train station. She told him about their performing and traveling experiences and all the different countryside they had seen. "Endless wheatfields, mining country, muddy rivers, no lakes. Everything is so different. I even managed to sleep in my seat on jostling train rides. I will be very glad to get back to our soft bed." She smiled flirtatiously. "With you in it, of course. I've missed you so much." They embraced again.

Walter described the movies he had shown while they were gone. There were a couple of new ones. *Pinocchio* was his favorite, but *Dante's Inferno* had been very popular. Freda was eager to hear about the newest actors and actresses who were appearing on film.

"We had some extra excitement too," Walter said. "My brother John had been hired by the American Moving Picture Theater as acting manager because Mr. Codd was on vacation. He hired me to operate the projection machine, which you know I've done many times."

Freda nodded. "Yes, and you're very good at changing reels. Hardly anyone can tell when you do it."

"I appreciate that. It is quite a trick to get the timing right." He went on with his story. "Well, just before 10 pm we were preparing to change reels. I smelled something burning and saw smoke. A film had overheated and started a small fire in our booth."

"Oh my!" exclaimed Freda, knowing that theater fires were frequent and deadly.

"Right away I shut the doors to the booth – it's fireproof, you know – and found the emergency appliances to put out the blaze. I succeeded, but someone had turned in a fire alarm. The fire was out before the firemen got there. No one in the audience suspected anything until then. They even wrote it up in the newspapers."

"Thank goodness." Freda said with relief. "I'm so glad it wasn't more serious. Please don't mention this to Betty. She still has nightmares from the Iroquois Theater Fire when she was in school in Chicago. That's the only time I've ever been glad I was sick. She had to miss accompanying the orchestra there that day to take care of Mother and me. Did you save the newspaper describing your fire? I'd like to read it when we get back."

"I don't think so, but Mother may have," said Walter.

Orville composed another letter for the Eau Claire newspaper to keep the group in people's minds. "This is our last day in the western state[s] and we are glad of it. The weather has been extremely warm and when we remarked about the hot weather (105° in the shade), we were told that was nothing, we ought to have been here when it was hot . . . Joplin is a place of 35,000 population and the main industry in the surrounding country is the mining of lead and zinc ore. . . In taking a trip to Webb City, 15 miles distant [there are] thousands of mammoth holes caused by the miners withdrawing the supports . . . and the ground caving in. One curiosity at Joplin is the Calcite Crystal Cave. The miners . . . broke into a natural cave of crystal formations; the cave is over 100 feet underground . . . and is a beautiful sight. . . . Oklahoma City is a new city only 20 years old, has 65,000 population and is growing rapidly. The only drawback is the lack of rains; this is their fourth successive dry season. . . . The fresh drinking water is bottled here the same as at Hutchinson, Kansas, only the water here, instead of having a salty taste is full of alkali and not fit to drink even after it is filtered. We leave tonight for God's country, that is, Chicago and vicinity."

Reuben kept a copy of that newspaper too.

On the third day of their long train ride home, they had an argument about the future of the *Musical Reeses* as they approached Chicago. Things did not look promising for them. The train fares for Babette, Orville, and Freda amounted to $610 and did not include their costs for lodging and food, (although they had tried to get by on the meals offered by the boarding houses) nor did they factor in the cost of Walter's train fare of about $140. They had been paid a total of $750 on the tour.

Walter had a paper and pencil and was figuring something. "I don't see how we can keep this up." He tapped his pencil on the armrest. "Our act earned about $750 for all these performances, and we spent more than $600 on train fares, not to mention lodging and food. And this is for just the three of you. If you split it 4 ways to include me, we don't even break even."

Freda sat forward and said, "Oh, Walter, stop being such a killjoy. I have had the time of my life on this trip."

Walter smoothed out the paper and slowly circled the number at the bottom. "Believe me, Freda, I know how much you want to find success on stage, but we have to be practical about our future. How on earth we will pay our bills if we don't make any money?"

"But, Walter, we're really good. Have you read the reviews I've cut out? They all say great things about us and how classy our act is. I'm sure we will eventually succeed." Freda said, raising her voice a little.

"Freda, I know our act is good. Very good, actually. But 'eventually' may take more time than we have," said Walter. "We can't keep relying on our families for support. And how can we live with no real and steady income?"

Babette added her perspective. "We have really worked hard for this, and Orville has invested so much money into our instruments and costumes and training. We have four shows booked this fall in Freeport, Illinois, in November at The Orpheum. I think we need to honor those dates and see what happens after that. I would hate to give up yet."

Freda raised her voice again. "Give up!? I'm not ready for that. We're just getting started!"

Walter said, "I know you really want to do this, Freda, but we have no more bookings after this November."

Orville had been quiet, but his face was turning red. "Give up? After all the money I have poured into our act? I really don't think we have given it enough time. I'd hate to think of you as a quitter, Walter. You haven't even been with us most of the time. How do you know it won't work if we keep at it?"

Walter responded calmly and deliberately, "I'm not a quitter, Orville. I am just being reasonable. You know I would have joined you if I hadn't had to take care of my prior commitments. Freda and I need some income. If the act isn't making money enough to cover expenses, we need to consider what else we could do."

"Could you be implying I didn't plan things out well enough? Or spend enough time and money preparing our act? We worked on it for almost two years, and I spent $2,500 on instruments and our costumes, I'll have you know," fumed Orville.

Walter tried to reassure him. "It's not that we aren't prepared. I think our act is better prepared than the most seasoned ones I've seen. But somehow, they have better booking connections than we do. I'm beginning to believe a saying I heard once. 'It's not how good you are, it's who knows you're good,' that determines success. And it seems like we haven't known the right people."

Orville cleared his throat, calmer but still offended. "I think Mr. Moss and Mr. Keith were pretty good connections. And we have Professor Parraent to thank for our polished performance."

Walter said, "Nobody is accusing you of any negligence. We have all given it our best effort. I know you have put a lot into this. Babette and Freda have too. But it seems foolish to throw good money after bad."

Babette began, "You know, Orville, Walter has a point. We can't keep drawing on your savings to make ends meet. Soon we'll have nothing left."

Orville looked at her. "Not you too, Babette. I really thought showcasing our talents would work on stage. I'm not sure how to think about this. It would be very disappointing and embarrassing to return to South Bend as failures."

Freda began to cry. "I can't believe you're thinking of giving up, Walter. You know what this means to me. It has been such fun watching the audiences enjoy our act. We really are good."

Walter put his arm around her shoulder, but she shook him off.

He said, "I know we are, Freda. But we have to be realistic. We just don't seem to have made the right connections. With no future bookings beyond November, and many of the theaters around our home area closing for the winter months, it doesn't make much sense to fight a losing battle. Even I wonder if I can find enough work in illustrated songs."

Freda was too upset to answer.

Through clenched teeth Orville said, "Well, if you won't keep trying, Walter, and Babette isn't sure either, I guess 1911 will be the end of the *Musical Reeses*."

"It's not a question of will or won't," said Walter. "It's that I don't see any way we can."

The group passed the next few miles in frustrated silence, trying to absorb Walter's words and work out their next steps.

Freda finally calmed down and quietly admitted to Walter that she realized they needed to find a new path. "But" she said emphatically, "I don't want to go back to South Bend and have people feel sorry for me."

Babette overheard and agreed, "It would be hard to face the students I was teaching. I still feel like I abandoned them. Certainly, by now, they have found other teachers, and I would not want to steal them back."

Walter said, "I have an idea. Why don't we return to South Bend and stay with our families until the next bookings. We can show them the posters and newspaper clippings Freda has been saving and tell them about our adventures on the road. We can announce the end of our touring and performing after our last bookings, so we won't have everyone wondering. By then, we should have new future plans in place."

Babette agreed and said, "This sounds like a reasonable plan. I do think it would be best for the two of us to stay with Orville's family in Michigan."

Orville was very upset that his dreams of fame had not materialized. He had known adversity before and was aware he couldn't continue alone. It was hard to accept that, after all his efforts, they had failed. He brooded for several miles. Babette occupied herself with a book, trying to ignore his mood.

Walter and Freda sat together quietly. Freda too, was upset that her dream of stardom was ending. After a while Walter suggested, "Why don't we try living in Chicago for a bit? I can try to do illustrated songs or other singing. You could sing with me. Or I could work in sales. And there is always work for people who can operate movie equipment. Once we earn some money, maybe I could take some classes."

Freda snapped, "As long as you don't have any more fires."

"Freda, you know that was a freak accident," Walter said defensively. After a moment he continued. "I have seen that you are good with numbers. You could get a job in a bank. They always seem to be hiring tellers."

She remained quiet. She knew Walter was right, but that was not her vision of her future.

As the train neared Chicago, Orville grudgingly admitted to Babette, "I don't agree with Walter, but we can't continue if we don't all feel we have a chance to succeed. In South Bend most of the members of my Reese's Band have moved into other positions. I can't expect them to return. The other bands I led have all found replacement directors. Maybe we can find a different town near South Bend that needs music instructors and band conductors. I can make some phone calls when get home."

Babette was relieved.

The train pulled into the Chicago station. Orville and Babette took the xylophone, aluminum bars, and two saxophones with them. Since they had decided to go to Eau Claire, they needed to take another train there. They sent a telegram to Reuben to ask him to meet them.

Walter and Freda had to decide whether to stay at the Heyer's or the Christensen's homes before moving to Chicago. Finally, Freda said, "Oh, I really want to see Mama and the boys for a little bit and try to get back into Papa's good graces. He might be more cordial after our 'successful' tour. I'm also not sure I could bear Tillie's negativity toward me. We don't have to explain our future plans, just say that we need a rest. It will be fun to show them my collection of articles and programs. Besides my old bedroom is empty."

Walter agreed. The two couples walked off in different directions with curt farewells.

Freda said," I will send my parents a telegram to let them know we're coming. You should send one to your family, too, Walter. I hope we can visit them. Your mother was very nice to me when we stayed there last June." They gathered their two saxophones and luggage and got on the streetcar to South Bend.

Freda and Walter were welcomed warmly by Susanna and the boys. Fred was reserved but listened as Freda told a few of her tales from life on the road. They looked at a few of the newspaper reviews and programs.

Freda said, "People did seem to like us, and the crowds were pretty big. I was sorry Walter couldn't be with us most of the tour, but we did have a great show in Oklahoma City when he joined us. He told me he had a little excitement back here while we were on tour," she added, looking at Walter.

Walter nodded and Susanna said, "I suppose you're referring to the fire at the American Theater. I read about it in the paper and saw that Walter was operating the movie machines. I decided not to worry you about it, Freda, since everyone was safe, but it must have been frightening for you, Walter! I'm so glad you weren't hurt."

Walter said, "Thank you. Yes, fire in a theater is a terrible thing. I'm glad we were able to put it out. Unfortunately, it did $300 worth of damage to the machines. But they were a little outdated, so they were probably going to be replaced anyway. Seems they come up with improvements almost every day. That's why inventors are so important." He motioned toward Fred Sr. who seemed pleased at the compliment.

Susanna had an idea. "What would you say if I invited Walter's family over Saturday afternoon for refreshments? Then you wouldn't have to tell everything twice. We haven't met them yet, and it would be good to get to know them. I'll write an invitation. Do you think they would come, Walter?"

Walter thought that was a good plan. He said, "We will visit them tomorrow and bring them your invitation."

Walter's family was glad to see them and hear a bit about the *Musical Reeses'* musical tour.

Walter said, "We'll be staying with Freda's family since Freda's bedroom is available. Freda's mother, Mrs. Heyer, has invited you all to their home on Saturday for refreshments." He handed Christina the note. "She would like our families to meet each other. Then we can hear about all the adventures on the big tour together."

"How nice. I would love to meet your family, Freda, and I'm sure Tillie and John will too," said Christina.

John said he would be glad to come. Tillie said nothing.

Saturday afternoon, the two families gathered in the Heyer's parlor. After introductions, they all looked at the clippings Freda had collected spread out on the table. Everyone exclaimed at the accolades. "Swell lookers!" read Herby out loud, looking at Freda. "I guess I'd agree with that."

They all chuckled.

"One of best instrumental musical acts ever seen!" read John. "That's impressive."

Christina picked up an article and read, "'The Musical Reeses offer what is easily one of best instrumental musical acts ever seen here.' My, some of these make your act sound amazing."

Freddy said proudly, "They are amazing."

Everyone chuckled again.

Susanna brought out two apple pies and served them with ice cream. There was coffee and apple cider to drink.

As they enjoyed their treat, Walter repeated their harrowing tale of the theater fire, with more scary details to entertain Herb and Fred, who regarded him as a true hero.

Christina said, "I am so glad nobody them was hurt."

"So are we," said John.

"I saved the newspaper report, if you want to add that to your clippings, Freda," Christina said.

Freda said, "Thank you very much. I would appreciate that."

They all enjoyed the descriptions of the land Freda saw, how it was so flat in many places that you could see all the way to the horizon. Fred wanted to hear more about the mining, and Susanna wanted to know what kind of houses people lived in. Freda told them how hot it was. They were all happy they didn't need to put up with those temperatures in Indiana.

The boys were fascinated by the postcards of the Crystal Cave near Joplin. Herb said, "I want to see that when I grow up."

When they finished with the stories and pie, Fred cleared his throat and asked, "What is the next step for the *Musical Reeses*?"

Freda and Walter looked at each other. Freda began. "We haven't exactly decided. We have some appearances scheduled for November . . . " Her voice trailed off.

Walter took over. "We have a few shows scheduled in November, but nothing after that. We have talked about pursuing some other opportunities in 1912. Freda and I have discussed moving to Chicago where she can find a regular job, maybe in a bank or financial institution. They always seem to be hiring. I am thinking of attending some classes. I am pretty sure I can find a job in sales and maybe continue with showing movies and doing illustrated songs. Although the last two don't provide much income or security, I enjoy it. Freda could sing with me, and of course she could see all the latest movies for free. They usually give free passes to the operators' families. Maybe you could visit us and see the latest films."

Herby and Freddy thought that was a great idea. The women enjoyed shopping in Chicago, so they were interested in this chance.

Again, Fred cleared his throat. "Does this mean the end of the *Musical Reeses* after you have worked so hard? And spent so much money? What about Orville and Betty?"

Freda responded, "You know they are staying with Orville's family in Eau Claire for now. I imagine they are entertaining everyone with their stories. They talked about using their teaching skills to start a music school in one of the towns around here. Orville will look for other band directing opportunities, and Betty will do as much accompanying as she can."

"To be honest, we weren't hired by a big vaudeville circuit, just a minor one. They can't pay us much. It hardly covered train and lodging expenses even when we lived very frugally. So, it seems the handwriting is on the wall." Walter glanced at Freda who was looking at her hands.

"Oh, I'm so sorry. You all had such a splendid act," said Christina. "When we saw you perform in Dixon, you were wonderful."

John said, "I was really impressed."

"Closing the show does seem a shame," said Susanna. "If you are serious about giving up your act, maybe you could give a farewell performance at the Star Theater here and invite friends and family again like you did for your dress rehearsal. There are so many people who have supported you and hoped for your success." She looked at Fred, part owner of the Star. "What do you think, Fred?"

Fred paused, resisting the urge to say, "I never thought it would work." Instead, he said, "I think that would be possible in December if it stays mild like usual. We have a couple of openings around the 10th. But I don't think you should call it a 'Farewell Performance' when you invite folks. Perhaps call it an 'Appreciation Performance.' You could do a full hour-long show and perform all your numbers, then at the end, come out to announce your future plans."

"Oh, Papa, that sounds like a perfect idea. Thank you so much. We need to ask Babette and Orville what they think. And we must invite Orville's family from Michigan too. I'm sure they would attend. They have been very supportive." Freda hugged him.

After everyone had said goodbye, Walter told Freda, "I still get the feeling your father does not like me."

Freda objected, "I don't think that at all. He seems very nice to you. I think he's upset that we are ending our vaudeville career. Or maybe that we even tried it."

"I still get the distinct impression that he is unhappy with our marriage. I guess it's wise to live in Chicago for a while. Maybe when he sees that I am good provider and husband, he will come to like me."

"Walter, I just think you're too sensitive. I'm sure Papa will accept you in time. And I am excited about living in Chicago," said Freda.

In November all four of the *Musical Reeses* met in Freeport, Illinois, for the four shows they had booked there from November 16-19. Then they gathered in South Bend to rehearse for their hour-long "Appreciation Performance." Orville avoided conversing with Walter after they had talked over and decided the sequence of their numbers. It was bittersweet as they recalled the effort they had put into learning and coordinating their vaudeville act.

The Heyer and Christensen families were invited to the Reese farm for Thanksgiving. It was a pleasant gathering with some of them meeting for the first time. Reuben was proud to show off his prize-winning poultry breeding projects. Herb and Freddy loved seeing all the animals and playing in the hay barn with the other youngsters. Josephine prepared an exceptional spread of turkey and all the fixings. Babette, Freda, Susanna, Christina, and even Tillie helped with the dinner. The four Reeses performed some of their act following dinner, which everyone enjoyed and applauded earnestly.

Then Orville stepped out and announced that they would be pursuing other opportunities in the future. "It has been harder than we expected to get good bookings and earn enough to cover our costs."

They all felt the undercurrent of disappointment.

"Oh, no." someone said. "You're too good to quit."

Another shouted, "We love hearing you!"

Betty thanked them and told how much they had appreciated their support. They invited everyone to their upcoming "Appreciation Performance" at the Star in South Bend.

Many of the Eau Claire relatives and friends made the effort to attend the Star performance, as did many from South Bend and Elkhart. It was a full house. As Fred had suggested, their invitations did not mention that they were ending their act, although some of the audience already knew.

After the curtain closed, the four of them stepped out in front of the curtain. One by one they expressed their appreciation for the support and encouragement they had received and told how much they had enjoyed being a part of the *Musical Reeses*. Each told a story from their performances that made the audience laugh. But when Orville said they would be pursuing other opportunities in the future and discontinuing the act, there were gasps and even sobs from the audience. Everyone knew how much effort and energy they had put into their performance. It was a poignant moment for everyone.

On their way home Babette said, "Now I suppose I will be 'Betty' again!"

"I think, to me, you'll always be Babette. It's such an elegant name," said Orville.

"I guess I can be both," she said, squeezing his arm.

CHAPTER THREE

THE INTERVENING YEARS: 1912 - 1919

After New Year, 1912, Betty asked Orville, "What should we do next? I really don't want to return to South Bend. There are so many people there who had a lot of faith in our prospects. It is hard to disappoint them. And I know I want to keep teaching piano, but my former students have all moved on."

Orville said, "I agree. It's the same with the bands I directed. Do you want to stay in this area?"

"Yes," answered Betty, "I think so. I would like to be close enough to my parents and your family to be able to visit them now and then."

"I have been asking around, and it seems like the city of Peru, Indiana isn't overrun with music teachers. Maybe we could start a music school there. It's not far from South Bend," said Orville.

Betty said, "That sounds like fun. I do love teaching young people. But how could we afford to do it?"

Orville answered, "I do still have some savings left, and you know that I get a little money from my army duty. If we could find a suitable building to lease, we could set up music studios and rent them to teachers. We would maintain the building and the big instruments like pianos, and other teachers would pay a small fee to use the facility. Of course, you and I could teach our lessons there too. We need to come up with an inspiring name for it."

Betty thought a minute. "How about *The Star Academy*? We could name it after Papa's theater in South Bend."

"I like 'Star' but 'Academy' sounds too academic." They laughed at his play on words. "What about *The Star Conservatory*?" Orville asked.

"I think that's perfect," Betty responded.

They visited Peru and found an older building to lease. It even had some apartments above. One was empty and they could live there. They arranged to move the things they'd stored in South Bend to Peru, and began advertising and recruiting music teachers, encouraging them to establish studios. They also announced they were available to teach and emphasized their unique qualifications. Orville and Betty soon had lists of their own students.

They worked hard at building their fledgling enterprise. Things went quite well. The faculty grew to include eleven piano teachers, along with three band and two orchestra instructors who worked on a commission plan. 300 students were enrolled at one point.

Orville busied himself managing the school and the business details involved such as billing, collecting payments, and dealing with maintenance of the structure and the musical instruments. He taught lessons to some instrumental students.

One day, Orville came home with a new idea. "I have been asked to return to directing the Brown Commercial Band. It pays a little money and doesn't take much time."

"How much time?" asked Babette, remembering the lonely evenings she spent before their vaudeville days.

Orville answered, "They practice one evening per week and there will be some concerts too. I think I could do that and still keep up with everything here."

Betty sighed. "I suppose that will be all right. I know how you love directing. It's your decision, dear. And we do need the money."

He soon added the Murden Ford Band, the Woodmen of the World Band, the Twentieth Century Band, and the Bunker Hill Band to his responsibilities.

Orville found they needed more stable income to meet expenses at the Conservatory. He complained. "We seem to be short of money at the end of each month. Maybe I should look for a steadier job."

Betty said, "The income from the Star isn't as dependable as I thought it would be. Teachers come and go, students start and quit, or get sick and miss lessons."

"I have quite a bit of sales experience, and I have always been interested in furniture sales. Maybe I could get a job as a salesman at the Murphy Furniture Company here in town. I saw a 'help wanted' sign in their window."

He applied and was hired. He could work there in the days and teach or direct in the evenings. At the furniture store he learned about the buying and selling of furniture and when and where manufacturers' exhibits of the latest styles were presented. He also discovered that stores could get a discount if they purchased items in large quantities. That allowed them to charge their customers less, which they could advertise to their advantage.

As Babette Reese was still a well-known pianist in the area, she was often hired to accompany soloists and performances. After one engagement, she had a very close call. Most of the audience had gone home and the performers were gathering their things to leave. Everyone looked up when a delivery boy came in with a large bunch of roses for the performers. The anonymous sender requested that the pianist be given one of the flowers.

The delivery boy asked, "Could someone tell me who played the piano tonight?"

The performers indicated it was Babette, who said, "I was the accompanist."

"I was instructed to make sure you got this." He plucked out one of the blooms and presented it to her.

"Oh, my," she said reaching for the rose. "How beautiful." Raising it toward her nose to enjoy the lovely aroma, she stepped backward and suddenly found herself falling through a stage trapdoor that had accidentally been left open. She screamed. Three men standing nearby heard her and immediately recognized her danger. They managed to grab her as she tipped backwards. Struggling to keep their balance, they lifted her back on the stage, saving her from a nasty 12-foot fall to the cellar below. Shaken and frightened, she swooned for a minute as they helped her to a chair.

After she regained her composure she exclaimed, "What a fright! Thank you so much for catching me."

"You are welcome," one of the men said with relief.

Another added, "That would have been a terrible fall."

"Yes, I can see that." Babette peered into the hole in the floor and shuddered. Then she looked at her hand that was still holding the rose. She held it up. "And look, here is the cause of all the trouble."

When she described the incident to Orville, he took her in his arms, kissed her and murmured sincerely, "I'm so glad you weren't hurt." He took the rose from her and placed it in a vase. "When we see this beautiful rose, it will remind us to be thankful for that."

Walter and Freda moved to Chicago. Both the Heyer and Christensen families were sad to see them leave South Bend but understood their need to start over. Freda found a job in a bank and loved living in Chicago again. Every once in a while, she felt a pang of sadness that her dream of stardom had ended, although Chicago was exciting. There were so many things to do and see, from museums to art galleries, from symphony concerts to ball games. There were always new vaudeville acts and movies.

Shopping occupied many of her free hours. She could visit the fancy department stores like Rothschild's, Carson Pirie Scott & Company, and Marshall Field's. Then she could go to a store called The Fair and find similar things at lower prices.

Walter found a day job in a local furniture store. He had worked in sales before, but this was something different. He liked showing customers the newest styles and suggesting combinations they might not have imagined. He was friendly and enjoyed talking to people. His sales numbers were among the best at the store. When they had saved enough money, he decided to learn more about running a business and enrolled in some evening classes.

One day Freda read an ad in the newspaper announcing that Rothschild's was installing a special aquarium display. She showed the ad to Walter and said, "Wouldn't that be interesting to see? There will be 125 glass tanks displaying fish from all over the world. And the best part is that admission is free. Will you go with me?" she begged him.

Walter said, "I'm not really interested in seeing fish in tanks. I'd rather catch them and eat them from the lake." He went back to reading his textbook.

When Freda finally had a free day, she went to Rothschild's seventh floor by herself. She spent the whole day wandering among the tanks of exotic and common fish, from sea horses to sunfish.

She came back to the apartment and said, "Oh Walter, it was amazing to see all those different fish. There was a sign saying that this display is the biggest in the whole country. I wish you could have seen it."

"That must have been something," he said half listening. He added, "Now I really have to finish this assignment for my class."

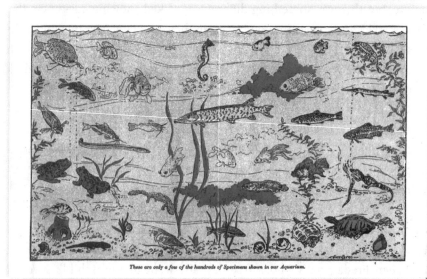

These are only a few of the hundreds of Specimens shown in our Aquarium.

from the private collection of Sue Thurman

Freda was upset that Walter wasn't interested in joining her activities. She said, "Walter you are so busy studying and working all the time, there's no chance to do anything just for fun. There is so much to do and see in this city."

He agreed but repeated that he was just too busy. "Freda, I have to figure out how to make a decent living for us. The best way seems to be in business of some sort. I am a pretty good salesman, but I need to learn about how to run a business. I love singing, and singing with you is a real treat. But there's not much money in it." They had some engagements singing together in illustrated songs, but, as he noted, it didn't pay well.

So, she visited the galleries and museums on her own. Sometimes Walter would accompany her to evening events, if they could find affordable tickets. But mostly she went by herself.

Time passed, with occasional visits to their families, but little else. One afternoon, a couple of years after they had moved to Chicago, Walter came home and found Freda seated at their one table, surrounded by disorganized piles of clippings from newspapers, old programs, posters and other memorabilia. "Freda, what is all this clutter?" he asked, annoyed that their dinner table clearly was not available for dinner. It might complicate mealtime for several days from the look of it. "Are these from our *Musical Reeses'* tour?"

"Oh, Walter. It's not clutter. Some of it is from our vaudeville days. I don't want to forget any of it. I was living my dreams. There are clippings I saved from our appearances. They were all in this envelope. Looking through them I realize that I already have trouble remembering the exact month we were in these places. At least I wrote the location on most of them. I'm trying to get them in order so I can paste them in this scrapbook." She held up a red scrapbook with an Indian chief's head embossed on the cover. "Mama saved the first few, and I've collected them since then. There are also articles about your theater fire that your mother saved. And Reuben gave me clippings from the Eau Claire newspapers with letters Orville wrote on our tour. And I have some other things I have gathered that I want to keep."

Walter chuckled with a tinge of sadness. "Those were exciting days. But I'd just as soon move on. There should be good days ahead of us too."

"Well, I don't want to forget it," said Freda. "They were extraordinary days, and I had a swell time. I wish they had never ended," she said, looking down at the articles spread in front of her. She continued, "I also found some things I saved about other performers I admire, and make-up and beauty advice. I'll put them in it too. Look at this." She pointed to a pamphlet. "Here is the flyer from the aquarium display I saw at Rothschild's. Remember when I showed it to you after I went? I still can't understand why you wouldn't go. It was fascinating. Anyway, I am going to include that, too."

*from the
private collection
of Sue Thurman*

"It seems like a daunting project, Freda, putting this all together. Are you sure it's worth so much of your time?" he asked, sounding slightly peeved.

"If I don't do it who will? No one could understand what these clippings are all about and they'd just throw them in the trash," said Freda. "I am certainly going to include this Jack Wilson quote that I cut out from *The Show World Paper*," Looking amused, she read, "'Now-a-days When You Are Crazy, They Don't Put You in an Asylum, They Put You in Vaudeville.'"

Walter commented dryly. "That sounds about right. I'm not so sure we want to be listed among the crazy. It still seems like more work than it's worth."

Freda put her hands on her hips and glared at him. "Making the scrapbook will be a lot of work, but I think it's a wonderful idea. We will have a real record of what we did or tried to do. And some other good memories. Besides, it's not like I have much else to do." She glared a minute more, then went to sit beside him. She took his hand. "Don't fuss, Walter. It's fun remembering, though we might have to eat on trays for a bit."

Walter grumbled. "Humph. Just how long do want me to eat in a chair?"

"I should be able to finish it in a week or two." Freda gently ran her fingers through his hair. "I also found that horoscope that was done for you when you were younger. It predicts so many things about you quite accurately. Listen to this," she read from the booklet. "'He depends upon his head and adapts himself to personal business plans, management etcetera . . . has a great love of order, harmony and elegance.' That is exactly you, Walter. And here, 'his practical, utilitarian disposition . . . causes him to see how best to use every cent to the utmost possible advantage.' And this part 'With proper . . . education would make a successful Business Manager and Promoter.' I can't believe how accurate these predictions are."

"Goodness. I had forgotten all about that," said Walter. "It seems sort of silly now."

"Oh, I don't think so. It's interesting how it fits you. Do you mind if I keep it in the scrapbook?" asked Freda.

Walter answered, "I guess it would be all right, if you want to hang on to it. I don't believe in those, anymore. I wondered then why it didn't mention my sense of humor. If you want to spend your time this way, it's up to you." He went back to his books.

In the fall of 1914 Orville received a letter from his friend, George Herrick. Herrick had played saxophone in one of Orville's Indiana bands and had relocated to Winona, a community in Southeastern Minnesota. He was hoping to move to a place with more opportunity for him as a musician.

He had chosen Winona at the urging of relative who had settled there. Dr. Herrick, a dentist, had bragged about Winona's booming economy and encouraged young George to consider moving to the city. It was a port on the Mississippi and also an important railroad stop crucial for distributing crops grown in the Midwest. It had large milling and lumber industries. The thriving J.R Watkins Medical and Baking Products Company was located in Winona. Educational opportunities were outstanding with excellent public and parochial schools, plus the Winona Normal School, the College of St. Teresa, and St. Mary's College. At that time, it was said Winona had more millionaires per capita than any other American city.

George Herrick thought it sounded like the town would be ripe for a dance orchestra and perhaps a music store. Dr. Herrick invited George to stay at his home and become acquainted with Winona. George liked what he saw and soon moved to Winona. He spent a few years playing with the existing dance bands and getting to know musicians in town. When he knew enough players of sufficient skill, he formed his own dance orchestra and started performing for social and community events. Herrick's Orchestra grew in reputation and popularity.

Herrick read in the Winona newspaper that a group of citizens was trying to organize a municipal band in the city. There already were other bands, but they were mostly affiliated with organizations or businesses. The Association of Commerce wanted to create a band that represented all of Winona. They had gathered subscriptions from the public and had enough money to hire a director, so they were advertising for qualified applicants.

Herrick immediately thought of his friend, Orville Reese. The Herrick family in South Bend were friends of the Heyers and had stayed in touch with Orville and Betty after the *Musical Reeses* ended their act. Herrick wrote a letter to Orville describing Winona and encouraging him to apply for the position.

"What would you think of living in Winona, Minnesota, if I were appointed band director there?" Orville asked Babette after reading Herrick's letter.

She said, "Where is that?"

"It's on the other side of Wisconsin, on the Mississippi River," he answered.

Orville handed her the letter that Herrick had sent her. She read it with interest. "I suppose it wouldn't hurt for you to apply, I guess. I am ready for a change."

Orville composed a letter of interest in the position, listing all of his experience directing and organizing bands. He waited for a reply.

A few weeks later, Walter and Freda came to visit them in Peru. Relations between the sisters had healed, but Orville still was upset that his dream of fame and fortune had been thwarted by Walter's truthful assessment of their situation. He hadn't completely forgiven Walter for pointing out reality.

Orville told them that he had applied for a new band director position in Winona, Minnesota. Their response was the same as Babette's, so he described Winona's location and read them the letter George Herrick had written about the city.

Freda asked, "Would you be willing to move so far away from everyone you know, Orville?"

Orville answered, "I think so. Another of my dreams is to direct a band and shape it to my expectations. And there don't seem to be many opportunities around here."

"How do you feel about making such a big move?" Walter said, looking at Betty.

She responded, "I know it would be a big change and have its challenges. But I told Orville that I think I am ready for something new."

The next day they were sitting around the table eating lunch. The mail was delivered, and Orville found a response from the Winona Association of Commerce. He had not been chosen for the position. Chicago composer, George Colburn, had been offered the job and accepted it. The letter was signed by Dr. Oswald Leicht, Band Board president.

"Humph," sputtered Orville, slapping his hand on the table. He read the message aloud. "They hired George Colburn? A composer? What would he know about directing a band?" He crumpled the letter and threw it on the floor.

Betty took the letter and smoothed it out. "I remember him. When I was a student at the Chicago Musical College, he was an instructor of harmony at the Conservatory of Music. I'm pretty sure he does have conducting experience because he directed bands at the Northwestern Military Academy. I seem to recall he had quite a large family too."

Orville frowned at her. "You don't have to defend their choice," he grumbled.

Walter changed the subject slightly. "Didn't Colburn compose the music for the movie *Antony and Cleopatra*? I remember that it was filmed on location, not in a studio like most movies. That was pretty novel. Colburn's music was quite an innovation, too, and it made a big hit. We ran that movie for weeks. I bet I could recite every line in it. The music added a lot to it."

Freda agreed, emphatically saying, "I loved it! I saw it three times."

"I still can't imagine that this Colburn would know how to organize a community band program. That's quite different from teaching in an academic setting," Orville said, returning to his original line of thought.

"You're right, dear," Betty agreed. "You have had a lot more experience in that area."

Orville continued, "Besides, how on earth can they pay him enough in Winona to support a big family?"

The answer to that came about three years later when Mr. Colburn's contract expired. He had been well liked in Winona, especially after he composed a special song for the city. Aptly named *Winona*, it was presented to the public and, according to the day's newspaper, "made a decided hit." The article predicted that the song "will soon find a place in all public gatherings held in Winona."

But despite his popularity, Colburn realized that it would be financially best for his family if he returned to teaching. In January of 1918, he announced that he had accepted a position as a theory and composition instructor at the Cosmopolitan School of Music in Chicago.

Orville sent another application for the newly open position. He lost out again. Dr. Leicht, informed him by letter that Emile Michaux had accepted a one-year contract as new director of the Winona Municipal Band. An accomplished composer and French horn player, he had studied music at the Royal Conservatory of Music in Brussels, winning prizes for French Horn performance, harmony, counterpoint, and composition.

When Orville received this news, he tore the letter up. "Another composer? And this one apparently with NO directing experience. The Winona citizen's board doesn't seem to have enough money to pay a full-time director. I think that in order to make a success of directing this Winona Band, a person would need to have an independent source of income. I'll be interested to see how long this director will last."

In the summer of 1919, Orville was offered a job preparing and directing a band for a concert in Mankato, Minnesota. He was excited about it and told Babette that the concert would be in late July.

Betty said, "That sounds like a great opportunity. Is that near Winona?"

"It's west of Winona, more in the middle of Minnesota. But the train makes a stop in Winona on the way, so I could see the town, and maybe have a chance to get together with George Herrick," said Orville.

"If you do that," said Betty, "be sure to say hello from me."

"I will be happy to," answered Orville. "I hope he can tell me how things are going with their Municipal Band."

Betty asked, "Why don't you see if Walter could come along to sing in the Mankato Concert? People always enjoy hearing his beautiful voice." She was hoping that Orville and Walter would be able to smooth over the tension that lingered between them since the end of their vaudeville act. And she missed being near Freda. Maybe they could stay together at their parents' home while their husbands were away.

Although Orville still harbored some resentment, he could see the wisdom in bringing Walter along as a featured guest. Walter's presence might be helpful. He was friendly and easy going, and people loved listening to him. Orville had been told that he, himself, could be a bit difficult. Maybe they could play some of their old act's saxophone duets in the concert, too. Orville guessed it wouldn't hurt to ask.

He called Walter to see if he would be interested and available.

Walter said, "I would love to do that. I haven't sung with a band for quite a while. Let me know what arrangements I should make for missing work."

Walter described Orville's offer to Freda.

"Where is Mankato, Minnesota? Is it near Winona?" Freda asked.

Walter pulled out an atlas and showed her.

"That's quite a long way away. You'll be gone a while, I suppose," she remarked.

"I imagine about a week. We'll take the train. Orville will let me know when he has more details."

Walter still loved to perform and was glad that Orville invited him. Freda was hopeful that he and Orville could become friends again. She missed being near Betty. Maybe they could stay with their parents in South Bend while the men were gone.

When Orville called with exact dates, Walter made arrangements for taking a few days off.

Orville had been thinking about the band director job he had applied for in Winona. He was fairly sure it would open up again. He also wondered if Winona would have any business opportunities available that he could consider purchasing. He still had some savings and a small inheritance from a relative.

Orville knew that his job at the Peru furniture store had been a great sales experience. It wasn't necessary to keep track of so many small items like he did in dry goods sales. He had taken advantage of the opportunity to learn all he could about the business.

He called his old friend, George Herrick, who had told him about the first Winona band director opening and was still living in Winona. After they caught up on family news, Orville said, "I am coming through Winona on my way to Mankato for a one-time band directing job. My brother-in-law, Walter is coming with me to sing at the concert. Remember, he was sometimes part of our vaudeville act."

Herrick said, "Sure, I remember Walter. He married Freda Heyer, right? You must plan to stop here to visit. I would love to have you meet my new wife, if time permits."

"I have an unusual request for you. Could you ask about the local furniture stores and find out if any of them might be considering selling their business? I'm thinking about moving to Winona if there is an opportunity there," Orville said.

Surprised, Herrick said, "I thought directing bands was your big goal. If you're truly interested in running a furniture store, I'll see what I can find out. I have heard rumors that Frank Winkels might be ready to retire. He has owned Winkels Furniture House for a long time, since the 1890's, I think. Maybe we can meet with someone at the bank to inquire. They handle a lot of the real estate transactions in town."

Orville said to Walter, "I would like to allow time for a stopover in Winona to see my old friend George Herrick. I think you met him. At least he said he remembered you. I'd like to find out what Winona is really like, since I already applied twice, unsuccessfully I might add, for the band job there."

Walter said, "That would be fine. I've been curious about Winona too, after you read Herrick's letter. Yes, I did meet him back in South Bend a couple of times."

Orville and Walter bought their train tickets for the evening train from Chicago, so they would arrive in Winona the next morning. They would have the day to meet with Herrick and take a look around. There was an evening train from Winona that would get them to Mankato the following morning.

© *Winona Republican Herald - 1907*

They boarded the train in Chicago, found seats by each other, and arranged their luggage on the overhead rack. The train whistle blew its warning signal, and the train slowly began to chug along behind the soot and ash of the noisy steam engine. The ride to Winona would take ten hours. They sat in uneasy silence for a while until Orville swallowed his pride and asked Walter, "Tell me about the furniture store where you have been working."

Walter thought it was an odd request but answered, "Our store isn't very big, but we have a lot of customers. Many times, they order things from a catalogue. I like working with people and showing them possibilities they may not have considered. But I think the store would make more sales if they had more choices available on the floor."

Orville talked a bit about the Murphy Furniture store in Peru where he worked and eventually invested in. They compared notes on prices, what furniture sold well, and what were the newest styles. They discussed the best ideas for effective advertising they had seen. Orville said, "Between us, we seem to know a lot about the furniture business."

Walter agreed, but he still wondered what Orville had in mind.

Then Orville told him that he had been thinking about owning his own furniture store.

Walter finally had an inkling about what Orville was considering. He said, "Yes, that would be a good idea if you could afford it. Being your own boss must be nice. Where would you locate?"

"I have been thinking about Winona. From what Herrick said, Winona is an up-and-coming town with a growing population and many large businesses. Besides, I am interested in that Winona band job. They are on their second director now. The first one only lasted three years. They couldn't pay him enough to feed his family. Not much has changed since then, so the job might open up again. It might work out as a part time job. If a furniture store happens to be for sale in Winona, I would consider buying it."

Walter was surprised. He asked, "How does Betty feel about moving?"

"We have talked about it. She said she wouldn't be opposed to it," replied

Orville. "Herrick told me Frank Winkels has run Winkels Furniture House for 25 years and that he might be getting ready to retire. His store is sort of an old-fashioned one with all the tables, dressers, beds and chairs arranged in groups. Winkels should have an established customer base." Orville paused, then added, "If his store is for sale, would you be interested in joining me in this enterprise?"

Walter was again surprised. After thinking a minute, he said, "It sounds like an interesting opportunity. Heaven knows, I'm not making much money showing films and doing illustrated songs, even with my sales commission at the furniture store. But I need to find out how Freda would feel about moving. She loves Chicago."

Orville said, "You can tell Freda that Babette and I have already discussed it. She thinks a change would be a good chance to start over. I still have enough money saved for a good down payment. I don't know if you would be able to help finance the deal, but I might be able to borrow some from my father. Would you be interested in helping manage the store if I decide to buy the business?"

Walter answered, "It sounds like a good opportunity, and yes, I would jump at the chance to manage it. I do have a little money put away. But we certainly should have a good look at the store before we make a decision."

"I agree," said Orville. "If Winkels' store really is for sale, I will trust you to look over the finances, and we both can examine the styles and condition of the furniture there."

Relations between the two men thawed as they conversed. They both realized that it would be best for them to let go of their grievances if they were entering business together, especially since their wives were sisters.

They had not reserved sleepers so they dozed as best they could in their assigned seats until the conductor announced, "Next stop, Winona, Minnesota."

They got off the train at the Winona depot, and George Herrick was there to meet them. Herrick did have some information about the furniture business in Winona. He told them, "Winona currently has three furniture stores, Hillyer's, Breitlow's, and Winkels'. A fourth store, called Winona Furniture, closed in 1917 and is now Purdy's automobile and implement business."

Herrick had made arrangements to take them to Merchant's Bank to inquire about the potential sale of Winkels Furniture House. They were told that, yes, Mr. Winkels was thinking of retirement. The banker said, "I'll make a call to see if you can stop by the store this afternoon."

Mr. Winkels answered. "Yes, I'll be happy to meet with them around two p.m."

They thanked the banker and left to take the five cent bumpy streetcar ride down 3rd Street to the Frederick Hotel Café for a quick meal. The streetcar passed by Winkels Furniture House, so they gave it a good look from outside. After they ate, Herrick went with them to the store and introduced them to Mr. Frank Winkels. Then he left the three of them to discuss business.

Mr. Winkels said, "I have run this business long enough. It has provided me and my family a very adequate income. Keeping the store up to date has been a priority for me. I brought electricity in as soon as it was available downtown, to show off my inventory to its best advantage." He told them about the Great White Way effort of 1916. That campaign was led by business owners and interested citizens to install six streetlights per block in the downtown business area. He said proudly, "We contributed to support it and found the lighting greatly increased our evening business. However, I am getting older and feel like I am ready to retire."

They discussed the details of a purchase, the building, the inventory, what sold well and what did not. Walter asked to see the store's accounting records and looked through them carefully, while Orville and Mr. Winkels wandered about the store, checking out the furniture styles and displays which were as old-fashioned as Orville had expected. Walter finished looking over the sales and financial records.

Orville and Walter agreed that things seemed to be in good order. Orville said, "Mr. Winkels, I think that you have built a fine business here. Everything appears to be organized very well."

Frank Winkels looked pleased.

Orville went on, "I would like to offer to purchase it from you. Let's sit down and talk things over."

Mr. Winkels stated the price he was expecting to get for the building, inventory and the customer base.

Walter winced and looked at Orville, who was scribbling something on a piece of paper.

"Based on the cost of your inventory, which I calculated as we went through the store, and the condition of this building, which you must admit needs some updating, I would be willing to pay about three quarters of what you are asking," Orville finally said.

Mr. Winkels frowned. "I'm not sure that would be enough."

Walter spoke up, "We realize how much of your life you have invested here and how much effort you have put into this business. But we will be starting over completely. The building does need repair. The roof is leaking in a couple places, and we'll need to repaint and redo all the rooms. Plus, we'll have to purchase some more modern furniture. There will be a lot of advertising costs, since we don't know anyone in this town besides our friend, George Herrick."

Mr. Winkels said, "I agree with the need for repairs here. But the furniture we stock is of very good quality. We have many customers who buy all their furniture here."

Walter said, "Yes, there are many positive things about your store."

"We are interested in buying it from you," said Orville. "We have to take the train this evening to Mankato where I have an engagement directing their city band this week. I suggest that Walter and I talk it over on the way to and from Mankato. We will write a letter now stating our interest in this sale and put some money down to reassure you of our intentions." He quickly dashed off the letter and pulled some bills out of his pocket.

"We will stop here again when our Mankato obligation is over and we are on our way back to Chicago, to see if we can come to an agreement," said Walter. They shook hands on that.

Walter and Orville took the streetcar back to the depot. George Herrick was waiting there to see them off. "How did it go?" he asked.

Orville said, "I think it looks promising. We'll be back in about a week to see if we can finalize things."

Herrick said, "Congratulations! I hope it works out. This town is growing so quickly, I'm sure you'll sell a lot of furniture to people moving here."

The evening train soon arrived, and the conductor shouted, "All aboard!" Orville and Walter climbed up the steps to the platform, entered the coach car, found a pair of seats together, and stowed their belongings.

Orville said, "I'm hungry,"

Walter agreed. They wove their way down the aisle between the seats and cars to the dining car, found a table and ordered food.

"What did you really think of Winkels' store?" asked Walter.

"It needs some updating and modernizing," said Orville, "but aside from the building repair, I don't see any major problems."

"The financial picture I saw was mostly positive. Profits aren't huge, but I think we could improve on that with some effort," replied Walter. "I also think he is asking too much. I hope he's willing to negotiate."

They returned to their padded coach seats and tried to get some sleep. They would be in Mankato by morning.

The engagement in Mankato went well. Orville had a few days to rehearse the band, and the city put them up in the Vendome Hotel. It was located in the heart of the business district, so it was a handy location for them.

At the first rehearsal the players were disorganized. Orville rehearsed them carefully and gave them time to practice the hard passages. Finally, they could play their parts adequately and produced a sound that satisfied him. They were ready to give a concert. As expected, Walter's singing made a big hit and inspired the musicians to rise to his level.

Betty and Freda did stay at the Heyer home while their husbands were gone. Susanna was not feeling well, so they helped their father with her care when he was busy working on his inventions. Herbert had taken a job in another city, but Fred Jr. was still living at home. The new jazz music he'd been hearing obsessed him, and he loved playing the new percussion styles. He earned enough money performing with dance bands to buy his own drum set and could practice for hours. He wasn't much use with Susanna's needs and the sound from his drums did little to soothe her, even though the drums and drummer had been relegated to the cellar.

The sisters saw that Freddy's playing kept Susanna from resting. Betty took him aside to talk to him privately. "I think you should restrict your playing to the times Mama is awake. We are all proud of your ability, but she does need her rest."

Freddy agreed but said, "I could play more softly and maybe just use my brushes when she is sleeping. That shouldn't be too loud."

"We'll see," answered Betty. "I'll ask Mama."

When asked, Susanna said, "I really enjoy hearing Freddy play. He is so good. But if he could be quieter when I'm resting, I would appreciate it."

Freddy made sure his mother was awake when he practiced.

The telephone rang. Both Freda and Babette ran to answer it. The Heyers had the latest in telephone equipment due to Fred's involvement in that technology. Their telephone was a candlestick model with the new rotary dial that Fred had worked on developing. An operator and switchboard were still needed to connect most phone calls, but the Heyer's phone just had a four-digit number.

Orville was on the other end calling from the Mankato hotel.

The sisters held the earpiece between them so they could both hear. Betty asked, "How is the concert preparation going?"

Orville replied, "I think the players are doing quite well. The concert should be a success. I'm so glad you suggested asking Walter to come. He adds a great deal." He paused, then added, "We have a little surprise for the two of you. When we stopped in Winona, we found out that Frank Winkels was thinking of selling his furniture store. So, we talked to Mr. Winkels and looked at his store. I remember you saying you were ready for a change, Babette. How do you think Freda would feel?"

"I'm right here, Orville," Freda said, "although it is a little hard to understand you. You are thinking of buying a furniture store in Winona?"

"Yes, we are," responded Orville. "Walter thinks it's a good idea, too."

Freda didn't answer right away, so Betty took over. "Did you have enough time to really look things over?"

Orville said, "We talked to the owner and looked closely at the store and its stock. Walter examined the books. Everything looks quite positive."

"Walter knows I really love living in Chicago, but I suppose I could adjust to a smaller town again," Freda said, reluctantly. "You told us a little about Winona a while back. Wasn't there a band directing job you were interested in?"

"Yes, there was, but I didn't get the job," said Orville. "Walter and I are thinking of making a firm offer for the business on our way back through

Winona. We hope the owner accepts it. Who knows, I might have another chance to apply for that band job. And if we have a steady source of income, I might be their first choice."

Betty spoke again. "It would be a good chance to truly start over. Orville, do we have enough money for this big step?"

Orville answered, "I'm sure of it. I have saved up a lot. And I could borrow some, too. We can't talk too long, so I'll let Walter and Freda chat a little."

As soon as Freda got on the line, she asked Walter, "Are you in favor of this move?"

Walter replied, "Yes, I am. Orville has asked me to manage the store, and I know I will be good at it."

"Well, if you think it's the right thing to do, then I guess I can go along with it," Freda said. "I'll miss Chicago, but I suppose a change would be healthy." She was glad Orville and Walter seemed to be getting along again. "Good luck with the concert. I hope it goes well."

They said their goodbyes. Freda and Betty sat down, too stunned to speak.

Susanna was in the room and asked, "Now what was that all about?"

The sisters explained the plan their husbands had proposed. Betty hoped starting over in a new place would give her more time with Orville. Freda hoped she could find some excitement in such a small town. Both were worried about being so far from their family.

Susanna said, "I think it sounds like a wonderful chance for a new beginning. But I will be very sad to have you go."

"Oh, Mama," Freda said. "You and Papa can move there with us."

Betty added, "We can get settled there and send for you. Papa has talked about retiring."

Fred Sr. and Freddy came into the room. "What is all this fuss about?" asked Freddy.

Fred asked, "And did I hear someone mention my retiring?"

The sisters told them about their husbands' plans.

Betty explained, "You and Mama could move to Winona after we find places to live. You could still tinker with your gadgets there."

"That's a big piece of news. I suppose we could move to Winona. It would be quite a change. If I am able to keep working on my projects there, I should be happy. But I warn you, I'll have a lot to pack up," Fred responded.

"What about me?" asked Freddy. "Where will I live? I'm only 19 and I can't afford to buy a house and stay in South Bend. I don't even have a real job here. But I do have a lot of music connections."

Freda laughed. "Betty and I were both settled and married by your age." She reached up and ruffled his hair teasingly. "Don't worry, Freddy. You could move to Winona, if you want to. I am certain you could have a job in the furniture store."

Betty added, "And lots of opportunities to play your drums too. After all, George Herrick has his own dance orchestra there."

The afternoon of the Mankato concert was cool and lovely. Walter's singing was well received, as was the saxophone duet he and Orville played. The very appreciative audience rewarded the whole performance with several calls for encores. Orville thanked the band members for their hard work and excellent performance. Representatives from the city encouraged Orville to apply for the director's position, which they were currently filling with guest conductors. He replied that he was considering purchasing a furniture business in Winona, so he would have to decline.

He and Walter walked to the train station for the 5:00 pm return trip to Chicago via Winona. They discussed the performance. Walter observed, "You know it sounded like some of the band sections needed more practice."

"I agree, particularly the cornets. And it would have helped if the saxophone section had better reeds. The audience really appreciated your singing, Walter. Thanks for coming along."

Walter said, "My pleasure. All in all, I think it went pretty well. They liked our saxophone duet too. It reminded me of our vaudeville times."

George Herrick again met them at the train station in Winona at around 9 p.m. He invited them to stay that night at his new house nearby and meet his wife. They accepted. Walking there, they talked more about buying Winkels Furniture House. Herrick said, "I hope it works out for you. I think that would be a great business venture. Especially with both of you having experience in furniture."

"I hope we are offering enough. My offer is the upper limit of what we can afford," said Orville.

George assured them, "I don't think you are competing with many other offers, so things should work out."

"We'll soon find out," said Walter.

They arrived at George's house where they met his wife, chatted a little more, and went to bed.

Orville had made arrangements to meet with Mr. Winkels and the banker at 8:30 a.m. before the store opened. Following another streetcar ride, he and Walter stepped down and approached the store. Frank Winkels unlocked the door and welcomed them in. The banker arrived a few minutes later. They all went into Winkels' office, and he waved them into chairs.

Winkels began, "I have thought a great deal about your offer. I believe you would do a great job with this store that I have created. Its continued success is very important to me. I am willing to take your offer. I have asked my banker to draw up some papers for you to sign."

Walter and Orville felt a rush of relief. They looked over the documents and found everything in order. Orville, who would be the majority owner, signed them confidently.

"Thank you, very much." Orville said, standing up to shake Winkels' hand. "We will take very good care of your store."

Walter added, "We certainly will."

They spent the rest of the day with Herrick touring the sights of Winona, including parks, businesses, the grand post office, and the courthouse before they boarded the evening train back to Chicago.

They settled in their seats and talked over the day's exciting and surprising events. Finally, Walter said, "It's getting late. Shall we get something to eat?" They made their way on the swaying train to the dining car and celebrated with a couple of beers and a big meal of roast beef, mashed potatoes, and gravy. They felt quite mellow and may have swayed a bit more than the train's movements required as they returned to their seats.

As they made themselves comfortable, Orville said casually, "Babette told me that your father died when you were quite young."

"Yes," Walter paused and then said, "He was murdered."

"Oh, I had no idea." Orville responded. "I just assumed it was an illness. Do you want to talk about it?"

"I guess so. I don't think about it often. My father was a policeman. There were many thefts happening in the freight yards. A gang of hobos was looting the parked boxcars. My father was sent to investigate. The thieves saw him and one of them fired a gun in his direction multiple times. A shot hit my father. He died instantly. I was only three in 1897 so I didn't understand much, but there were articles in the paper about the killing that I read later. It was very hard on my mother and older siblings. Mother scarcely had time to bury him and grieve before she had used up our savings and needed to find a way to put food on the table. It was difficult for her to ask Tillie to drop out of school and find a job. Tillie was just 13 and almost done with school. Mother decided that they could afford for Tillie to take a course in stenography. With that skill she found a job that paid well enough to support us. They did catch the murderer, a guy named Mullaney. For some reason there were a couple of trials with hung juries. They tried a third trial in 1899, but they could not locate the star witness. So Mullaney got off scot free. My mother was so disappointed and disillusioned. I can still hear how she cried. Tillie became very bitter."

Orville had been listening intently. "That was a real injustice for your whole family. Your mother did a good job raising you."

"Thank you. It might be why I am so methodical and deliberate about things. That's what Freda says. I learned to take things carefully and seriously. But my singing? Mother was always interested in music. Apparently, my father was a good singer, and both of their families were musical. She encouraged me. My brother, John, also is a good singer but Mother thought he should become a plumber so he would be sure to find work. A singing plumber. I used to kid him about using his voice to clear clogged pipes." Walter and Orville laughed.

"What about your childhood, Orville?" asked Walter. "I know Josephine is your stepmother. She is a lovely person."

"Ah yes," he began. "Josephine is a wonderful woman, and she is good for my father, Reuben. I am so glad they met each other and got married. We were living in Kansas when my own mother, Eva, died in the spring of 1883. She had been a schoolteacher but wasn't teaching after I was born. My father had bought a farm. I was about seven, I guess, and have great memories of roaming the fields with my father. He had an old cornet and sometimes he let me try to blow it." Orville smiled at his recollections.

He went on. "After my mother died, my father didn't know what to do with me because I was so young. He sold the farm and we moved to

Kearney, Nebraska where he got a job with the post office and enrolled me in a boarding school. At first, I hated it, but then one of the teachers learned I had some experience with the cornet. He took me under his wing and gave me cornet lessons. Later on, I joined the band. I learned a lot about getting along with people, playing in band. During the summers, my father would send me to Michigan where most of his family lived."

Orville was silent for a little while, then continued, "Now here's something I don't tell everybody. My father had a rough time after my mother's death. He got into some financial difficulties in the 1890s. I'm not sure if he was drinking or gambling. I never really wanted to know. But he was accused by the postmaster of embezzling some money orders. He swore he was innocent, but there was a trial in 1895 and he was sentenced to the penitentiary for four years. I was around 19 and on my own by then. I found a job working as a clerk in the Blak Flag store in Kearney. That's when I helped capture the guy who was stealing things from our store."

Walter turned to look at Orville. "What? That could have been dangerous. Especially if he had a gun. Remember what happened to my father when he went after the robbers."

Orville sat back and folded his arms. "We weren't even thinking of that. We just knew someone was coming on Saturday nights and making off with merchandise. But it was a mystery because there was never a sign of a break in. One night in September, my coworker, Mr. Mason, and I decided to try to solve the puzzle. We brought some pillows and blankets and bedded down in the storage closet. About 4 a.m. we heard a noise coming from the ceiling. We looked up and saw someone open the skylight. He lowered a long, hooked pole toward the display line. Sure enough it hooked some jackets and he pulled them up through the skylight. We weren't positive, but the fellow looked like the young man who lived in the upstairs apartment with his family. We didn't confront him; we called the police. They came right away and caught him red-handed. When the police searched their apartment, they found a lot of the merchandise our store had been missing."

"That's quite a story, Orville. The owners must have been very glad to find out what was going on!"

Orville added, "Yes, that was one of the most exciting events of my sales career. The owners promoted me soon after as a reward. But back to my father. He didn't serve his whole sentence. He applied to the governor for clemency and was pardoned in 1897. He came to see me to tell me he was moving back to Michigan where most of his brothers and sisters still lived, the ones I visited in the summer. He asked if I would come with him. At that time, I didn't want to move because I was making pretty good money and recently had that big promotion to head salesman. Two years later he wrote to ask again if I would come. He was going to marry Josephine. Of course, I wanted to meet her and be there for him. In June of 1899 I resigned my position in Kearney and moved to Benton Harbor before the wedding, June 30. I sometimes wonder if my ambition to succeed and earn sufficient money was influenced by my father's experience in Nebraska."

Walter commented, "You certainly do have plenty of ambition. I saw that when we were the *Musical Reeses*."

Orville went on, "My father has lived an exemplary life since returning to Michigan. He has become the unofficial historian for our family and the whole county. He loves farm life and has spent a lot of effort and time experimenting with poultry, breeding and crossbreeding chickens for various traits. He even gives presentations on his results. Babette is so fond of him that I've never told her the Nebraska stories. I trust you to keep it to yourself as well," Orville concluded.

Walter assured him, "Freda thinks highly of him too. She clipped that long poem he wrote about the old days and put it in her scrapbook. My lips are sealed. You can count on that. I think your father has more than made up for his bad choices."

They both drifted off and slept fitfully until the conductor announced, "Next stop, Chicago. Please exit at this end of the car and watch your step while detraining."

Babette and Freda were at the station to meet them. On the interurban back to South Bend, the sisters peppered them with questions. "Did you really buy a furniture store?" "Are you sure you got a good price?" "Do you think Freddy could have a job at the store?" "When will we move?"

Walter and Orville answered as fast as they could. "Yes. Yes. And Yes. August!"

"August!" Freda gasped. "How will we get everything ready by then?"

Betty raised another concern. "You know, Mama is not well. It's all Papa can do to take care of her. Freddy tries to help, but it's not easy. She was excited for us but also sad when we told her we thought we would be moving to Winona. We assured her that we would have room for her and Papa to live with us in Winona when we get settled."

"I'm sure things will work out," said Walter. "We'll take one day at a time."

The rest of the summer, they were kept busy making arrangements to move. It was a complicated process. Fred Sr. had said he would agree to move to Winona. "But," he stated, "I need some time to sell the South Bend house and its contents and organize my inventions for the move. Also, I am very concerned about Susanna. You can see her condition is not improving."

The sisters assured him they would do everything they could to accommodate her.

Fred Sr. said, "I will try to find someone to stay with her during the day, until she can join you in Winona."

Betty and Orville had to organize, pack, and move their belongings from Peru to South Bend. Freda and Walter cleared things out of their lodging in Chicago and stored some of the boxes at the train station. Then they all gathered in South Bend to help the Heyers.

Little by little they got the big things boxed and crated to be moved to Winona by train.

Orville and Walter would be driving to Winona. Orville made a trip to Detroit where he had some friends who worked at the Ford Plant. They advised him on purchasing a Model T Ford with a back seat, on the payment plan. He drove it to South Bend, where they packed it with smaller items, breakable things, and their instruments. They tied some things to the top.

Orville and Walter said goodbye to their wives, the Heyers and the Christensens, and set out from South Bend to Chicago. From there they followed the Black and Yellow Trail, originally laid out as a route from Yellowstone to the Black Hills. The route had expanded eastward through South Dakota, Minnesota, and Wisconsin to Chicago. It was fairly well maintained in some areas, not at all in others. Outside of the cities most of it was just a trail of gravel and dirt.

They had heard that the trip would probably take a week because the potholes and mud puddles they'd encounter could result in flat tires, broken axles, and getting stuck. They drove each day from dawn until dark, then found friendly farmers who let them pitch their tent in a field. Some of the more enterprising farmers' wives offered to fix them meals for a small fee.

There was rain, and they found themselves stuck a few times. Once they were mired so deeply that they had to tramp across a field to a farmhouse to find a farmer with strong draft horses who could pull them out. Walter and Orville were prepared for the anticipated flat tires with extra inner tubes, a small jack to raise the wheel, patches for the holes, and an implement to loosen the bolts. They had several occasions to use this equipment after hitting deep holes or sharp stones. When they heard the pop of a punctured tire, they had to pull off the road, kneel in the dust or mud, jack up the flat wheel, remove it from the rim, pull the innertube out of the tire, repair the hole and reassemble and reattach the whole apparatus. They endured constant anxiety waiting for the unmistakable sound of a blown-out tire or the clunk of a broken axle.

While the two men were on their way to Winona, their large crates and boxes were stored in a warehouse by the train station in South Bend. Betty and Freda stayed with Susanna and Fred, helping them pack and caring for Susanna.

When they heard from Walter and Orville that they had reached La Crosse, Wisconsin, the sisters knew it was time to get their things on the train and start the 10-hour journey to their new home. They tearfully said goodbye to their parents, went to the station, and directed the loading of their crates. They were relieved that Fred Sr. had found a neighbor who could tend to Susanna during the day. They boarded the overnight train so they would arrive by morning.

George Herrick had found a large home they could rent at 201 East 5th Street. It was big enough to accommodate all of them. Walter and Orville had agreed it would be ideal. Checking out the address on a city map, Walter noted, "From there it will be an easy two-block walk down Market Street to the store."

"Until we get the store up and running, it will be helpful to be so close," said Orville.

MUSICAL CHAIRS

CHAPTER FOUR

WINONA: 1919-1940

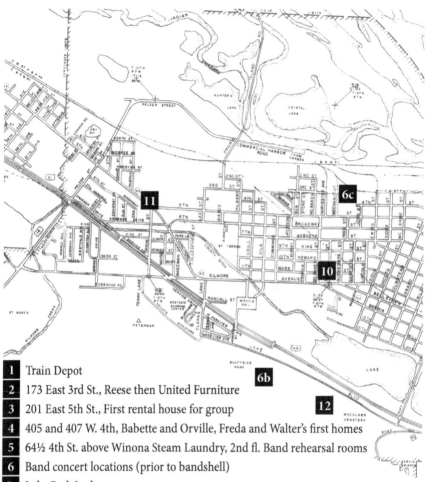

1 Train Depot
2 173 East 3rd St., Reese then United Furniture
3 201 East 5th St., First rental house for group
4 405 and 407 W. 4th, Babette and Orville, Freda and Walter's first homes
5 64½ 4th St. above Winona Steam Laundry, 2nd fl. Band rehearsal rooms
6 Band concert locations (prior to bandshell)
6a Lake Park Lodge
6b Bluffside Park
6c Athletic Park
6d Municipal Dance Pavilion
6e Levee Park
7 Winona's permanent bandshell
8 La Moille (approx. 11 miles)
9 358 W. Sanborn St., Walter and Betty 1937
10 804 W. Mark St., Freda and George 1937
11 101 Orrin St., Walter and Betty
12 Woodlawn Cemetery
13 West Burns Valley

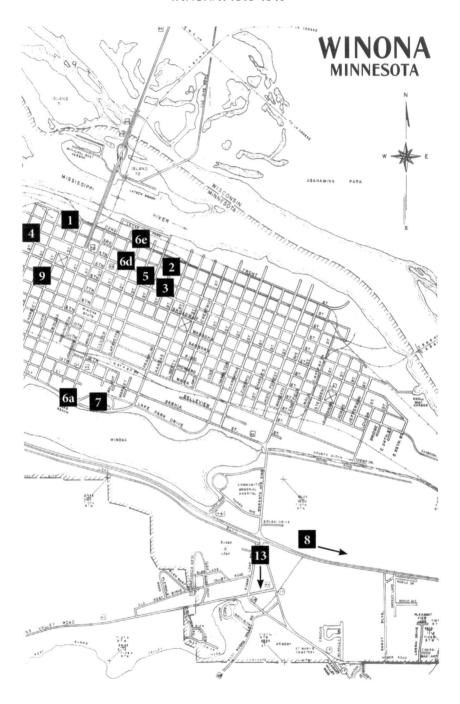

Map of Winona, Minnesota courtesy of Winona County Historical Society

1919

One late evening in August of 1919, Walter and Orville arrived in Winona, found their new home, and unloaded everything from the car. They put some blankets on the floor and quickly fell asleep. The next morning, they drove to the train station to meet their wives. Herrick also met them there. He had borrowed a horse drawn cart to load all their belongings from the train and move them to the rented house. Betty and Freda were happy to see their husbands, although they both noticed and remarked that the men really needed to bathe.

As soon as they were settled, Orville decided they needed to announce their purchase of the furniture store to the public. He was an excellent writer and had honed his skills in both sales and music promotion over the years. He put together the information he wanted in the article and sent it to the *Winona Republican Herald*. It appeared on September 20, 1919, with headline "MUSICIANS BUY PIONEER LOCAL BUSINESS HOUSE" in all capital letters, followed by the subtitle "O. W. Reese and W. W. Christensen Purchase Interests of Winkels Furniture Store."

According to the article, their intent was to "improve stock" and "make it modern."

When they got the newspaper Orville gleefully said to Walter, "Listen to this." He read aloud, "'Four professional and talented musicians of wide experience took over the interests and stock of the Winkels Furniture company.' Then it lists all of us and goes on, 'Messrs. Reese and Christensen will remodel and restock the store, which is one of the oldest of its kind in the city.'"

Walter remarked, "Well, that should stir up some interest. I suppose you wrote most of that yourself?"

Orville said, "Well, I did furnish the basics. Let me read you some more. 'They will carry a complete and up-to-the-minute line of furniture, rugs and draperies. Furniture booths will be built in the store, potted palms and tasty interior decorations will be added, and the stock will be greatly enlarged, so that the store will be among Winona's most up-to-date establishments catering to the best trade.' I guess they printed it exactly as I wrote it. They even included this detailed description of our musical experience and accomplishments." He pointed to that paragraph. "I really wanted them to put that part in. Especially if the Band Board will be looking for a new band director soon."

"Is that the real reason you wanted to move to Winona?" asked Walter.

Orville admitted, "It is one of them."

The next several weeks all of them spent cleaning and rearranging the new Reese Furniture Store. They only closed the store for a few days to get the painting done and to decide how to display the furniture in home-like groupings, as promised. They found a few young boys who were willing to move the heavy things around for a few extra coins. They hired painters, who painted walls and ceilings with the most modern palate according to Freda, who took great interest in these things. Floors were polished, windows cleaned, and updated lighting installed to show things off. Freda, and sometimes Betty, decided how to arrange things most attractively. Plants, smaller pieces, and accessories were carefully distributed.

There was an open balcony on the mezzanine between the first and second floors. It had served as Winkels' office, and they decided to keep it that way. There were desks and cabinets for paperwork plus a system of wires and pulleys connected to the first-floor counter that whisked baskets of cash and receipts back and forth when sales were made.

One day, after the store had been set up, Betty announced, "I truly don't want to be involved in the furniture business. I want to teach music to children, and I want to continue giving lessons. I need a place for my studio." She put aside her broom and pointed to the stairs. "Could I have a corner upstairs in the store for teaching?"

"I don't see why not," said Orville. "There is some space that we won't be using for sales or storage."

Walter added, "We do have to make sure that the sound doesn't disturb store customers."

"Maybe they would enjoy it," Betty responded huffily. She went upstairs and found a former storage room in the east corner at the back of the building. She thought it would be a perfect teaching studio. One wall was on the alley side with large windows facing south, making it cheerful and light. It was close to the top of the side stairway so students could come and go quietly.

She brought everyone up to see the room. "It needs cleaning, but I am sure that no one in the business area will be bothered by the sound from way back here."

Orville said, "I think that might work, but you will need to test that. We can't lose customers because it's too noisy."

Betty put her hands on her hips and frowned at her husband. "My students make music, not noise," she said testily. But she decided to try to dampen the sound by hanging curtains along the inside walls. She acquired some heavy draperies from a theater that was going out of business and hung them against the inside walls. She then added a rug that would keep the sound from going through the floor.

Once the room was prepared, she asked everyone to stay downstairs and tell her if they could hear anything. She brought her saxophone up into the room and played as loudly as she could.

When she went back downstairs, Orville said impatiently, "Are you going to test your saxophone sound soon? We have a lot of work to do here."

Betty answered, "I have been playing for the last five minutes! Obviously, you didn't hear a thing. I think that room will work out well for my studio." She was very glad. It would be the most spacious studio she'd ever had. And no one else would be sharing it.

Her piano was carefully moved up the stairs into the room. A few out-of-fashion chairs and a bookshelf for her stacks of music were borrowed from the old inventory to furnish the room.

On October 24, 1919, an ad appeared in the Winona Republican Herald with Babette's photo. It announced that "Babette Reese, Teacher of Piano and Saxophone has opened her studio on the second floor of the Reese Furniture Store."

That fall, Orville joined the Association of Commerce as a business owner. The Association of Commerce had been involved with starting and supporting many civic projects, among them the Fire and Police Board, the YMCA, the new high school, road improvements, parks, and, of course, the Winona Municipal Band. He got to know many of the influential people in the group including Dr. Oswald Leicht who had worked particularly hard to develop the Band (and had written Orville the letters informing him of Colburn and Michaux's hiring.)

When the store makeover was complete, it was time to get down to business. They had made a few sales while they were reorganizing. Now they spent their efforts learning about the competition they faced from existing furniture stores in Winona. Breitlow's and Hillyer's both doubled as mortuaries, since they built coffins. They had existed in Winona for many years. Orville and Walter were not interested in the mortuary business.

One thing that Orville and Walter had learned from their own experiences was the importance of advertising constantly. A business had to keep its name in front of people in addition to offering good value and friendly service.

Orville began placing weekly ads in the newspaper in December to encourage Christmas shopping at the store. These ads were eye-catching and utilized the newspaper staff artists who drew detailed pictures of furniture. Orville's copy noted that the newly opened Reese Furniture offered "everything in furniture, Cedar Chests, Rocking Chairs, Reclining Chairs, Davenports, Sewing Tables, Library Tables, Dressers, and Framed Pictures" to name some of them. His ads invited customers to visit the store and see the extensive assortment of gifts for every member of the family. He tried his best to make people aware that Reese furniture was a store with the most modern merchandise. Walter did his best to make sure every customer was treated well and felt welcome.

© *Winona Republican Herald* - December 8, 1919

For Your Shopping This Christmas Visit Our Store

and see our complete and extensive assortment of gifts for every
member of the family.

THE REESE FURNITURE STORE

© *Winona Republican Herald* - December 18, 1919

1920

As 1920 began, Orville said to Betty, Walter, and Freda, "I encourage you to make yourselves as active as possible in Winona's music community. Babette, you will attract more students to your studio by accompanying groups and soloists, along with advertising in the newspaper. Walter and Freda, if you offer to sing for events that come up, Babette could be your accompanist. It would make your names more recognizable in Winona, and that would help our business grow."

They followed his advice. As a result, their names were frequently seen in the newspaper. Orville made sure to send in articles that highlighted their individual talents and appearances.

When he was chosen band director in Rollingstone, a smaller town about 10 miles west and slightly north of Winona, Orville submitted an article to the newspaper saying, "During the few months he has been here, he has shown himself to be a musical leader." The article went on to describe his experience in Peru, Indiana where he had organized commercial club activities and arranged events drawing thousands of people. He was sure that it would help him if the position as director of the Winona Municipal Band became available, as he suspected it would.

Orville also sent information to the newspaper Society page for an article introducing his wife to Winona. She read it to herself when it appeared on February 7. "Miss Babette Heyer Reese, who in the late fall removed from Indiana to Winona, is a gifted and accomplished pianist who, in the comparatively short time she has been here, has attained a recognized place in the local musical world." The article summarized her awards, accomplishments, and vaudeville expertise on the xylophone.

"Oh, Orville," said Betty, embarrassed after reading it. "Why do you make my past sound so impressive? It seems a bit overwhelming."

"You want to attract students, don't you?" asked Orville.

"Of course, I do. Teaching music is very important and satisfying to me. But this sounds too much like bragging."

"One thing I have learned," said Orville. "You have to get your name out there and let people know who you are. You are an amazing teacher and performer, Babette. They should appreciate that."

"Thank you, Orville. So are you. I suppose you're right, but I don't like to make so much of myself."

In mid-February, Fred Heyer Sr, sent them a telegraph from South Bend saying, "Your mother is declining quickly. Tending her has become too much for our neighbor. Could one of you come home to help me care for her for a few weeks until we are ready to move?"

They decided that Freda should go since Betty already had several students signed up for weekly lessons. Freda packed a bag and took the train to South Bend. She helped with Susanna's care and cried herself to sleep every night. She remembered the post cards Susanna had sent them when they were practicing their vaudeville act, telling her how proud she was of their hard work. It was heartbreaking to watch her mother get sicker and sicker since there was nothing anyone could do to help her.

Susanna woke up and noticed Freda quietly weeping. She gathered her strength and said, "Freda, don't be sad for me. I have lived a wonderful life with your brilliant father. He invented so many things to help people. It's too bad that he never got the recognition he deserved. But we have seen you and your sister and brothers grow up and develop your abilities and try amazing things. Now it's this furniture store. What a future you have."

"But, Mama, I will miss you so. You have given us all so much."

"I'm not gone yet." Susanna sighed with a little smile. "I really would like to see your new home in Winona." Her eyes closed and she drifted back to sleep.

In mid-March, the Association of Commerce adopted a new plan for the Winona Municipal Band. When the Municipal Band had been organized in 1915, it was placed in charge of a Band Board elected by those who contributed financial support. In 1919, the band was made an activity of the Association of Commerce. President Gardner said, "The band will be conducted again along that line in the present season with Dr. Oswald Leicht to head the new music bureau."

Dr. Leicht had been a strong proponent of forming the band back in 1915. He had continued to support the Association of Commerce's role in managing the band and providing the finances to continue it. Subscriptions still played a big role in raising the money it required.

As expected, Emile Michaux did resign from his directorship of the Winona Municipal Band to enter Chautauqua Work. Orville chortled when he read the news in the morning paper. He said to Betty, "I knew Michaux wouldn't last. Now is my chance to apply. Oswald Leicht knows I am interested. I will call him to ask his advice."

Oswald advised Orville, "Simply submit a letter stating your interest and qualifications. That should be sufficient." Orville got busy writing his application. He delivered it to Oswald in person.

Returning home, he told Betty he had delivered his application for the position to Dr. Leight. Betty scooped up some plates and put them in the sink. "The Band Board would be missing an opportunity if they chose anyone else. You are certainly the most qualified."

A few days later, Orville was reading the paper. Suddenly he whooped with excitement and said, "Babette, Look at this. I've been selected municipal band director for the coming year! The article says that the Winona Association of Commerce music bureau met and chose my application Monday evening." Orville grabbed Babette in a big hug, spun her around, and kissed her soundly.

REESE TAKES CHARGE OF BAND TUESDAY NIGHT

All Band Musicians of City Invited to Attend Important Organization Meeting.

© *Winona Republican Herald - April 5, 1920 p. 3*

"My goodness, Orville." she said, breathlessly. "Congratulations."

He replied, "It's my dream come true." He clapped his hands together.

At the next meeting of the Association of Commerce when his appointment was formally announced, Reese rose and said, "Thank you for your confidence in me. I will work with the Association of Commerce and immediately take charge. I will drill the band for the upcoming summer. Our concerts will feature both popular and serious music. We will include special features and continue the instruction of new players. I will use the band in any way I can to help the businesses in town."

He began rehearsing his new band in the band rooms on the second floor of 64 ½ 4th Street above the Winona Steam Laundry. It wasn't an ideal place to practice, but at least the humidity was good for the woodwinds.

Orville and Walter worked hard at their furniture store, showing people around, arranging terms for them to buy furniture, and placing ads in the paper. Orville was fascinated with the emerging world of recorded sound. He said to Walter, "Will you look into the New Edison phonograph machine? Maybe we could sell them at the furniture store. They have made big improvements over the old wax cylinders they used to sell. Those wore out so fast."

Walter said, "Do you really think these new cylinder recordings are the way to go? I hear there has been a great deal of progress with the disc recordings and turntables."

"Edison's cylinders have a constant speed, so the sound is supposed to be better than the discs," Orville said.

Walter went ahead and asked an Edison representative to come to the store and explain the New Edison Phonograph cylinder and demonstrate how it improved the sound. Both Orville and Walter were impressed.

Walter said, "I've never heard such lifelike sound from a machine before."

"Neither have I," said Orville. "I think customers will be very interested in purchasing them. And then they need to buy new cylinders to hear new music. That could be very profitable for us."

They decided to purchase the Edison Phonograph Agency in March. Walter agreed to organize and manage it. They selected a special area of the store and called it "The New Edison Shop."

Hear it for yourself
—the phonograph which
amazed all Winona

ARE you one of those who believe that no phonograph can match the voice of the living human? An astonishing discovery awaits you — like the thousand Winonans who attended the Amy Ellerman-Fleming Sisters recital.

Thomas A. Edison gave his famous Tone-Test last week Thursday in the Winona Opera House. He had Miss Ellerman sing in direct comparison with the RE-CREATION of her voice by the New Edison,* Then he had the Fleming Sisters Instrumental Trio play in similar direct comparison with the Re-Creation of their art by the New Edison. Music lovers were completely baffled. Their ears were unable to distinguish the RE-CREATED art from the living. You have never heard any phonograph that approaches the New Edison. It RE-CREATES not only the musical notes, but every elusive quality of tone and color which identify the original artist.

The NEW EDISON
"The Phonograph with a Soul"

Come in and hear the identical instrument* which was used. Make the great discovery for yourself.

REESE FURNITURE STORE
173 East Third St.   Winona, Minn.

*The instrument used in the Tone-Test is the regular model which sells for $295 (in Canada $431) It is an exact duplicate of the Laboratory Model which Mr. Edison perfected after spending Three Million Dollars in experiments

© *Winona Republican Herald* - May 1, 1920

Selling more expensive items and letting people pay for them in installments was a popular trend. Orville and Walter discussed this thoroughly and finally decided to set up their own plan. Walter said, "Why don't we call it 'systematic spending' because it takes the purchase price out of your income so gradually that you will hardly notice it."

Orville said, "That's a great idea, Walter. Let's do it. We can use your words in our ad."

They found this new approach increased sales a great deal.

In March, Freda, Fred, and Fred Jr. helped gather Susanna's belongings for the move from South Bend to Winona. They got her to the train station and found a seat where she could rest comfortably. They sat nearby, ready for the long trip. Betty and Orville met them in Winona and drove them to their rented home. They settled Susanna in a quiet room.

Freda stayed busy caring for her mother, but she missed the excitement of Chicago. She said to Walter, "I've pretty much seen everything in Winona. I've visited Choate's department store and a few others. They certainly don't offer as much as the stores in Chicago. There are no art galleries or museums here. I've been to the Winona Library, and they have some impressive artwork, but nothing like Chicago has. I've checked out books to read and I've gone to a few shows and concerts, but . . . ." She trailed off.

Walter said, "Freda, I understand. The store could use your help in bookkeeping. You are very good at that, and maybe you could modernize our system. Would you want to try that?"

"I guess it would give me something to do," she said flatly.

Walter said, "I'll talk to Orville."

When Walter asked about employing Freda at the furniture store, Orville said, "I've observed that she has good skills with numbers and the experience to go with it. I think she would be an asset to Reese Furniture. If she wants a job, we'll hire her."

She did want a job, but she told Orville that she didn't want to start while her mother still needed her.

He said, "That will be fine. I know Susanna needs you and Babette as much as you can be with her. But we need to let people know who you are, so they have confidence in you. I will write something up for the Winona newspaper."

On April 3, Freda brought in the newspaper and quickly looked through the pages. Walter was still finishing breakfast. She paused and let out a squeal as she read a headline out loud, "'Mrs. Freda Christensen, An Accomplished Musician Has Made Success Both as a Vocalist and Saxophone-Xylophone Player.' That's nice of Orville to write."

She kept reading the article which described her musical and singing ability and said that she and her husband, Walter Christensen, had often been featured in duet work. "Listen to this," she read. "'Mrs. Christensen is a thorough businesswoman having held a very responsible position in Chicago. She now has complete charge of the bookkeeping system of the Reese Furniture Store in Winona, of which concern Mr. Christensen is the junior partner.' Do you suppose Orville knows I was just another teller in Chicago?"

"Orville probably wouldn't include that if he did know it. He likes to embellish things," said Walter. "Still, that's quite an endorsement coming from him."

Throughout April, Susanna became weaker with each day. Betty and Freda did their best to make her comfortable, but nothing could be done to stop her from deteriorating. Herbert was summoned from his home in Chicago. He came with his wife, Harriet. Fred Sr. sat by her bed every day, talking to her softly. On Friday, May 5, 1920, she breathed her last.

The following Monday they arranged an afternoon funeral service for Susanna at their rented home, following custom. Many of their new acquaintances came to pay their respects. Betty, Freda, and Harriet bought traditional black dresses, and the men all wore black armbands. They purchased a plot in Winona's beautiful Woodlawn cemetery, big enough for the whole family to be laid to rest eventually.

Fred Sr. sold the house in South Bend and moved his things to Herbert's home in Chicago. He needed to return there to finish some projects. He would come to Winona as soon as he could to live where most of his family had settled.

Orville had been working hard to get the Winona Municipal Band ready for the summer season of concerts. Since he had taken over, they had been having two rehearsals a week preparing their music. He was quite a taskmaster and insisted on members practicing their music until it was as perfect as they could make it. He was also rehearsing the Rollingstone Band on a regular basis for their summer season.

Betty came to Orville one Sunday when he was at home. For once, the furniture store was closed, and he had no band obligations. She said, "Orville, I hardly ever see you anymore. You are always at one rehearsal or another or busy planning sales promotions. It reminds me of the years before we started *The Musical Reeses* when we were both so busy trying to make ends meet. Even though preparing the act and traveling around performing was exhausting, we at least got to spend time together."

"You're right, Babette," Orville said. "But you know the only way to succeed is to work hard. I am determined that the furniture store will do well. And my heart's desire is to be a successful band director. I don't know if there is anything I can change. I am still proving myself to the Band Board and I need to put on a successful series this summer if I want to keep that position."

Betty answered, "I know how important both of these things are to you, especially the band. I keep quite busy with the students I have. But it would be nice to have more time with you."

Orville answered, "Maybe things will settle down once the band is established. Walter is doing a great job managing the store."

Betty responded, "I'm sure he is. But I do hope we can spend more time together." Privately, she felt that nothing would change.

On June 5, Orville was pleased to read the newspaper's assessment of him to Babette. "It says that I am a businessman as well as a musician and plan to place the Winona Municipal Band on a business foundation." He turned toward her and said, "Did you know that the band now has about 40 members? Walter and George Herrick have joined."

Betty answered, "That's wonderful, Orville. Didn't you start with about 10 members?"

"Yes. I have worked very hard to build that number up," he said proudly.

"I know. That hard work means you're never home."

Orville looked at her quizzically but didn't argue.

The first concert of the 1920 summer season was to be on June 13 at Bluffside Park on the south side of West Lake Winona. A walking bridge on a former streetcar trestle crossed over the west end of the lake connecting Lake Street to Bluffside Park. A temporary bandstand had been erected there.

The concert received a glowing review in the newspaper. Orville happily shared it with Babette, who was sweeping the floor. "Hear this," he said. "'The Winona Municipal Band under the leadership of O. W. Reese gave the first concert Sunday.'" He skipped over some parts and continued, "'The original program of seven numbers was considerably lengthened by encores, which were demanded after every piece and responded to with popular music of the day.'" He stopped reading and commented. "They couldn't seem to hear enough. And here's what they wrote about Walter's solo, 'The introduction of a vocal number was an appreciated feature of the concert. W. W. Christensen, baritone, sang *Sunny Weather Friends* and in response to an insistent encore gave *Freckles*.' The audience really enjoyed Walter's singing."

Betty and Freda had, of course, attended. "How nice for Walter and you," she commented, still sweeping. "It was a very fine concert."

By July, business at the furniture store was going well. Betty said to Freda, "I wish we could buy our own homes. It would be nice if we lived near each other but not in the same house. I think we have good enough credit to get a loan."

Freda said, "The place we're renting is nice, but I would also love to have a home of our own. Let's ask Orville and Walter to see what they say."

The next time they were all together Freda said, "Betty and I have been wondering, do you think we could afford to buy our own homes? We love living in the same place, but I think we would all enjoy some privacy."

Betty added, "We would like to find houses near each other and not too far from the store. I will need a house with enough room for my piano."

"Well, there's no harm in looking," said Orville.

Walter said, "But first we need to go to the bank real estate department to find out what properties are for sale. I think we should go with you."

After Walter and Orville accompanied them to the bank and met with a representative, an agent took Freda and Betty to tour the homes that were for sale. The men needed to "mind the store." Nothing the sisters saw seemed exactly right. The houses were too big, too small, too far apart, or too far away from the store. After a few days, they were almost ready to give up when the agent excitedly told them he had two nice, similar, big houses for sale that were next door to each other, at 405 and 407 West 4th Street.

Betty said, "That sounds exactly like what we are interested in."

"When can we see them?" asked Freda impatiently.

The agent said he would call them back with some specifics for visiting both homes. He arranged a time that worked for all four of them.

After touring the properties, Freda exclaimed, "These are perfect. What do you all think?"

Walter agreed, "I think these would be very suitable."

Orville nodded his approval.

"I think so too," Betty said. "They both have many rooms, and we could fit pianos into either of them. Freda and Walter, you will have room for a new piano for yourselves."

Betty and Freda were thrilled that the houses were close, but separated from each other.

They offered $6,500 for each of them. Since the houses were nearly identical, Betty and Orville chose the 405 addresses. They happily moved out of their rented space to become neighbors rather than housemates on July 24.

Although they had all been kept busy with the move, Orville managed to conduct weekly concerts throughout the summer at various locations: the Municipal Dance Pavilion opposite the Post Office at 4th and Main, temporary bandshells in Levee Park and Lake Park, as well as Bluffside Park and Athletic Park on West 5th Street. The band also played for parades and other special events.

Orville said, "Since we are organizing the band on a business basis, we need a business manager. I think that George Herrick would be a great one."

Herrick agreed to the responsibility even after Orville told him that one of his chief duties would be keeping track of musicians who failed to appear or came late to rehearsals. He would have to make sure their pay was reduced.

The municipal band concerts presented during the summer featured guest artists and were well received. Orville made good use of their vaudeville experience and featured Walter singing, and Babette playing her xylophone. The saxophone quartet that had been part of the *Musical Reeses*' act was scheduled to play as well. They enjoyed having an outlet to perform again.

Orville was impressed by the saxophone players in his band. He told Babette, "It would be quite a feat to put together the largest saxophone band in the United States. I asked the band's saxophone section if they were interested, and 12 of them are willing to join. I would like to have 25 of them. That would be noteworthy." He chuckled at his own joke.

Reese Furniture ads featured the phonographs frequently all year, promising that the recordings truly sound to the listener as if they are in the same room. In September, Walter showed Orville some advertising materials the company sent telling them how to invite customers in to test it.

"How do they suggest we do this test?" asked Orville.

Walter answered, "The Edison Company provides the script. I have read these materials over and can conduct the test myself. I hand people the instructions to follow and ask them at the end, 'Do you get the same emotional reaction that you experienced when you last heard the same kind of voice or instrument?' Most people think they do."

Orville said, "We can certainly try it." He wrote up an ad challenging people to come in to take the New Edison Test for free. Curious folks did come in, and Walter sold many units that way. Even when they didn't buy a New Edison, they often found something else they needed to buy before leaving. Orville noticed that.

In September the band had a money crisis. The city had pledged money to the Association of Commerce to support the band. They understood the appropriation was for one year and needed to be requested in subsequent years. With the change in structure and leadership, this had been neglected and the band was left with no city money. Orville said that they could continue concerts if they could obtain enough funds to finish the year. There was not enough time to resolve the dispute before the September 22 concert which was to feature the saxophone quartet. So that concert was cancelled. Enough people complained, and the matter was resolved in time to schedule the quartet for the season's last outdoor concert on October 2.

By the end of the year Orville had divided the band into three sections. Class A, B and C. Class A included the better musicians, class B the less skilled players and class C the juvenile department. Reese planned to teach them a course in opera since he firmly believed that "All classical and standard musical numbers were founded on grand opera." He hoped to have members educated in music before the upcoming summer. Indoor concerts were planned for the colder weather.

1921

The New Edison Company came up with another advertising ploy that they sent to their dealers. Walter read it over and shared it with Orville, saying, "The manufacturers believe that hearing music can change one's mood. Have a look at this chart. People are supposed to listen to music played on their phonograph and write down their mood changes."

"Being musicians, we know from our own experience that music has an effect on moods," said Orville.

"You're right," said Walter. "They seem to be using a well-known idea to sell their machines." He paused a moment, then said, "I wonder if they are worried about competition from the turntable devices?"

Orville said, "That's possible, but I've heard some of those and the sound really isn't as good as the Edison."

Walter said, "Not yet anyway. I heard one too. The music it produced seemed sort of thin and scratchy. The phonograph's sound is much better. I guess there's nothing wrong with making people aware of music's effect on them. I think we should use it in our ads."

Soon Reese Furniture ads appealed to people to fill out a mood change chart after listening to music on a New Edison Phonograph. They were informed that their responses would help Mr. Edison's research. They could take the test at the store, or, if they already owned a phonograph, they could get a supply of charts from Reese Furniture and invite their friends to a Mood Change party. It would be more entertaining than a Ouija board, the ads promised. Completed charts returned to the store would be sent to Mr. Edison. These ads, along with their usual furniture display ads, brought in a lot of business.

Reese Furniture sold fiber and oriental design rugs. Walter had been reading about the new Congoleum Rugs. They were similar to the earlier linoleum flooring products but were made with asphalt which gave them more durability. He said to Orville "Why don't we add Congoleum Rugs to our stock? They seem to hold up well and are very easy to clean. They have designs just like our regular rugs."

Orville agreed and told Walter to go ahead and order a few. "We'll see how they sell," he said.

They ordered a selection and placed many ads extolling their advantages. These 'rugs' didn't need vacuuming or beating on the clothesline and didn't attract moths like wool did. You could simply wipe up messes with a damp mop. They came in different sizes and were made in patterns that mimicked rugs. They became very popular.

In January of 1921, Reese told the Band Board, "If we are to have a quality Municipal Band, we need to

© *Winona Republican Herald -*
March 1, 1921

start students at a young age. I want to propose a training plan. We will invite boys above fourth grade to join the juvenile branch and learn to play. They could have 25¢ weekly lessons. For young players I earnestly believe that hard work should be balanced with play. I would like to offer refreshments and games after rehearsals once a month."

The board approved. They soon started their first group of beginners and added a second section later in the spring. The young band members worked hard and eagerly anticipated the special activities.

Reese and the Band Board president, Oswald Leicht, made public pleas for donations of band instruments. They ran appeals in the newspaper saying, "There are probably many unused band instruments lying around that could well be brought into service again. Many youngsters have the ambition to join the new boys' section of the Winona Municipal Band but their families can't afford to purchase an instrument."

Orville told Oswald Leicht about another idea he had. "I would like to plan a band tournament for Winona."

"What would that involve? asked Dr. Leicht, looking slightly skeptical.

"It would be scheduled for August, so we have time to prepare. Bands from surrounding towns like Alma, Wabasha, Rollingstone, Galesville, Arcadia, Plainview, and Cochran will be invited to participate. As tourney host, the Winona Municipal Band would not compete."

Dr. Leicht asked, "How would you entice them to come?"

"There will be prizes awarded, of course," explained Orville. "When I visited Elkhart last month, I acquired a trombone valued between $75 and $100, donated by the Conn Instrument Factory. We could use that as the first prize. We could make the second prize a cash award."

"It sounds like you've given this some thought, Orville," said Dr. Leicht. "It will take a lot of work to organize."

Orville said, "Yes, I have thought about it. I am sure people from the band and the Band Board will help with the details. The Association of Commerce should be especially interested since the contest will bring people to Winona from all the nearby towns. Besides the band members, think of all their families who will come to see them. And they will spend money here too."

"You make a good point, Orville. I will propose it to the Band Board for their approval," said Dr. Leicht. The board thought it was a great idea.

Orville spent hours preparing the music for the regular summer concert series. Many nights he came home from his office in the band rooms very late.

Betty said, "Orville, how can I feed you dinner when you don't get home until almost bedtime? The meals I've cooked are all cold by the time you eat them."

"Babette," he said, a little testily, "you know how important it is for me to have all these concerts planned ahead of time. I have to make sure we have all the parts for the music, and I need to become familiar with the scores. Some of the popular pieces I even have to arrange myself using the piano music. That really takes time. And I do that after spending most of the day at the store."

"I know, Orville, but I get so lonely. Sometimes I teach lessons into the evening, but when I come home to an empty house, it makes me sad," Betty answered.

The next evening, he came home in time for dinner. He told her, "I am almost finished planning the summer concerts. Have I told you about the band tournament we're planning in August?

"No," she answered, wondering how much time he'd need to devote to this project.

"The Band Board is really excited about it. We are inviting bands from surrounding communities to participate in a contest on August 14. The bands will gather at the band rooms on 4th Street and march to the Levee, where they will give concerts of music I choose and be judged on their performance. Dr. Leicht is taking care of the location details, and Walter offered to help with planning refreshments. My big job will be to choose the music and invite the bands," Orville said.

WILL SING AT BAND CONCERT FRIDAY NIGHT

W. W. CHRISTENSEN   FREDA CHRISTENSEN

A popular feature provided by Director O W Reese for the concert of the Winona Municipal band to be held Friday night at Lake Park will be the appearance of W W Christensen, baritone, and Freda Christensen, contralto, who will sing "Mammy." Judging from the reception accorded the Christensens when they sang at a recent concert, they will be required to sing several encores in addition to the program number. The Christensen duets are much in demand and Director Reese complied with a popular wish in providing the feature for the Friday evening concert

© *Winona Republican Herald* - July 28, 1921

"Goodness, what a lot of work. You certainly have big ideas," Betty said halfheartedly.

Orville, apparently missing her tone, took it as a compliment and said, "Thank you. It will be very good for Winona."

Betty finished the dishes, swept, and cleaned up silently. Then she went to their bedroom to read a book. He went to his desk to write invitations to the tournament.

Orville read the reviews of the first summer concert to Babette. "'The Winona Municipal Band has made a gain of fully 100% in ability according to music lovers who attended.' Did you hear that? 100%."

Betty was unable to resist his enthusiasm. "That's wonderful, Orville."

The regular summer concerts were presented at the usual locations with one new one, the Normal School campus. Special features were duets by Walter and Freda, and a piece that used the new chimes, played by Fred Heyer Jr. The band had grown to include 50 musicians.

The band tournament Sunday afternoon in August was a huge success. Thousands came to Winona to enjoy it. Lanesboro won first, Galesville 2nd, Alma 3rd, Rollingstone 4th, the Strum Ladies band 5th, and the Winona Boys' Band 6th.

Oswald Leicht told Orville, "Well, this is another feather in your cap. It truly demonstrates that you are serious about using the bands to help Winona businesses."

Orville was happy that Betty was close enough to hear Dr. Leicht's remark, but she just kept watching all the activity.

Orville had been quite vocal about the problems with the various locations for the band concerts. He told the Band Board, the City Council, and anyone who would listen, "We need a permanent place for concerts. Along the levee, boats go by while we're playing, and their noise covers our music. The stand at Main and 4th doesn't seem safe. We can't use the lake park location often because of high water. There is a problem with trains whistling and chugging by. Many people complain that Bluffside Park is too far away."

The City Council acknowledged the problem. The mayor said he was in favor of improving the location along the levee, but the council decided to discuss the matter with the park board.

In December Reese announced a plan to increase the numbers in the Boys' Band. "I propose that we affiliate with the Boy Scouts of America. There are already eight scouts in the band and fifty more in scouting."

Parents and the Band Board agreed.

Orville told them, "We will rename the band 'The Boy Scouts' School Band' and we are going to wear scouting uniforms. I see three advantages to this arrangement. One, it will increase the number of players. Two, we will acquire uniforms, and three, we will gain a dedicated group of mothers to arrange monthly social meetings with refreshments after rehearsals."

1921 Winona Band Tournament
photo courtesy of Winona County Historical Society

1922

Orville announced his plans for the Municipal Band's coming year to the Band Board and members in January. "We will continue weekly rehearsals in the winter months in the band rooms. I am happy to announce that the Boys' Band, after the merger with the Boy Scouts, has grown to 70. We will divide rehearsals between Tuesday and Wednesday evenings. I will act as scoutmaster, and the boys can wear their scouting uniforms. But I'd really like to outfit them in band uniforms, so I am working on a plan for that."

Orville and Walter knew they needed to attend the big furniture markets in the East to keep abreast of the latest in styles and designs. Orville usually went and sometimes Walter or other store employees accompanied him. They would order quantities of new furniture for the store. It was a great opportunity to keep Reese's up to date. When a market was in Chicago, Babette, Freda, and Walter came along and had a chance to visit Walter's family and other old friends.

Orville said to Walter one day, "I think the store is too crowded. We don't have room to display things properly. We do get a better price when we buy more furniture, but we need to be able to show it off."

Walter said, "Yes, it has gotten hard to feature everything we have. Do you think we should build an addition? There is an empty lot to our west."

"That space would be ideal. I will see if it's for sale," said Orville.

Soon he had negotiated an agreement to purchase that lot. They had plans drawn up for the addition. Building began after the spring thaw and was expected to be finished by the fall.

The senior Municipal Band was invited to play for the yearly 'Spring Opening' when stores could show off new seasonal wares. Orville proposed to the Association of Commerce that they combine it with an exhibit at the armory, saying, "We merchants could show off new items from our stores. I would be glad to help with planning the exhibit. I can draw on my experience in South Bend, when I put together the Pure Food and Manufacturer's Exposition. It was very successful."

"Of course," he told Walter afterward, "Reese Furniture must have a booth with our newest pieces. The Winona Municipal Band has been asked to play at the event. That will ensure good attendance the first night."

As he predicted, hundreds of people thronged to downtown Winona. The Municipal band marched and played, generating much excitement.

Betty had a dozen saxophone and piano students who were ready to present a recital, so she scheduled one for June 8. It was open to the public. She said to Orville, "I hope you can come to see how much progress these young people have made."

Orville replied, "I really would like to be there, but I have so much work to do preparing the Boys' Band for our summer outing with the Rollingstone and Weaver bands on the 26th. And I am preparing for the Municipal Band summer season. Concerts start on June 28. And I think there will be a second band tourney in August, so I need to think about that."

"Yes, I know." Betty couldn't keep the disappointment from her voice.

The next evening when Orville was having a rehearsal, she went next door to Walter and Freda's. She said to them, "I asked Orville to come to my students' recital. Some of them have made so much progress. But he said he was too busy."

"That's unfortunate," said Walter, sensing her feelings. "Freda and I will be there."

"Thank you. The students have worked very hard and deserve an audience," said Betty.

Freda said, "Of course we'll come."

They talked a little about the upcoming summer concerts. "Orville has asked us to present some special duets at this summer's Municipal Band Concerts," Walter said. "I really enjoy being in front of an appreciative audience again."

Betty said, "Orville suggested that I play a feature on the xylophone with the band. I told him that I would. Freda and I will be at all the concerts regardless."

Freda said, "I have an idea. Since Orville is so busy, why don't the three of us form our own band and see about playing some dances ourselves? It would be fun, and we could bring in a little money."

"That sounds like a great plan. We know so many new songs and there are lots of standard numbers we remember from our vaudeville act. It shouldn't take much practice to polish our act and learn some new songs," said Betty.

Walter added, "I would appreciate a little distraction from all the store business. Freda and I could sing, and you could accompany."

"Maybe Freddy Jr. could join us with his drums if he's free," Betty said.

Freda thought for a moment. "I have some friends who always go to dances on Fridays and Saturdays. Sometimes they go to the Witoka tavern up on the bluff. I bet Witoka would like some variety. I'll ask my friends who we should call."

Since Walter and Freda now had a piano, they got together at their home to put together their program. They practiced in the evenings when Orville was off rehearsing one of his bands. Betty stopped feeling so lonely.

The summer was a busy one for the Municipal Band. Not only were the usual concerts presented, but the band began to accompany trade tours. The Association of Commerce arranged car caravans with the band and participating merchants. They drove to neighboring towns where the band played a concert and businesses distributed souvenirs.

Orville regularly read the summer concert reviews to Babette. After a concert in July, he scanned the newspaper and said, "Listen to this. 'The standard and classical numbers on the program were well received and excellently given. The rehearsals during the winter and spring months under the leadership of Director Reese were well reflected in the worthy presentation of the different numbers.' I hope the community appreciates our efforts," he said, tapping his finger on the article.

"I'm sure they do," said Betty.

Orville had warned the Band Board and anyone else who would listen, "These flimsy temporary band stands that you have erected around the city are not satisfactory structures. They could collapse at any time. Besides, there is no way for the band to be heard properly without a solid surface behind them." But it seemed no one was listening.

During the concert on July 29, 1922, the night that Babette was going to be featured on the xylophone, Orville was proven right when the band stand at Lake Park collapsed. Everyone was horrified. Many children had been climbing under the wooden platform while the band was trying to play. Orville and other band members warned them repeatedly to stop. The weak supports finally collapsed, and the stand sagged backward toward the lake, flattening out. The music stopped and the players jumped to the ground, afraid that children had been trapped underneath. Thankfully the platform was close to the ground, and no one was hurt.

Orville was very upset, and shook his head, saying, "I've been so afraid this would happen." He helped the band put things back in order on the platform, which was now lying flat on the ground. The concert resumed, and Babette was able to perform her xylophone solo.

After this occurred, Orville addressed the Band Board and the City Council, mincing no words. "Unruly children spoil the experience for everyone. I advise parents to control their children. It should be standard to have a policeman present at concerts to control these impudent young folks. This is another case for erecting a permanent bandshell."

Policemen were present for the following concerts.

Orville organized a second band tourney to be held on August 27. Eighteen bands from Minnesota and Wisconsin entered, and even the Wabasha Band planned to participate. Orville suggested organizing the bands into divisions, so there could be more winners. He had gathered several impressive prizes to award. The tourney had a surprise ending when the Pine Island Band, entered in Class B, was elevated by the judges to Class A and awarded first prize.

The nearby communities of Alma, Strum, and Minnieska requested Orville's service directing their bands. Minnieska, Minnesota, was only about 15 miles north west of Winona, but Alma and Strum were in Wisconsin, 26 and 50 miles north respectively. In a conversation with Dr. Oswald Leicht, Orville explained his expanding opportunities and said, "I am flattered that my directing expertise is being recognized."

Dr. Leicht put up a warning hand. "Hold on. Are you sure you are up to all this work and travel? I fear you are taking on too much responsibility. I am concerned about your health. After all I am a physician."

Orville said, "I know I can handle this. I thrive on directing music. You've seen that."

Dr. Leicht looked him in the eye and advised, "Make sure you are not neglecting other aspects of your health and family. Life is more than directing bands."

"I hear what you are saying, Oswald, but I have always dreamed of doing this. I have a great deal of energy."

In spite of Leicht's warning, Orville agreed to direct these bands along with Winona and Rollingstone bands. He worked out a complicated schedule of rehearsals that had him on the road a great deal.

The C. G. Conn company provided a special, gold "director's medal" set with three stones to be given to O. W. Reese in recognition for his work organizing the band tournaments, in addition to his direction of the Winona Municipal Bands and three area bands. On the back was inscribed "to the most popular director of the tournament." Dr. Leicht, as board president, announced that the medal would be given to Orville Reese at a future band rehearsal.

On the day he learned of the award, Orville came home in high spirits and proudly described the meeting to Babette saying, "I was so pleased with this recognition. It seems my hard work is paying off. And now there will be two medal winners in this house."

Betty looked at him with mixed feelings and responded, "Congratulations, Orville. Receiving a medal is a special thrill. I am glad you feel that way. But your band work takes a great deal of your time, and you are on the road so often. It seems that the furniture store and the Winona Municipal Band would be enough work for anyone." She added, almost too quietly to hear, "You are hardly ever home."

Orville answered, "Yes, I know I need to be gone a lot. But I consider it my duty to offer people the opportunity to play music wherever I can. What more can I say?"

Betty had no answer but was clearly unhappy. She, too, understood the importance of imparting musical skills to her students. But she didn't think she had to neglect her personal life in order to do it. She went into the kitchen.

In the fall, Walter, Freda, and Betty placed an ad in the paper announcing themselves as Christensen's Orchestra, a real snappy bunch. They could play all the new songs and other popular tunes. They were hired for jobs at Witoka and occasional private parties. They all had fun.

ANNOUNCEMENT!

Christensen's Winona Orchestra

Including Freda and Walter Christensen, Popular Entertainers.
We are ready to please you with music for

Dance, Concert or Party

Featuring Babette Reese at the Piano, and Fred Heyer, Jr., with his Bass.
Write, phone or call

W. W. CHRISTENSEN, NEW EDISON SHOP

Phone 565-J or 1425-R   173 East Third St., Winona, Minn.

© *Winona Republican Herald* - September 28, 1922

The new addition to Reese Furniture was completed and would be ready for a grand opening in early November. On October 29, Orville sent information to the newspaper announcing the formal opening of the addition, including a concert by the Winona Municipal Band on the first night. The second floors of both buildings would be used for furniture display. Toyland would be located at the south end of the new building. New electric lights with wiring in conduits had been installed to display the furniture to its best advantage.

Orville included details of the extensive musical experiences of the former *Musical Reeses*, (himself, Walter, Freda and Babette) and their current duties in the Reese Furniture Store (except Babette). In case folks had forgotten, he noted that he was currently conductor of the Winona Municipal Band. Fred Heyer Sr., father of Babette and Freda, who was a well-known inventor, had wrapped up his commitments in Chicago and moved to Winona where Reese Furniture employed him as "efficiency man" for the New Edison Shop mechanical division. Orville ended with "My father, Reuben, plans to join us when he closes out his interests in Michigan." What attracted the most people to the opening, however, was the announcement that prizes would be given to attendees.

Walter remarked to Freda as he read the formal opening ad, "Between you and me, it sounds like Orville thinks people come to our store because we're musicians, not for furniture values."

© *Winona Republican Herald* - November 29, 1922

Erecting a band shell in the Lake Park area had been discussed for several years. The secretary of the Park Board, Frederic S. Bell, a Winona banker and philanthropist, owned and was willing to donate the land and fund a permanent bandshell by the lake, but persistent drainage issues and flooding had stalled construction. Finally, the city engineer, E. E. Chadwick oversaw improvements which involved dredging and diverting water flow. The area had now been dry for two years, so plans for building the structure could go ahead.

At the end of 1922, Mr. Bell announced, "We are paving the road along the lake in preparation for the erection of a permanent band shell. The road will run in a loop from Franklin Street to the west, with the plan of placing the band structure in the center. Cinders are being hauled in to let them settle over the winter before construction begins."

Orville said to his musicians and the Band Board, "I am very glad to announce that progress is being made toward erecting a worthy structure for our Municipal Band concerts. We won't have to play from those flimsy band platforms when the new bandshell is completed."

1923

The Senior Municipal Band was busy during the winter months. They played for a Winter Carnival Beauty pageant, the Annual Auto Show, and the Spring Styles Exposition. Orville took over the directorship of the Minnieska band but didn't neglect his Boys' Band. His belief that hard work be balanced with play resulted in a very dedicated group of players. They always had monthly social events after rehearsals and occasional excursions to other towns for performing and picnics.

MONTHLY BAND SOCIAL—
The regular monthly band social arranged in connection with the practice sessions of the Junior Municipal band will be held tomorrow evening at the band rooms Parents and friends of the boys are invited to come The luncheon will be served after band practice

© *Winona Republican Herald* - February 6, 1923, p.2

Walter Christensen's Orchestra played for dances at the Armory and the Witoka Tavern. Walter and the sisters had a great time, but Orville was not as pleased.

He told Babette, "I think it is unseemly for you to be playing in a tavern. I hope you will stop this nonsense."

"But, Orville, we are having fun and making money too," said Betty. "It gives me something to look forward to when you are busy all the time."

Orville still demanded that Babette stop playing with the group.

Betty was in tears when she next saw Freda and Walter. She said, "Orville insists that I stop playing in our group. He thinks it's unseemly," she said bitterly.

Walter said, "I wondered when he would want you to stop. Don't be sad, Betty. We can still find acceptable places to perform. We really are a good group."

Betty dried her cheeks and said, "I know, Walter. But the people who come out to dance are a lot different from the people who go to PTA meetings."

Freda agreed, "That's for sure. I love the dance crowds."

The short lived Walter Christensen's Winona Dance Orchestra played their finale in April of 1923. The three musicians continued to perform for other, less exciting events, and Orville was fine with that. He knew that keeping their names in the minds of the public would be good for everyone.

By June, visible progress was made in preparing for the new band shell. Orville drove by every day and told anyone who would listen about the latest changes. One day he reported, "They say they are making parking spaces for up to 500 cars." Another day he said, "They are installing benches with seating for 1500 people." A while later he had the news, "They are leveling all the rest of the land and sowing grass seed. They have a bunch of shrubs and trees to plant, too." At the beginning of July, he exclaimed, "They are driving 30-foot piles for the foundation of the bandshell." Orville was beside himself. "It is actually going to happen. We'll have a permanent place to play our concerts!" he crowed to the Band Board.

Since the bandshell was not complete, summer concerts still needed to be held at the various alternative venues. Walter, Freda and Betty regularly presented feature numbers.

Orville complained about the crowd noise at concerts. "Rowdy youth, talking audience members, and other distracting sounds keep people who

photo courtesy of Winona County Historical Society

come to hear us from doing so." The concert reviews were rather brief that summer, so Orville just read them to himself, feeling gratified that they were at least positive.

Throughout the year Walter and Orville had purchased many display ads for Reese Furniture's various wares. Orville said to Walter, "We should sell pianos here. After all, Babette is attracting many students to the store, and they might want to buy better instruments. Maybe we could add saxophones and cornets since we can demonstrate them." So, they added musical instruments as well as Hoosier style kitchen cabinets made by Seller's from Indiana. They displayed these in their show window.

"You know they have electrified refrigerators now that are selling like hotcakes," Walter told Orville. "We have quite a stock of Alaska Refrigerators." These were essentially cabinets that held ice. Walter continued, "I think we should try to move those out. Let's offer a month of free ice with the purchase of one." They sold many with this added incentive.

Orville and the Band Board planned a third band tourney to be held in late August. Seventeen bands entered and 10,000 people were expected to attend. That day was perfect and pleasant. The Preston Band won the $125 first prize. Orville told Walter, "I am very pleased that my plan to promote music and business has been such a success."

In November Reese Furniture decided to highlight their extensive offering of toys. They had started this tradition the year before and found it very profitable. Their ads invited people to the opening of Toyland to see the wonderland of playthings that would make great gifts for little folks.

Betty continued teaching in her upstairs studio at the store. She presented a recital in November with 11 students. Orville could not attend, but Walter and Freda were there, along with the families of the students.

© *Winona Republican Herald* - November 24, 1923

1924

Walter suggested another promising marketing idea for Reese Furniture. "It might make it easier for people to purchase furniture if we would take their own used furniture as the first payment for the new furniture. They could buy new items and we could sell the used ones. The basement space could be cleaned up and made into a bargain basement."

Orville thought that was a great idea. "Why don't you come up with a new advertising campaign and have our staff get the basement in order?"

This approach proved very successful, and soon they had a supply of used goods to sell that had been acquired very reasonably.

Walter and his staff made sure that Reese Furniture continued advertising consistently in the paper, everything from aquariums and ironing boards to musical instruments and stoves, in addition to their regular stock of tables, chairs, dressers, beds, and so on. Walter was always looking for different things to sell and unique ways to sell them.

The Winona Playground Committee announced that they were sponsoring a buggy parade. Walter immediately spoke to the Committee Chair and said, "Reese Furniture would like to donate the first prize, a very nice doll buggy." The event was a hit. Kids decorated their buggies, wagons, trikes, or carts and paraded down Main Street from Central Park to 3rd Street. Reese Furniture's doll buggy was the most coveted prize and prompted many of the entries. About 200 children participated, entertaining throngs of parents and friends cheering from the sides. The participants were judged, and winners were given prizes.

A big event in 1924 for Winona was the completion of the new permanent bandshell. Band Board president, Dr. Oswald Leicht, met with the other members and appointed special committees to plan a suitably elaborate dedication ceremony.

Dr. Leicht told Orville, "At the next public Junior Band rehearsal, the Band Board is planning to recognize your contribution to the band's increasing success and improvement."

Orville said to Babette, "They are going to present me with the award I described to you at the Junior Band rehearsal Monday. I would appreciate if you would come."

Betty responded, "That's wonderful, Orville. I know how hard you have worked and how important the band's accomplishments and these awards are to you. But I have scheduled some make-up piano lessons that evening, and Papa has not been feeling well." Fred Sr. had been living with Freda and Walter. Every evening Betty stopped to see him and help Freda with his care. She felt justified in refusing Orville, since he had missed so many of her special events, but she still felt a twinge of guilt.

The occasion of Orville's recognition and gold medal award was reported in the newspaper. Reese was considered the most popular band leader in southern Minnesota. The article noted that when Winona thought of music, it had also come to think of Orville Reese for the many things which had been accomplished under his supervision.

Reese expressed deep gratitude for the public support given to the band. He said, "I have been inspired to still greater efforts and feel that my success with the Boys' Band is largely due to the mothers and fathers of those who make up the band."

Orville returned home from this recognition and was anxious to tell Babette about it. But when Babette was done with her make-up lessons, she had stopped at Walter and Freda's to sit with her father for a bit and then gone home to bed. She was very tired and didn't stay up for Orville.

In the morning, Orville described the previous evening's event and showed her the medal he received. Handing her the newspaper he said, "Here is the write up in the newspaper."

After reading the printed account Betty said, without emotion, "Congratulations, Orville. This has been your goal for a long time."

Orville was thrilled again when the Bandshell Dedication was held on the afternoon of Sunday, June 15. The Winona Municipal Band played the opening overture and the finale, and the Junior Municipal Band, the orchestra of the College of St Teresa, and a mixed chorus each gave two selections. Prayers and speeches were given by local clergy and dignitaries. A bronze tablet was attached to the back of the shell inscribed "Presented to Winona by Frederic Somers Bell 1923."

Dr. Leicht observed, "This bandshell is one of the finest, most modern and complete in the area." The shell faced a little to the south of west to bring some of the lake directly in front of the band, allowing people to enjoy the concerts from their boats.

The first regular concert in the new band shell was held on June 25. In spite of unpleasant weather, a large crowd attended. The next day,

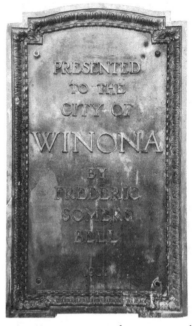

photo courtesy of Winona County Historical Society

Orville read the newspaper review to Babette. She listened as she dusted the furniture. "Well, this is gratifying," he said. "It says, 'One cannot but be impressed with the improvement in the band's playing over last year. It is more clear-cut and decided, with much better shading.'"

NEW BAND SHELL DEDICATED JUNE 15, 1924 WINONA MINN

photo courtesy of Winona County Historical Society

Betty paused long enough to say, "Playing from a bandshell really does help project the sound." She continued dusting.

However, Orville was not completely happy with the summer concerts. He repeated his complaint to the Band Board and band members about the noise from the audience. He continued, "And the sound from the car horns when the audience expresses appreciation by honking drives me crazy and distracts the musicians."

Oswald Leicht suggested, "Why don't you enlist Mr. Bell's assistance? Perhaps he could write a letter that would convince people to change their ways."

Orville approached Frederic Bell and said, "The Winona Municipal Band deeply appreciates the fine bandshell that you have given us. It truly is magnificent and improves our sound tremendously. But there is one thing that I have tried to impress on our audience over the years. The noise they create, particularly with their car horns, is very distracting. When I explain the problem and ask for their compliance, they remember for one or two concerts then return to their disrespectful habits. Maybe if you addressed this problem, they would listen to you."

Mr. Bell agreed. He followed up by writing a letter that was published in the paper. "I wish to express to you my grateful appreciation of all public and private expressions of commendation and of thanks which have come to me in relation to the new band stand. It would gratify me beyond expression if public approval of my gift should take the form of quiet and orderly enjoyment of the new facilities, and in particular I would suggest the doing away of the use of automobile horns in applause. It is a barbaric custom. The old poet sang, 'Music hath charms to soothe the savage breast,' but if he had been obliged to listen to honked plaudits on really fine music, he would have thought the savage breast needed a more powerful anodyne. Cannot Winona set a good example to other communities in this matter of applause by klaxon? Very sincerely yours, FREDERIC SOMERS BELL."

That seemed to do the trick. Audience behavior improved and klaxon applause ceased for the rest of the summer concerts.

The band performed for many old and new events, including the Winona County Fair, the big Fall Opening of stores that featured new goods for the coming season, and a trade tour to local towns to promote Winona businesses.

Winona Stores To Have Fall Opening 3 Days Next Week

THE annual fall opening of Winona stores will be held next Tuesday, Wednesday and Thursday, it was announced by E. F. Rogers, chairman of the Merchants bureau of the Association of Commerce, today.

The event will be inaugurated Tuesday evening at 7:30 o'clock with the opening of special window displays arranged for the occasion, accompanied by a display of fireworks and the blowing of whistles. Street lights will be turned on at 7:45 p. m. after the fireworks and the Municipal band will give a concert in the business district, starting at 8 p. m.

© *Winona Republican Herald* - September 20, 1924

Betty confided to Freda, "I am quite satisfied sharing my love of music with my students and developing their skills, but I miss having Orville be interested in my work. He doesn't even know my students' names, unless they play saxophone in his Boys' Band."

Freda sympathized and said she couldn't understand Orville's obsession with his bands.

But Orville was in his glory. He said to Walter, "We have a new bandshell and my band is being recognized as one of the best in the state, maybe the whole Midwest. I couldn't ask for more. But Babette doesn't seem truly impressed or appropriately respectful. She was much more fun when we were playing vaudeville. I haven't heard her laugh out loud since then."

Walter defended her, saying, "I think Betty is lonely since you are gone so much of the time. And you know her father is very ill."

Both Freda and Betty spent a great deal of time caring for their father. Fred Heyer Sr. died on December 22. His obituary noted his many inventions, among them the Heyer Storage Battery, improvements to the telephone switchboard, and innovations in surgical cautery instruments. He was laid to rest in Woodlawn Cemetery beside his beloved wife, Susanna.

1925

At the January meeting of the band board, Orville spoke about providing proper band uniforms for the Junior Band. He addressed the group, "From its beginning about three years ago, the band has grown from 17 to around 40. The progress these youngsters have made is very impressive considering most of them began with no musical knowledge."

President Leicht took up the cause. "I propose that one of our big projects for 1925 will be uniforming our junior band. Since there is nothing so attractive to the young person as a natty uniform, we are sure they will be a big incentive to join the band. Purchasing 65 to 70 uniforms will cost approximately $1,500 to $1,800."

Different ways of raising funds for the uniforms were considered. Finally, Dr. Leicht suggested, "The junior band could perform two concerts, selling $2 tickets for admission to both. If we ask someone like Horace Seaton, the music director at St. Paul's, to put together a program with a variety of local talent, I'm sure we can meet our financial goal. We could put some ads in the paper emphasizing that this is a whole community effort, and the program will be an exceptional entertainment value."

The first concert, presented on January 15, was very successful. The Boys' Band, under the able direction of O. W. Reese, performed two groups of numbers. Other performers on the program included W. W. Christensen, accompanied by Babette Reese. He sang *Your Blue Eyes* and *Tell Me You Love Me when the Lights Are Low*, songs that Babette had composed. The newspaper noted that "Mrs. Reese's songs have good melody and a good swing."

Toward the end of January, Freda saw an article about an upcoming wrestling match at the armory featuring a local athlete, George "Spike" Graham. She showed it to Walter and told him how interesting the event sounded. She would like very much to go. Walter agreed. They hadn't been out for a while so they went to watch. It ended in a draw.

On the way home, Freda gushed, "That was so exhilarating!"

Walter hadn't enjoyed it as much. "If you want to attend these sweaty spectacles in the future, I think you should go alone or with other friends," he said dryly. "Maybe your sister would go. I just don't enjoy watching muscle bound men slamming each other around."

"Oh Walter! You are such a . . . a . . . typical musician!" Freda sputtered. All of her life she had been around non-athletic, genteel, artistic, and intellectual folks. She had never witnessed a wrestling match. It was so dramatic.

The next morning Betty, as usual, was playing her piano. She heard the door open and saw Freda come in. Babette said, "Good morning, Freda. What brings you over here so early?"

Freda perched on the edge of a sofa near the piano. "I was wondering if you would be interested in attending some wrestling matches with me. Walter and I went to one yesterday. I thought it was exciting, but Walter made it clear that he did not enjoy it. He told me if I wanted to see another match, I would have to go by myself or with friends. Would you be interested in going?"

Betty shook her head. "No, I really don't enjoy watching wrestling. I'm always afraid that someone will get hurt. If Walter says it's fine, then you could go alone. Maybe another one of your friends would want to go with you. But be careful, Freda. You are a married woman."

Freda stood abruptly, "I know that. And I'm not doing anything wrong. But the matches are really fun to watch. And that George Graham, one of the wrestlers, is so handsome. He looks to be about my age. I think I will attend the next time he is in a match."

Babette repeated, "Be careful, Freda. You're a married woman."

Freda turned as she left and, with a toss of her head said, "So are you. I've seen the way you and Walter look at each other."

"Oh Freda, you have such an imagination." responded Babette, a little uncomfortably.

Freda managed to attend more wrestling matches. She caught George Graham's eye, and he winked at her. She winked back. After another of his wins, he made an effort to meet her. He introduced himself saying, "I am always so glad to see you among the spectators. Your cheering inspires me. I would like to get to know you better. Would that be possible?"

Freda said, "Yes, I would enjoy that. My name is Freda Christensen. I am married to Walter, but he doesn't care for what he calls 'sweaty spectacles.' He said I can come alone because I do like them."

"Would you let me drive you home after I shower and clean up the spectacle of my sweat?" asked George, smiling.

Freda laughed and agreed. The armory wasn't far from her home. George asked if she would mind taking the scenic route. Again, laughing, she agreed. He drove her down by the lake and parked while they talked.

Freda asked, "What made you take up wrestling? You are very good at it, it seems."

"I learned it when I was in the Navy. After I enlisted, I got training in the electrical school. But I wanted to do something for fun while I was there, so I started wrestling. I discovered I had a knack for it when I began winning." answered George.

"That explains why it looks so easy for you. But what brought you to Winona and what do you do besides wrestle?" Freda continued.

"Now that's a long story and a bit complicated. I got married when I was in the Navy. My bride apparently liked the look of my uniform. But when she learned I didn't come 'from money' as they say, she changed her mind after a year and a half and returned to her parents. Our divorce has taken a while, but she didn't even bother to come to the court proceedings." George laughed bitterly. "I began to look for a job in this area and found one in Winona at Watkins in the engineering department. After I moved here, I started wrestling again."

"I'm sorry," said Freda. "It sounds like you have been through a lot."

"It probably worked out for the best," said George. "I like it here. Winona is a nice city and there is so much to do outside in these beautiful hills. Enough about my life. Now tell me about yourself."

Freda told him about being in a vaudeville act, meeting and marrying Walter, and eventually settling in Winona, where her husband and brother-in-law bought a furniture store. "I work as a bookkeeper, and Walter runs the New Edison Shop there. We are asked to sing together quite often for different events. My brother-in-law is the Municipal Band Director, and he sometimes features us singing duets."

"That's amazing. I've heard you at the band concerts, but I never connected that Freda with you! You have a splendid voice," George exclaimed.

"That's kind of you to say. I love performing. Maybe that's why I have found your wrestling matches so fun to watch. You perform too, but you do it in such a different way." Freda looked at her watch. "Oh, my. It's gotten late. Walter will wonder where I am."

George started the car. "I lost track of time. I hope we can meet another time. It seems like we share many interests." He drove her to her home. She got out, shutting the door as quietly as she could.

She walked in the house, expecting to hear Walter ask where she'd been, but he was already asleep in bed.

Meanwhile, Orville was immersed in the effort to raise funds for the Junior Band uniforms. The second fundraising concert was held on March 9th. This program promised to be as good as the first, and ticket sales were enough to order the uniforms. Orville suggested to the Band Board, that they order the same uniforms for the Boys' Band as the Senior Band. "That way when players are good enough to move up to the next band, we won't need to buy them new uniforms. And if the two bands perform together, they will look alike."

The board agreed.

Some changes came to Reese Furniture in March. Walter saw the New Edison Phonograph system was being challenged by the new gramophones, which used turntables and disks instead of cylinders. He said to Orville, "You know, things don't look promising for the phonograph business. I've even heard rumors that the Edison Company is going to stop making them. Gramophones seem to be outselling our phonographs and cylinders. Maybe we should sell our inventory out and close the New Edison Shop. I've thought about it, and I actually would like to be more involved with furniture sales."

Orville agreed with Walter. He said, "What if Reese Furniture buys your interest in the New Edison Shops? You could become a junior partner in charge of sales."

"I like that idea." answered Walter. The change was announced in a large newspaper ad.

Fifty of the new uniforms arrived in April and the rest came in May. They were navy blue with visored caps. Orville said, "They will add a great deal to the appearance of the Boys' Band. Winonans will be more impressed by how well they play if they look like professionals."

On May 20, a photo appeared in the newspaper of the boys in their natty uniforms, accompanied by the caption, "Perhaps no happier group of boys could be found anywhere today than the boys of the Winona Junior Municipal Band."

Orville was very proud of this accomplishment and said, "I knew Winona would come through to support the boys. I look forward to giving their band more opportunities to perform."

Orville once more was engrossed in planning the coming summer series. When the concerts started, his musical selections were well received and earned positive newspaper reviews. Some of them were exceptionally laudatory. Orville eagerly read the write-up of their first concert and said to Babette, "This review is really something. It compares the return of the concerts with 'the arrival of our summer garden flowers.'"

Betty was trying to thread a needle. She said, "That's a nice comparison, Orville," followed by "Ouch!" as she accidentally poked herself.

"That's not all," said Orville. "It continues 'Conductor Reese, like a tall sunflower, dominated the garden. Symphony of color is replaced by the symphony of sound.'"

"I like the color part, but somehow I'm not able to see you as a sunflower," Betty said, and continued with her sewing.

Orville said, "The tall part is not accurate, I guess." But he was secretly flattered by this description.

In the fall Orville turned his attention back to the Boys' Band. He told the Band Board, "It is crucial to develop musical skills at this age so we can have enough players to fill out the Senior Band. There are many young fellows who want to join, especially after hearing that the Senior Band members are paid. I need to pick those who seem the most promising and motivated. I believe that interested boys should be given an exam to determine their suitability."

The board concurred.

In September, Orville informed the board, "Fifty-four youngsters enrolled at the opening of the Boys' Band. We expect about 25 more will join." He talked about the 81-question exam he had designed to determine a youngster's suitability for band. It included questions like, "How are tones expressed to the eye?" to assess their acquaintance with the way music is written. Other questions included "Where does the strong beat always fall?" and "How do you determine how high or how low the pitch of a note is?" Prospective band members were then selected from those with the highest number of correct answers.

The Senior Band played for many events that fall, among them the La Crosse State Fair, the downtown stores' Fall Opening and the October celebration of the improved dike road over the Mississippi between Winona and Wisconsin. Reese Furniture was among the businesses that had worked hard to encourage this better connection. Merchants realized that the improved access would help their sales. The newspaper proudly declared, "The new Minnesota-Wisconsin paved dike road affords every traveler who comes to Winona a safe approach to the most beautiful spot in the United States, the Gate City of Minnesota."

Betty, Freda, and Walter visited each other on the evenings Orville was at rehearsals. The three of them reminisced about their vaudeville days and their short-lived dance band. Sometimes they practiced songs they knew or wanted to learn. They still were being asked to perform in various combinations at a number of community events, and they had enjoyed appearing during the summer municipal band concert series. Walter said to Betty, "I wish you would write some more songs. The ones we did at the Boys' Band benefit were charming."

Babette blushed and responded, "Thank you, Walter. Your approval means a lot to me."

Back in May, Orville had heard about some land that was being sold along the river south of La Moille, in Richmond Township, about 12 miles southeast of Winona. "That would be a perfect place for gatherings with my bands in the summer." he exclaimed to Babette. "There would be room for water recreation and land games too. We could host gatherings for the staff at Reese Furniture there as well. Besides, I love fishing."

Betty said, "I can't imagine you having time for fishing, but that sounds like a pleasant spot for a summer place. Can we afford it? It would be nice to be by the water on hot summer nights."

"Elbert Lee, the owner, is asking $300 for all of it. I think we should buy it. I know we have that much."

Betty said, "That sounds like a nice idea. But it's just the land, right? Wouldn't we have to build a cabin there?"

Orville said, "That shouldn't be too difficult or expensive. We have enough credit here in Winona to qualify for a loan if we need it. A couple of the Junior Band members have fathers who are builders. They might be helpful."

Betty added, "We could use it ourselves as a get-a-way." She hoped it would give Orville a reason to spend more time with her.

Before the year was out, they purchased the land and hired builders to construct a cabin. They both looked forward to using the place when the next spring came.

1926

Reese Furniture was very busy advertising in 1926. Walter and Orville tried some different ideas and continued some that had proven successful. In February they joined a new city-wide "Dollar Day" campaign. Participating stores had chosen certain items to be sold inexpensively. Clues to the locations of these items ran in the newspaper, and bargain hunters were out early to find the goods they wanted. It was recommended that people bring copies of their newspapers for a guide. The newspaper article explained, "Even men, notoriously helpless in such matters, will find the path made easy to track the elusive bargains."

Walter had been promoting the Sellers Kitchen Cabinets that Reese Furniture stocked. In March the *Winona Republican Herald* sponsored a series of fifteen cooking classes, led by food expert and home economist Mary Brown-Lewers. Customers were invited to come see demonstrations and learn new cooking tips. She would also demonstrate the unique features of Sellers cabinets, like glass drawer pulls, roll up curtains, gravity catches, and ant proof casters. Attendees would be offered the choice of a free transparent measuring cup or an accurate measuring spoon as a souvenir. Walter remarked to Orville, "Look at how many people have come to these classes. We have sold a lot of cabinets."

Mrs. Mary Brown-Lewers

Chose the famous

SELLERS

KITCHEN CABINET

Because of its many exclusive features.

See it in actual demonstration at the Republican-Herald Cooking School

Reese Furniture Co.

"The Home of Fine Home Furnishings"

© *Winona Republican Herald* - March 1, 1926

Now calling their store The Home of Home Outfits, Walter and Orville continued to advertise new merchandise they brought in. There were more congoleum rugs, stoves, dishes, and all metal ferneries.

George Graham and Freda continued to get to know one another. In the winter George enjoyed ski jumping. Several nearby towns had constructed ski jumping structures, and these competitions became very popular. George said to Freda, "I would love to have you watch me jump. I know you thought wrestling was exciting, but ski jumping is much more thrilling. For me, it's almost like flying. There aren't many women who participate in it, but I would love to teach you if you're interested."

Freda said, "I would love to watch you, but I don't think I'm brave enough to fly off the end of one of those ramps. I'll be content with observing." George participated in many of the contests. He brought Freda with him to the meets to observe from the sidelines.

One day Freda told him, "I won't do ski jumping, but I would love to go down the Garvin Heights bluff toboggan run onto Lake Winona. It looks like so much fun, but I just can't get Walter interested in it."

George said, "I'll take you." Their next free weekend they decided to try it. They laughed and yelled all the way to the bottom.

Rosy cheeked and exhilarated, she said, "Thank you, George," and gave him a big hug. They made plans to do it again soon.

photo courtesy of Winona County Historical Society

Since the March cooking class had attracted so many people to their store, Orville and Walter organized another cooking school in May, featuring Garland stoves. Presenting classes by the Garland School of Culinary Art at 2 p.m. each day, they called for 100 women to come to their store to learn the culinary arts and possibly win prizes.

Walter stayed very busy at the store. When Betty was finished teaching her lessons, it was about time for the store to close. The employees went home, and Walter locked the doors. Then he would quietly walk up the steps where he could hear her practicing and knock on her door. They would practice a few songs together and then sit and talk.

Orville arranged for his Junior Band to play as often as possible. He again busied himself organizing the summer concert series at the bandshell. He told the Band Board, "I have decided not to list popular music on the programs. We will use those pieces as encores. Each concert will have a soloist or special feature." That sounded like a good plan to them. He continued, "I have organized the band into three groups now, the Beginner Band, the Junior Band, and the Senior Band." The board was impressed.

The summer concerts were presented and received the usual newspaper accolades. He read a very gratifying review to Babette that said, "Band director O. W. Reese displayed throughout an exceptionally accurate control of the band."

Betty tried to be supportive, saying, "That's nice, Orville." But secretly she wished he would pay attention to something besides his bands.

Orville planned special features for all the concerts, including a cornet duet and several appearances of Walter and Freda Christensen, who were always appreciated.

Reeses' cabin was ready by August. On different days, the Senior and Junior band members and families were invited to bring picnic lunches and gather there. Orville had organized boating, canoeing, and fishing activities that drew many to the river. Those who stayed ashore played kittenball (a version of softball), pitched horseshoes, and used the swings. Lemonade was on tap all day, and there was plenty of ice cream for everyone.

In the fall, when the health of Orville's father, Reuben, started to decline, he finally moved from Michigan to Winona. Josephine had died in 1922, and he preferred to live by himself, so Orville rented a big upstairs apartment a few doors down from Reese Furniture. Orville also found a place for him to work at the furniture store, where he continued to feel useful and productive.

On November 1, Orville invited the staff members of Reese furniture to their new river cabin. Fourteen employees left the store at closing time and drove in a caravan to La Moille. It was too cold for outside games, so they gathered inside. When they arrived, a large log was burning in the fireplace, and Betty was preparing a turkey dinner. Reuben Reese gave a toast, "Thank you all for welcoming me to Winona. May every new day bring you more happiness."

Later in November, the president of the Association of Commerce, announced, "We are facing a deficit in our treasury. Money is tight for everyone. The city has generously appropriated another $1,000 for the Winona Municipal Band. We have been providing $2,000 annually to maintain the band, but we are no longer able to commit that amount of money." They voted that instruments and uniforms would be turned over to the Band Board and held until they could be released to the next financial supporters.

This was a heavy blow to Orville, who had worked so very hard to demonstrate how important the band was to the Winona community and its businesses. He was despondent. "How could the Association of Commerce not understand what the band means for commerce in Winona?" he protested to Babette. "I admit that ponying up $2,000 a year is not easy and recently funds have become tighter. But still, the band provides so much for so many." He slumped into his chair, shaking his head.

Betty felt sorry for him even though she had frequently resented his overwhelming commitment to the band. She tried to comfort him saying, "I'm sure something will work out."

He went into the furniture store the next day to talk it over with Walter. "I have given so much of my energy to developing a strong band program here. I feel like I've failed." He sat down heavily in his desk chair. His head drooped.

Walter said with sympathy, "I know how much the band program means to you. This must be extremely disheartening for you, after all your efforts. But I think there is a glimmer of hope." Walter handed him a small clipping from the newspaper. "Did you see this, Orville? I cut it out of the newspaper in August when you were so busy with band matters."

Orville quickly read through it. It featured a picture of Major George W. Landers from Clarinda, Iowa. He was called the 'Father of the Band Tax Laws.' His efforts had been instrumental in passing laws to support municipal bands and orchestras through taxation. Band taxes had now been passed in twenty-six states.

Orville nearly jumped for joy. "That is certainly good news!" he said brightening considerably. "I wonder if we could get that done here in Minnesota? I've been so busy with rehearsals and concert responsibilities that I wasn't aware of this movement."

Walter continued, "I have heard that the Minnesota legislature will consider a similar band bill in the next session. If it passes, this could solve the band's problem of support."

"Yes!" Orville pounded his desk for emphasis. "We will have to advocate for this kind of legislation. I will ask the band members and the board to write some letters to our representatives."

Major George W. Landers, of Clarinda, Ia., "Father of the Band Tax Laws," whose efforts have been instrumental in making taxation in support of municipal bands and orchestras legal in twenty six states, according to a survey of the Conn Music Center.

© *Winona Republican Herald* - August 27, 1926, p. 10

1927

The "Future of the Band" was the headline of a letter published on January 14 in the *Winona Republican-Herald*. Orville and the Band Board had written it together, and he was pleased that the newspaper had given it a prominent place. Orville signed it along with five other members of the Band Board. He shared it with Babette, saying, "I hope it makes people remember the enjoyment the band brings."

The Future of the Band

No more summer night concerts by the Municipal Band will be sad news to many Winona families. Yet such will be the case unless some means will be found to finance this project. The Association of Commerce retires from the position of sponsor on February first. The money provided by the City Council is not sufficient to carry on. Rent, light, music, and the many other items making up the expense budget must be paid for. And there is no money. More than one hundred and fifty boys and girls who have bought their own instruments and are getting their instruction at the band rooms will be left out in the cold.

The years of labor and thought expended in building up the organization will be lost unless some prompt action will bring assurance of financial help. Once the organization is disrupted it may be a difficult matter to build it up again. Director Reese has labored hard and for a meagre stipend to build up and train the musical talent. His efforts will be lost. The band directors have in the past signed a personal note to obtain money for the concerts and instructions. This should not be necessary. The people get the benefit and must express themselves if they wish the band board to continue.

A final meeting of the band board directors to wind up affairs of the band has been called for Wednesday evening, January 19. Any suggestions as to an alternative action will be gladly received by any of the following men:

O. W. Reese	Robt. R. Reed
Fred Schaffer	Horace G. Seaton
A. V. Gardner	A. T. French

© *Winona Republican Herald* - January 14, 1927, p. 9

Betty said, "That sounds suitably dire. You make a strong case. You certainly have devoted a large share of your energy to the band."

A day later, Orville opened the paper to see another editorial supporting the band. "Well, this is interesting," he said to Babette. "Here's a letter that makes some other points." Without asking if she was interested, he began reading. "The Band Board has functioned exceptionally well, so that people haven't worried about the band's future. Every year it has grown in size and importance to Winona, concerts have become more frequent, programs more varied, the quality improved significantly." Orville raised his voice dramatically as he read the ending. "It is a ringing challenge to Winona to come to the support of their band in need. Without doubt the city will find a way to meet it."

"I certainly hope so," Babette responded. "Many people would miss it terribly." Even though it took so much of Orville's time and attention, she agreed that the Municipal Band was important.

"We know that the Band Tax Bill is going to be taken up by the state legislature in the coming session. But there is no assurance that it will pass. Winonans who appreciate and enjoy the band must let our state lawmakers know that they should support this bill," Orville declared.

Betty said, "I agree. Tax support would take a lot of pressure off you and the board members, not to mention your players. Women having the right to vote now should certainly work in favor of the band."

Orville was very happy when the City Council, which had supplemented the Association of Commerce commitment every year, formally endorsed the State Band Tax Bill on January 18. It was clear that the usual city appropriation alone would not be sufficient to cover the band expenses. The state bill would allow Minnesota cities to tax citizens not more than 2 mills to support their municipal bands. "This shows that the council recognizes that the proposed Band Tax Bill could solve the band's funding problem," Orville told Walter.

Orville and the Band Board met on January 19 and decided that $2,000 had to be raised soon to pay the band's bills, or the band would need to be dissolved. Editorials and ads ran in the paper regularly through January telling people that the future of the band was in their hands. By the end of the month, a fundraising effort was underway with the rallying cry of

"Lend a hand to help the band." By February 10 over $2,000 had been raised. Nearly 1,500 people contributed to the band fund, most of them in small amounts. The band was safe for now. Orville breathed a sigh of relief.

On February 22, the Band Board reorganized itself to operate without the support of the Association of Commerce. The present board members offered to stay on to form the new Band Board and administer the funds for salaries, equipment, rental and other necessities. Orville Reese would remain band director.

In order for the band tax question to be placed on the ballot that spring, a petition needed to be circulated and signed by 10% of eligible voters. Although the statewide legislation had not yet become law, the Winona Band Board wanted to be ready if and when it did.

That winter, George Graham had joined the Winona Odd Fellows Humboldt Lodge #24 because he was supportive of their mission which promoted "philanthropy, the ethic of reciprocity, and charity." Community members trying to survive tough times could find help from the organization. George became very involved in many of their works. Since he was not a Winona native, their meetings served as a great social environment for him to meet other members, including some of the city's prominent citizens. In 1927 he was elected to an office in the organization.

George was also enjoying his reputation as a ski jumper. He helped found the Winona Sugar Loaf Ski Club to promote the sport that was gaining such popularity. More communities built wooden jumps that skiers could race down to soar through the air until they hit the ground, preferably with both skis at the same time.

George often brought Freda to the out-of-town meets to watch him compete whenever she could get away. Freda told him, "I'm fascinated by how graceful you look as you sail off end of the jump. How wonderful that feeling must be. Aren't you ever frightened?"

"Not really," answered George. "But it is scary if I feel that I'm not balanced right when I hit the ground. You've seen me make some of my more spectacular failed landings."

"Yes," said Freda, "and I'm afraid you'll hurt something. You are going so fast."

George was flattered by her concern. "I don't want to worry you. But it's hard to explain how thrilling it is."

Freda said, "I can imagine how fun it would be to fly like that. It looks easy, but I know it's not."

As spring approached, Walter decided that they needed to do something to improve business and generate sales. A recession, which had begun the year before, had made people cautious about spending. He talked to Orville first and said, "Sales have been slow. I think it would be a good idea to make a few changes in our displays, paint things, and move things around, maybe put up new dividers. We could have a big clearance sale to make room for the remodeling."

Orville agreed, so Walter consulted with Freda, Betty, and others, and made plans, hiring some painters and builders. He placed large newspaper ads in March to drum up interest, declaring that they had to make room for a remodeling and redecorating sale. Walter needed to take care of most of the arrangements since Orville was preoccupied with the band funding problems.

The ads featured detailed drawings of hundreds of pieces of furniture that needed to be sold to make room for the workmen. The big sale was slated to run from March 27 through April 2. But a smaller, classified ad on April 2 announced, "Because so many farmers and out-of-town customers were unable to get in on account of the bad roads, we are going to continue our sale another week. Reese Furniture Company."

Hoping to appeal to more customers, Walter quoted Frank Winkels the former owner of the business in an ad, saying, "Trade follows the flag, but you have to wave the flag." To keep the Reese name in people's minds, he bought many classified ads promoting their bargain basement and other special items. By fall they were giving out S and H Green Stamps as an incentive to purchase things. Business improved.

To Orville's delight, on March 29 both houses of the state legislature passed the statewide bill allowing Minnesota cities to collect taxes to support their municipal bands. The governor signed it on April 1.

Winona band supporters had succeeded in gathering enough signatures to add the question to the local election ballot. Letters supporting the band tax measure appeared in local newspapers stating, "Vote Yes For the Band" and "There appears to be no good reason why anyone should not vote 'Yes' on the proposition to support the band."

April 4 was the date of the election. Orville was anxious and restless.

He paced and drummed his fingers and tried unsuccessfully to stay calm. When results were reported, there were about 500 more "yes" votes than "no" votes. However, a bigger number of voters had left the question unmarked. These were counted as "no" votes and caused the measure to be defeated. Orville was dumbfounded.

Orville went to the band rooms where some of the Band Board and a few members had gathered. He vented his frustration. Striding back and forth he thundered, "What is the matter with people? They all come to the concerts and enjoy them. Do they think that good music just happens? Don't they know how much work we all put in?" He stomped over to a chair and plopped down, folding his arms.

Oswald Leicht stood up. "Yes, most of us here know that. But a lot of people think we are just having fun. They have no idea what goes into having a good band. And there are some who don't think it's important. Almost everyone is finding money hard to come by these days. We need to do some education before the next time this question is put to a vote. We should make a real effort to encourage women to vote. And people must understand that leaving the question blank is a 'no' vote."

By law, two years had to pass before the band tax measure could be voted on again. That would be in 1929.

Orville settled down a bit as they talked over ideas to encourage a positive outcome the next time. He said, "I plan to have the band continue to play until the money runs out. As we speak, I am planning the summer concerts." He looked around the room and saw heads nodding.

The board decided that nothing more could be done until they held their annual meeting in April. Orville concluded "We will do our best with the money we have to demonstrate what we bring to Winona."

The Band Board invited all known band supporters and contributors to the April meeting. They discussed the situation. There was enough money in the band fund to support the band for most of the current year. The band would present the summer concerts at the band shell as usual, with many feature numbers. Moving the concerts from Wednesday to Monday evenings would be tried to avoid conflicting with other events. Everyone was asked to think of ways to fund the band for the following year, 1928.

The summer concerts were well attended. The usual reviews appeared in the newspaper, but one notable concert mid-July received a special write up. It told how the band began to play *Blue Skies* just as the clouds broke and a downpour ensued. The concert continued between cloudbursts and some numbers had to be cut. The applause was loudest for the most popular feature, the duets by Walter and Freda. The songs they sang, *It Made You Happy When You Made Me Cry* and *Lonely Eyes* were sung through the rain and much appreciated.

In August, Babette and Freda played their saxophones in a quintet with 3 other players and were the hit of the concert. Orville particularly liked a review that he read with relish to Babette calling the concert "one of the most successful of the season."

The senior and junior bands were invited to Reese's La Moille cabin for picnics in August. Guests brought their own picnic baskets and the Reeses served coffee and ice cream. Some attendees went canoeing, and some went fishing while the rest were organized into teams to play kittenball. A few of the participants pulled humorous sliding and base stealing stunts, including Freddy Heyer. Everyone was well entertained.

The fall of that year the band played again at the County Fair in St. Charles, Minnesota (25 miles east of Winona), and for the annual Fall Opening displaying new seasonal merchandise, but Orville needed to scale back a few of the usual events like trade tours due to cost.

Mid-September, a notice appeared in the newspaper. "The Reese Furniture Company will close their store for all business at 12 o'clock, Wednesday. Reason! The annual picnic for the employees of the store will take place at the summer home of O. W. Reese at Richmond." People brought lunches, played games, and did water activities. Everyone had a good time.

Walter invested in many ads for Reese Furniture in anticipation of the Christmas season. The ads touted the band instruments they sold as great gift ideas. A whole month of lessons could be bought for $1.

The number of Betty's students continued to grow as the word of her teaching expertise spread. Her feelings toward Walter grew as well. Freda was gone much of the time with George, so Betty and Walter spent many evenings in each other's company at the store after her teaching was done. They had so much in common, they never ran out of things to talk about. Orville, as usual, was busy with band business.

Hundreds of Fellows Earn All College Expenses Playing Conn Instruments

When you give a good musical instrument you give a great deal more than the money value of the gift—you give a better opportunity for success in life.

See Our Window

and then come in and make your selection. •

We will make delivery on Christmas Eve or any other time you choose.

Cash or Club Payment Plan.

Beginner's class starts January 1st. Instructions weekly at only $1.00 per month.

Reese Furniture Co.

Listen to the Conn Radio Half-hour each Sunday afternoon, 2 o'clock to 2:30, station KYW, Chicago.

© Winona Republican Herald - Dec. 13, 1927

1928

As the new year dawned, Orville was very worried about the future of the band he had worked so hard to create. Much of his success as a director was due to his musical and directing skills, but another important factor was his effort to create a feeling of camaraderie and unity among the members, young and old. He had developed a tradition of beginning each year with January gatherings of the Senior, Junior and Beginner's Bands.

This year he announced, "The Senior Band will meet with their instruments to play a few numbers and then enjoy a time to socialize and have a meal together. The younger bands will meet the following evening and hear the older division perform a few numbers."

When the younger bands gathered on their designated evening, Orville announced he had a surprise. A gasp of anticipation went around the room. He explained, "Do you see this covered container? It is full of gifts." Another gasp was heard. "There is a hole in the top. Every band member, along with their siblings, has a number. When your number is called, you can reach in and pull out a gift." Everyone cheered and clapped. As numbers were pulled out of a hat, each youngster eagerly selected a gift. Orville knew how these youths looked forward to this yearly gathering, especially now since so many of their parents were struggling to make ends meet.

The results of Reese Furniture's remodeling and redecorating were shown off at a Grand Opening of their new and improved Bargain Basement on January 24. Walter continued to place the usual ads for things like carpet sweepers, porch swings, and 49-cent pillows. As promised, Walter closed out their stock of Edison phonographs.

When the Edison Company formally ceased producing their phonographs, Orville said, "Walter, congratulations on seeing that coming. We reduced our stock just in time. We will still be able to sell out the cylinders, since a lot of people own the machines."

Walter was always coming up with ways to increase traffic and sales at Reese Furniture. He received a book of Bartlett's Famous Quotations for Christmas. He loved the wisdom of the great thinkers of the past and thought about sharing some of these insights with Winona citizens who might not be familiar with them. He said to Orville, "I have an idea that might give our ads a bit of distinction over the usual ones we run." He handed Orville the book of quotations and said, "I could pick out a saying and incorporate it the ads for Reese Furniture."

Orville paged through the book and answered, "I don't doubt that a few Winonans could benefit from some of these noble thoughts. Go ahead and try it."

Walter ran his 'Thought for Tomorrow' ads daily from February through April. They featured quotes by famous figures like Cicero, Bacon, Dickens, and Thackeray, and were framed in rectangles with the words "Reese Furniture Co. Better for Less" on top and small ads for items like bedroom suites, mattresses, rugs, and glass tumblers underneath. The quotes were mostly about positive characteristics and admirable behavior like George Elliot's, "Our deeds determine us as much as we determine our deeds." Walter wasn't sure if the ads helped business, but he felt good about the effort.

© *Winona Republican Herald* - April 12, 1928

Another of Walter's novel advertising ideas involved featuring artists working in the store's windows. In the winter, Reese Furniture announced that the well-known artist, Mr. E. C. Maxham, "will give the public an opportunity to see him complete his oil paintings in the east window of the store." A local painter, Celia Duffy, displayed her painting skills in the Reese Store Window in August and November. Business wasn't booming, but it was steady.

George "Spike" Graham continued to distinguish himself in ski jumping contests. Freda followed his successes and accompanied him to many local meets. She told him, "I wish I could learn how to ski, but not necessarily to jump. Because of you, I find I like being outside in the winter."

George said, "Maybe I could give you some lessons in Nordic skiing. You stay on the ground for that."

Freda smiled. "I think I would enjoy it."

Both Junior and Senior Bands played for the Memorial Day Service in May. Knowing that funds were low, the Senior Band members donated their time for the performance.

Once again, the Band Board and Orville organized a big fundraising campaign to sustain the band until 1929 when the measure could be placed on the ballot again. They recruited enthusiastic volunteers and provided them with materials supporting the band. Beginning on May 31, their goal was to visit every home throughout Winona to collect donations. The Board placed a full-page ad in the newspaper with an illustration of the empty bandshell. The words, "Our Empty Bandshell" printed underneath reminded people that there wouldn't be concerts that summer without money. It was followed by the question "How long are Winona Citizens going to be without a band?" Orville next provided a list of eight reasons to support the band, and the board supplied a detailed breakdown of how the needed funds would be used. The campaign was successful enough to support the 1928 summer concerts.

Orville was again able to plan and present the series. But, as before, the crowd noise was a nuisance. He complained loudly to the Band Board and members, "I can't stand the distractions from people talking, kids yelling, cars starting, and drivers honking during our concerts. People who want to listen, can't," he fumed, emphasizing "can't" by striking his baton across his palm. His message was heard. The newspaper's weekly listing of upcoming concert pieces began to include Orville's plea that "listeners kindly refrain from visiting, talking, blowing of horns, or starting of automobiles while the band is playing."

The Band Board requested a larger police presence to maintain order. At the next concert it was made clear that no moving of automobiles during concerts would be allowed. That worked. Orville asked that police be present for the rest of the summer concerts.

Walter and Freda sang duets that the newspaper review called a "high spot in the program for most" as they "have become a popular institution and may always depend on a good reception." Orville read that review and called Babette's attention to the part that said the concert "was one of the best programs in several years" due to the "toning down of the brasses, producing better balance." He remarked, "I have had the band work hard to improve their balance. Those brass instruments just don't realize how overpowering they can be."

Betty said, "I agree, but that is quite an admission, coming from a cornet player." She turned back to her book.

Orville pretended he didn't hear her.

By July the volunteers announced that donations to the band fund had reached almost $2,000. That was short of their target of $6,000 but they hadn't finished visiting all homes in the fourth ward. At that point, the Minnesota Valley Public Service Company conducted its own campaign and gathered enough donations to meet the goal. Orville was ecstatic.

The Winona Playground Committee leaders presented an idea to Orville. "If we have the children create paper lanterns, could they show them in a lantern parade at one of the Municipal Band summer concerts?"

Orville realized it might eliminate the noise and distractions that youngsters were creating at concerts. "I think that's a great idea, provided the children know they need to be quiet when they are marching around."

The committee assured Orville that the youngsters would be quiet. They would be holding the lanterns they had created over their heads. The children would know they had to be careful because their lanterns would be lit with candles.

"That sounds fine then," Orville said. "I'm sure all their parents and relatives will attend."

The lantern concert was a great success. Over 80 little cherubs lined up holding their creations as they paraded through the crowd. It was a beautiful sight. One observer likened it to a procession of huge fireflies. To Orville's delight, the concert had record attendance.

Orville had been asked to direct the school band in Arcadia, Wisconsin, about 30 miles north, for the 1928-29 school year. He had gradually stepped back from directing the bands in Alma, Minnieska, Strum, and Rollingstone, as replacements were found. But the position in Arcadia was tempting enough that he decided to accept it, saying to Babette, "I believe it would be a good opportunity for collaboration between the Arcadia and Winona Bands."

Babette's response was lukewarm. She simply said, "If you think so, dear."

A recital of 20 of Babette's saxophone and piano students was presented on June 29. Her reputation and student numbers continued to increase. Walter attended, but Freda and Orville had other obligations.

Orville was determined to demonstrate the importance of the band to Winona. He arranged for the band to play at many new events, trade tours, the state labor convention, and county fairs.

There was no money left for the last summer bandshell concert, scheduled for September 19. The players decided to present the concert anyway, and Orville made it clear that the players were donating their time. No more Senior Band performances were held in 1928.

The Junior Band had an exciting event that had already been scheduled for Saturday, September 25. The great march composer himself, John Philip Sousa, would be directing a 2:00 p.m. concert of his famed band at the Winona Theater. And the Junior Band would be playing two numbers under his direction. They were very excited when Orville told them, "You are going to play for the famous John Philip Sousa. That is truly an honor." Orville was very proud of these young players and was sure that this display of their ability would increase public support for the bands.

Reese Furniture put a large ad in the paper publicizing the event. It noted that Sousa thought "complete equipment of Conn instruments enhances the musical value of any band at least fifty per cent." Conn instruments were, not surprisingly, available at Reese Furniture.

At the concert, Sousa's 100-piece band presented a varied selection of music that included old favorites like Sousa's own marches, *Manhattan Beach*, *Semper Fidelis*, and *Stars and Stripes Forever*. He presented two newer ones too, the *Gridiron Club March*, composed in 1925, and the *Golden Jubilee March* which Sousa had composed that very year to commemorate his fiftieth year as a conductor.

During the concert intermission, Orville's Junior Band filed on stage and took the places vacated by Sousa's players. The youngest were barely able to reach the floor from the edges of their seats. Sousa conducted them in *The United States Invincible* to thunderous applause. He then motioned to Orville Reese to come to the podium, gave him the baton and asked him to direct.

Orville was surprised but had prepared the band to play *The Iowa Band Law March* by Karl L. King, a younger composer of marches and band music. He was sure that Sousa would not object, since Orville had told him how the city was struggling to pass a band tax. King had been instrumental in the passage of the Iowa Band Law in 1921 and composed this march to celebrate that accomplishment. Sousa always had been very vocal in his support of teaching music to youngsters. He said, their "best experience can be gained in the band."

The city budget for 1929 was published in October. It included $1,500 for the Municipal Band, again not enough to sustain it. The next time Orville spoke with the Band Board, he said, somewhat heatedly, "I must tell you that I am upset that the playground budget almost doubled while our budget stayed the same."

© *Winona Republican Herald* - September 24, 1928

1929

At January's New Year's party for the Junior Band, Orville had a special meeting with the Junior Band parents. He explained that the municipal band program had grown and was now organized into 4 levels: Beginners, Advanced, Junior and Senior. For the first time, girls were officially part of the band.

Junior Band players had to pass examinations and meet qualifications to gain admittance into the Senior Band. Orville said, "This year when the youngsters come to their first rehearsal, Santa will distribute small gifts to everyone. Then the boys and girls will elect a chairman who, in turn, will select a committee for planning summer picnics and other events. If they have a say in things, they will enjoy them more."

He then extolled the value of music for young people saying, "The young musician has a different slant on life. His morale is different. His environments have been bettered. His ideas have broadened out. He has more confidence. . . and is better able to cope with the ups and downs of the world." In addition, he concluded, "Musical skills can help a young person earn money for college tuition, if that is his goal."

For the Senior Band, Orville planned the usual smoker and luncheon. He reminded the members of their attendance and practice obligations. Then he reviewed the structure of the band program. He said, "You all know what the upcoming band tax vote means for the Municipal Band. I encourage you to ask everyone you know to support the band tax proposal this coming spring."

While Orville was busy with the band, George Graham continued making his own name. No matter the season, George loved being outside. His ski jumping ability was well known, but he also enjoyed cross-country skiing. His job at Watkins had him working all day, so he decided to quit and find a job with more flexible hours. Selling insurance might give him more flexibility with his time.

He had seen quite a bit of Freda at his wrestling matches and ski jump meets. They usually talked over the events for a while afterwards. He liked Freda, who was so lively and willing to try new things. He remembered his promise to teach her how to ski, so one mild Saturday in late winter he called her. "Would today work to give you a ski lesson?"

"Oh yes. Absolutely," said Freda. "We weren't planning anything special. I would love a lesson."

After she hung up the phone, Walter, who was reading the paper in his easy chair, asked, "Who was that?"

She answered, "That was my friend, George. You know he is a good skier. His name has been in the paper a lot. He said he would teach me to ski when a suitable day came along and today the weather is perfect. He asked if I could go with him for a ski lesson. He has some equipment I can borrow."

Walter, who was looking forward to a day of relaxing at home, said, "He's the wrestler, right? I can't imagine wanting to be outside in the cold, but if you want to learn to ski, go ahead."

Freda went on, "I didn't think you would be interested in trying it yourself, but I would like to find a way to enjoy the cold weather and snow we have here."

Freda donned her warmest clothes and George came by to pick her up.

Betty walked over to Freda and Walter's house. She saw Freda get into a car and drive away. She went to the door and knocked. "Where did Freda go?" she asked as Walter let her in.

"Her friend, George, offered to teach her how to ski. She says she wants to find outdoor things to do in the snow. It seems too cold for me."

Babette kept her thoughts to herself, and they chatted companionably about her students. Walter told her about all the new furniture they would be selling in their upcoming 'Two Truckloads of Living Room Furniture' sale. Then he showed her the latest sheet music the store had ordered. He had brought some pieces home and asked her, "Could you play through these? I'd love to hear them and maybe learn them." They went to the piano, where they spent the afternoon going through the new music.

Freda and George drove out to Farmer's Park west of Winona. George helped her strap skis onto her boots and showed her how to skate on the unwieldy slats by sliding one foot forward and then the other. At first, she felt awkward and fell a few times.

Each time, George helped her up. Slowly she got the hang of pushing and gliding and they spent the day skating across the flat meadow. George liked her spunk and was enchanted by her sparkling eyes and rosy cheeks. Freda liked the feel of George's strong arms helping her up.

On March 6 Orville gave his annual director's report to the Band Board and supporters, going over the growth of the band and his plans for the coming year. Oswald Leicht had departed on a voyage around world to see the sights and listen to the music of other lands. He would be gone for some time. Vice President Robert R. Reed took his place, and Leroy Grettum stepped in as Vice President. John G. Libera continued in his role as secretary-treasurer. The temporary officer slate was approved at this meeting. Then they discussed strategies for encouraging support for the band tax measure. The first order of business involved organizing the circulation of petitions that were needed to have the question placed on the ballot for the April 1 election.

Vote "YES" for the Band Tax

The band needs money for instruction, Instruments, Uniforms, Band Room, Rental and Music.

The proposed ½ mill tax will not be a financial burden. The following table shows the additional amount over various amounts of present taxes:

If your present tax is	You will pay additional for the band
$10	approximately 5c
$25	approximately 13c
$40	approximately 21c
$50	approximately 26c
$60	approximately 31c
$80	approximately 42c
$100	approximately 53c

Endorsed by Trades and Labor Council
and many other Winona organizations.

This advertisement prepared and inserted by the Board of Directors of the Winona Municipal Band Association.

© *Winona Republican Herald* - March 23, 1929

Their campaign was successful, and they soon had the needed signatures. Over the next few weeks, Orville attended meetings of many lodges, councils and groups to encourage support for the measure. "Vote Yes for the Band" ads sponsored by the Municipal Band Board appeared in the newspapers. The entire board worked very hard to spread the message, "Remember, a Failure to Vote on the Band Tax Is a Vote Against It."

Orville relished and retold one particular story, "There was an ordinary freckled young boy with musical ambitions whose hardworking parents couldn't afford lessons. He found his way into the Boys' Band and learned music there. Then came his 'Big Moment'. Because of his hard work and that of the entire band, he played along with the band for the Great Sousa." He begged Winonans, "Please don't deny this opportunity to other children. The fate of this band and the entire Municipal Band Organization is in the hands of the voters. Recall this picture and vote 'Yes' Monday."

Orville arranged a parade and concert for the evening of March 28 to showcase the bands and hopefully generate more support for the band tax. The Junior and Senior Bands first marched down Third street. Then a free public concert was given in front of the Mississippi Valley Public Supply Company. He said to the new board president, "Certainly, attendees will realize the important role the bands play in the cultural life of Winona."

April 1 came. Orville, the Band Board and some Senior Band members waited anxiously in the band room, staying up late for the results. The count from the first, second, and third wards showed the measure winning. But when the fourth ward votes were reported, the question was defeated by 200 votes, mostly because of those who left the space blank.

"Damnation!" Orville shouted as he paced the room. "Just like 1927! What else can we do? Should a small minority ruin things for the whole town?" The Band Board muttered and mumbled with anger and frustration. No one could explain it.

Band Board president, Mr. Reed, said, "We did what we could. We told people not to leave the question unanswered."

Mr. Grettum added, "Now I guess we just scrape by and try again in 1931." The group slowly disbursed. Orville was the last to leave.

He locked the door and walked to the apartment he had rented for his father, Reuben. He and Babette had sold their house on 4th Street and were winterizing their cabin in La Moille, so they could live there year-round. For now, they lived with Reuben.

Orville walked slowly up the stairs. Reuben had gone to bed, but Babette was waiting up. When she heard his weary tread and watched him slowly come through the door, she knew what had happened.

"Oh, Orville, I am so sorry. After all you've done." she said, with as much sympathy as she could muster.

"It's so hard to understand. And now we must wait two more years." There was a note of defeat in his voice that Babette had never heard before. "I don't know if I can stand it," he added, looking older somehow.

"We will have to give more attention to our remodeling of our home in La Moille. That should help take your mind off things," she said.

But Orville wasn't looking for something to take his mind off the setback. He immediately began forming strategies to find support for his band. "I'm sure it will pass in 1931," he told himself.

There were many letters about the vote published in the newspaper. Orville read them all. People expressed their disappointment at losing the band. He shared one with Walter when he got to the store. "Listen to this, Walter. A writer is putting the blame where it should be, on the slackers who didn't bother to vote." Orville read out loud "Calculating from the results, an average of about 41.5% of eligible voters actually cast votes. So, the story is not one of the band's unpopularity, but rather one of slacker voters. Elections cannot be won unless people vote."

Walter responded, "That is true. We all have to figure out a way to get those votes out. I wish I'd had more time to work on behalf of the band. I enjoy playing. And singing. But the store needs most of my attention. Business is very slow.

On April 4, members of the Senior Band met to discuss the situation. One player stood and said, "It's more important to train players for the future than to pay us to play." Everyone agreed. They voted to disband in favor of continuing the Junior and Beginners' Bands. They expected the city council would continue to budget money for the band and that would be enough to support the younger bands.

The Band Board agreed with their decision and prepared the paperwork that was needed to conclude its affairs. Board Vice President Grettum announced, "The board will not work to solicit donations to continue the band. We consider maintaining a band to be a civic responsibility. If, however, any other outside organization decides to conduct a fundraising campaign, as happened before, it would probably be accepted."

By the end of May, Reese Furniture had a new look with the addition of the city's largest neon sign. Red and blue, it was shaped a bit like the letter I. The word 'Furniture' was across the top, over a vertical 'Reese.' The word 'Rugs' filled the bottom. Orville and Walter were so proud of it. They let everyone know that it had cost $2,000. People coming to see it ended up visiting the store. Walter regularly placed ads for selected items like fancy pillows, camp stools, plated lamps, and upholstery vacuums.

As summer arrived, a group of band supporters came forward to organize another door-to-door campaign. Their goal was to raise $6,000 to cover the band's expenses for the next two years when the tax question could again be put on the ballot. By mid-June they managed to raise $1,770. It wasn't what they were hoping for, but it was enough to fund some of the season's summer concerts.

Concerts began in July and were well attended and appreciated. Walter and Freda sang several times. The lantern parade was again a huge success, with over 100 children marching, and their families swelling the audience. Orville introduced a new idea for the summer. A request box was placed on the bandshell steps where people could ask the band to play a special piece. The band performed as many as possible in the order they were received. Automobile and other noise still troubled the performers, but once again police presence took care of the problem.

On August 29, the annual band picnic was held at Reese's remodeled La Moille river home, following Orville's philosophy of rewarding work with play. He invited his Arcadia School and Winona Junior Band members and their families to the picnic. The Reeses provided coffee and asked people to bring basket lunches. Close to 200 musicians and family members attended. Orville was excited when he told everyone, "We have purchased inflatable rubber horses for water polo games and tug of war competitions. We'll also play land games. Arcadia and Winona will form teams to compete with one another."

That fall the Senior Band played for some events, like county fairs, that could pay for their services. But the unpaid Junior Band took their place for other events like the Armistice Day Parade and the annual "Fall Stores Opening" when stores displayed new merchandise. The Junior Band was invited to play at the opening of the paved road between Winona and La Crosse. It was held at Dresbach with dignitaries from both cities present. Orville was gratified that the Junior Band played with such polish but said, "I personally believe the Senior Band should be doing these events. Unfortunately, there is no money."

The Winona Teacher's College offered Orville the chance to organize a band program for the winter session. He jumped at the chance. At the store, he said to Walter, "This could be very helpful for the Municipal Band effort."

Walter asked, "How would it be helpful?"

"If more people play in bands, there will be more appreciation for music performance," Orville responded.

At the college, Orville organized a beginners' band and a band of more experienced players. The school agreed to purchase some of the very expensive instruments. Orville was excited for this opportunity to teach at the college level. He told Babette. She just nodded as she organized a stack of music. "Did you hear me?" he asked impatiently. "I'm going to be a professor!"

"That's very nice. But it's not a permanent position, is it?" replied Betty, continuing her sorting. She knew this added responsibility would be something else that kept her husband away from home and took up his time.

"No," he replied. "But it will be my responsibility to organize the whole program. I could have a lasting impact."

"That does sound important," said Betty, with the modicum of enthusiasm she could muster. "I hope they appreciate your experience."

In September, Reese Furniture celebrated their store's 10th anniversary. "Can you believe it's been ten years since we bought Winkels' store?" Walter asked Betty one evening as they practiced together.

"No, I really can't. It has gone by so quickly," answered Betty. "I guess that's because we've all been so busy."

"Some of us more than others?" Walter said, indirectly referring to Orville.

Babette looked at him knowingly. "You understand and I appreciate that. It's been difficult at times."

Reese Furniture placed a two-page anniversary sale ad. Orville made sure the ad explained that Reese's could offer the best prices possible because they were able to purchase in such large quantities.

Business at Reese Furniture was fair through the end of the year, in spite of the stock market crash. Orville said to Walter, "That new sign must be magic! Sales picked up this year."

© *Winona Republican Herald* - September 30, 1929

1930

Orville started 1930 with the customary New Year's party for combined Beginner and Junior Band divisions. Orville was determined to be positive about the future of the program and was careful not to let them see his discouragement. First, he had the bands play a few selections after which Board President Oswald Leicht, who had returned from his travels, complimented the students and Director Reese for their hard work and progress.

A business leader then spoke, telling the young players, "You all work very hard at learning to play your instruments. It takes a lot of effort. But making music together requires cooperation and teamwork, skills that will serve you well all of your lives."

Then to their delight, Orville announced awards won by the students the preceding season. After a lunch, the Band Board gave the Junior Band members candy and apples. The afternoon ended after many games were played. Attendees voted it the best New Years' band party ever!

The following day the Senior Band held their meeting. They played for a short while, then elected officers and discussed future plans, which at the time, were minimal, since there was no funding. After their luncheon and smoker they heard Dr. Oswald Leicht give his impressions of music he heard in the Asian lands that he had visited. He enjoyed the music in Japan and the Pacific islands which were mostly European style military bands, and he was intrigued by music performed in Indonesia on the gamelan. He had pictures of a gamelan to pass around, since it was hard to describe this ensemble of large, elaborate brass gongs, metallophones, drums, and other instruments that were tuned in unique intervals. The music of China was not as pleasing, he felt. He compared it to the sound "a cat makes when its tail is caught in a door" to the amusement of his audience. Afterwards, Orville announced, "The band has some winter engagements for which sponsors were found. So, we do need to keep up our rehearsals."

Freda and George met on several occasions for her ski lessons, and he brought her to watch him in ski jumping meets. An important meet was held in Rushford in February. There were 18 competitors who attracted 1,200 spectators. Of course, Freda was one of them. Heart pounding, she followed George's first attempt and saw him fly off the end of the run, landing at an impressive 88 feet. But then he lost his balance and fell. The crowd gasped and Freda's stomach knotted as they followed George tumbling down the rest of the slope in a cloud of snow. When he finally stopped, everyone watched, stunned and silent, as he slowly dug himself out of the drift his descent had created, and arose to face the crowd. He clasped his hands above his head in triumph. They cheered and clapped as he gathered his scattered equipment and made his way up the steps for the next try. His following two jumps were a bit shorter, but again he fell. Every time Freda felt the same knots followed by waves of relief when he got to his feet. Even with his mishaps he managed to place fourth.

When they got into the car for the drive back to Winona, Freda said to him, "Oh George, my heart pounded when you fell. It seemed impossible that you wouldn't be hurt! But you handled it so well. I'm proud of you for finishing."

"What else would I do? Take a nap in the snow?" George joked. He shrugged. "Falls happen when you jump."

"I've heard about broken arms, legs, and heads from these meets. I love watching, and I know how skilled you are, but I don't think I could bear it if that happened to you," said Freda slowly. "I thought we were just friends, but I find myself caring a lot about you."

"I care about you too, Freda. I've never known anyone so fun-loving and high-spirited as you are. I vowed I'd never trust a woman again. You've made me rethink that," said George. "But what about your husband, Walter? He seems like a nice guy, and I have always liked him."

Freda sighed. "I thought I loved Walter when we got married. We were very young. He was a wonderful singer, and I was sure we'd be a hit in vaudeville. Then we ended up here and all he thinks about now is furniture and music. I still love singing with him after all these years. He IS a nice guy. But he doesn't have any sense of adventure. And I do."

"Yes." George smiled. "You sure do."

"Besides, he's been spending a lot of time with my sister. I think they like each other more than they realize," added Freda.

"Hmm," said George. "What about Orville?"

Freda said, "Orville is so wrapped up in his bands and the furniture store, the two of them don't seem to spend much time together. I think Betty is lonely."

George said, "That's too bad. Orville's done an amazing job with the band program here. Even I have heard his bands. It's too bad about the band tax measure. And something new is always going on at the furniture store. Your sister is a lovely person and an amazing musician. I have heard her play piano."

"Yes, she is a great sister, and she always looks out for me, sometimes a bit more than I'd like. Orville is very ambitious and has a great drive to succeed. But I think he neglects Betty. She was really young when they married, and Orville was a lot older. I feel sad for her," Freda said with real sympathy.

"I can understand why she's turning to Walter," said George.

"Yes. But Orville's father, Reuben has been ill. He is quite elderly and has had trouble breathing. I'm sure she doesn't want to do anything to upset him. Orville and Betty are staying in his apartment for now, to help him. We all like Reuben very much. He is an amazing man and has accomplished a great deal."

"It's complicated," said George who pulled her close to him and kissed her. She didn't resist.

At the end of the ski season, Freda and George talked about the summer. "I realize you are busy with work and all of your activities," said Freda. "But I know you play tennis a lot. I have seen your name in tournaments."

George said, "Yes, I do enjoy tennis. I like being outside and I like competing. But you will be busy with your singing appearances and your work at the store."

Freda smiled coyly. "I am pretty sure I would have time to try tennis, too!" She took his hand in hers. "Do you think you would be able to teach me to play? It always looks like such fun."

"I would be happy to give you some lessons." He squeezed her hand.

The uniforms purchased in 1925 for the Junior Band had seen better days by now. The Band Board decided that they should mount an effort to buy new uniforms for the Junior Band, since it was representing Winona in so many situations. They coordinated with the Watkins Choral Club to present an impressive concert and sell tickets to raise funds for the uniforms. The Junior Band played several other benefit concerts and were able to wear new uniforms by April.

Orville announced formally, "This organization will no longer be called the Boys' Band since several girls are now playing with us. In the future it will simply be the Junior Band. Girl members will wear the same uniforms as boys."

Being in Orville's Junior Band was a privilege. Orville was demanding and weeded out less committed players quickly. Over the years he had developed a system in which players had to pass several measures of their skills, including playing scales, knowing fundamental principles, recording home practice time, mastering their instrument, and attending rehearsals.

Orville spent a lot of time evaluating the young players according to his system. He sent letters to parents, explaining each student's progress. Those who successfully fulfilled all requirements would be admitted into the Senior Municipal Band in the fall, an impressive achievement.

Since the treasury of the Senior Municipal Band was depleted, most of the events they had regularly performed for in the past became the responsibility of the Junior Band. Proudly wearing their new uniforms, the younger band played for the yearly Spring Stores Opening with displays of new merchandise, the Memorial Day services, VFW events and other affairs. Orville arranged for them to give a series of concerts in the nearby towns of Dresbach, Kellogg, Arcadia, and Independence, all communities that had hired him to direct their bands.

Orville invited Walter, Freda, and Babette to participate in these concerts. He knew their performances were always very polished and professional so they would be crowd-pleasers. Babette agreed to accompany some duets and solos and play a xylophone solo herself. She arranged for a saxophone quartet of her advanced students to perform special numbers.

Orville had asked Walter to find some humorous songs to keep the audience engaged. Walter chose a few and took them up to Betty's studio to run through. Freda joined them to practice together. It was reminiscent of their old vaudeville times, but they all knew things had changed.

By mid-summer it was apparent that several upcoming events which had involved the Senior Municipal Band in the past were not feasible without it. No summer concerts meant that popular annual celebrations like the doll buggy parade and the lantern parade would need to be scrapped. And a new project being planned by the playground program, the re-creation of a life-like circus, was put on hold. Many people protested the loss of these summer highlights.

Sunday, July 6, Orville held his annual band picnic at their La Moille home to keep everyone's spirits up. All the Winona bands plus the Arcadia and Independence band members and their families attended, about 500 people. Many contests and games were planned for land and water, and a luncheon was served afterwards. The Winona Senior Band forgot the money crisis for the day and enjoyed themselves.

At the annual meeting of the Band Board, on Friday, July 7, six stalwart members of the body resigned, saying they felt that new ideas were needed to find ways to raise money for sustaining the band. One of them, who had become Orville's friend and champion was Board President, Dr. Oswald Leicht. He was retiring after 15 years on the board and was honored with a resolution expressing appreciation for his strong support. In all, seven new members were elected to take the six retiring members' places.

The new board met the following Monday to discuss funding possibilities. The business community had pledged to support the band, but only $750 remained in the treasury. There was an emergency fund available, but they hoped they didn't have to use it. The entire board was appointed to a committee to solve the money problem.

Hoping the Band Tax Measure would succeed in 1931, the Band Board made the decision to use its reserve fund and present three July concerts by the Senior Municipal Band. To present a fourth concert, the band members voted to donate their services. A few days after the 4th concert Orville announced that there would be no more concerts unless there was money to pay the players. They would play for the Winona County Fair, since the Fair Board would compensate them. By early September the board determined that the money had all been spent, so the Senior Band would not play again in 1930.

Many people were worried about their personal financial futures after the bank crashes of 1929. They were much more careful about spending their money. Walter assessed items in the store and stayed late at work, picking out things to feature that people might be able to buy. He decided to widely advertise the bargain basement used furniture and mid-winter clearance items, to strengthen sales.

Realizing that a lot of people were financially strapped, he publicized the store's policy of appraising furniture in people's homes. Reese's bought many items which they could resell and help these people at the same time.

© *Winona Republican Herald* - January 27, 1930

As usual, Walter advertised their wide variety of home furnishings, from saucepans to dining room suites and baby carriages. He often reduced the prices of these items so people could afford them.

In September he placed an eye-catching, two-page ad to publicize their 11th anniversary. The ad boasted about the store's 36,000 square feet of space where customers could see "the largest display of quality furniture in Southern

Minnesota." He invited customers to "Take advantage of lower prices than ever." More and more of the operation of Reese Furniture seemed to be falling on Walter, as Orville stayed preoccupied with municipal band matters.

Freda had taken to George's tennis lessons and was learning how to serve and return the ball quite well. At the end of the summer, George mentioned that he would be going deer hunting in the fall.

Freda said, "That sounds interesting. Do you think that's something I could do?"

"You would have to learn how to shoot a rifle, you know. And it can be pretty bloody. Are you sure you'd like to try it?" George questioned.

"Could you teach me? Could I hunt with you?" Freda asked.

George said, "Yes, to both, if you're really serious. You would have to get a hunting license though."

"I can do that," she answered confidently. "I hope we get a deer." She laughed. "Of course, you would have to deal with the butchering. I haven't the slightest clue how. And I'm not sure Walter would approve. He is a real animal lover."

On October 21, Freda's name appeared on a long list of about 200 hunting license applicants, of whom six were women.

As the days grew shorter and chilly nights returned, Walter continued his habit of visiting Betty's studio when she was done teaching and the store was closed. They were often alone in the building when the employees had gone home. They talked over music they were preparing, played through new songs and generally enjoyed each other's company. They also talked about Freda's growing attachment to George.

One evening, Betty turned toward him from her piano bench and said, "How are things between you and Freda?"

Walter looked away. "She is gone a lot. Last winter she went to several ski jumping meets with George. I just can't get interested in being cold. And she spent a lot of time with him, learning to play tennis this summer. And now she's talking about hunting with him."

"Are you sure George is just a friend? They seem to be together a lot," said Betty.

"No, I'm not sure," replied Walter. "She really wants a more active life than I like. George lives one. I am content with my job at the furniture store and being able to play in the band and sing now and then." He coughed, more to hide the catch in his voice than to clear his throat. "We do still enjoy singing together."

"Freda always was a doer," said Betty. "But your voices are so well suited to each other."

Walter shrugged. "I'm not so sure about our personalities, though. I have become very fond of my times with you, Betty. I so enjoy our conversations. I hope you do too."

"Yes, Walter, I do. I treasure being with you when we can talk about interesting things." She paused, then admitted softly, "Orville seems to love his bands more than he loves me, and I am often lonely."

Walter joined her on the piano bench. She leaned into him as he put his arms around her.

Betty felt tears in her eyes. With her head buried against his shoulder, she murmured, "I am almost glad my parents aren't around to see my marriage failing. Papa would say, 'I never thought it would work!'" She choked back something between a laugh and a sob.

Walter patted her shoulder. "I guess people change as they mature. Both you and Orville have different needs than you did 22 years ago."

Betty nodded. "You're right, but we can't do anything now. Orville has enough to worry about with the band situation and Reuben not being well. And Reuben is concerned about Orville and the band funding problems. He doesn't need anything more troubling him." She sighed and added, "Although I think Orville would be just fine without me."

"I wonder if Orville has guessed about us. Maybe he is just so overwhelmed with the bands and passing the band tax, he hasn't noticed," said Walter.

"I can't really tell. He is always pleasant to me. But I don't see much of him. He often comes home after I am asleep because he works late in the band rooms, or he's off rehearsing a band somewhere. If the weather's bad, it can be very late. And you know how treacherous the roads can be. He's had a few flat tires out in nowhere. Sometimes I feel I can't stand the worry anymore."

The clock on the wall chimed eight. Walter stood abruptly. "Speaking of worrying, look how late it is. Orville must wonder where you are. How time flies."

Betty rose too and finished the cliché, "When you're having fun." They smiled as they walked toward the door.

They hugged again, and he kissed her, saying "Let's give it some time. Things could change. I have learned to be patient." He walked her to the apartment entrance.

Orville was not yet home.

That fall, Reuben became much weaker. Orville and Betty's winterized and remodeled home in La Moille was ready, but they decided to stay with Reuben in his apartment. He hardly left his room. Betty brought him meals and helped him eat. Orville came often to sit with him. When Reuben was awake, they reminisced about the family in Michigan and his poultry breeding experiments.

One day, Orville, who was sitting by the bed, asked Reuben about his own mother, Eva, saying, "I wish I had clearer memories of her, but I was very young when she died."

Reuben smiled sadly, and said, "Yes you were only about seven. Eva was a delightful woman, smart and funny – and very pretty. I'm sure she would be very proud of all you have accomplished here. I am proud of you too."

"Thank you for that, Father. I am very honored that you recognize my efforts."

"I was in such a state after her death, I didn't know what to do. I had to take care of you too. Farming and raising a child are hard enough with two parents. So, I sold the farm and took a job with the post office. I found a boarding school for you because I didn't think I could be a very good father by myself. I lost my way and made a few mistakes. I think you've heard about them."

Orville nodded. "Yes. But since you returned to your family in Michigan, you have more than made up for them. I've never mentioned them to Babette. She has high regard for both you and Josephine."

Reuben's face relaxed and he smiled again. "Ah, Josephine. She was such a comfort to me. I have missed her. Thank you. That means a great deal to me, Orville."

Orville stood up and embraced his father.

When Reuben fell unconscious a few days later, they brought him to the hospital. On October 22, he died. After his funeral, Orville accompanied his body to Benton Harbor, Michigan for burial in the family plot.

Before Christmas, Walter put several ads in the paper for Reese Furniture with gift ideas. He shared his ideas with Betty, saying, "We'll announce the opening of Toyland, soon. This year Santa will make his first appearance in Winona on November 29 at Reese's. We'll have the latest toys on display. And all children accompanied by their parents will receive a toy airplane. I'm sure most of them will plead with Mom and Dad to take them to the Reese Furniture Store."

Betty said, "That sounds like it will attract a crowd. Who do you have in mind to play Santa?"

"I was thinking of Orville. I know he is still grieving for his father, but I don't think he would be insulted, do you? He is a bit rounder than he used to be," Walter answered.

Betty said, "He loves to play Santa with his Junior Band at their New Year's parties. He has worn a costume, but all the children know who he is. I don't think he'd mind another 'Santa' engagement. He would be disguised, too. If anyone does recognize him, it might create some interest in joining his band. He'd like that."

Orville agreed to play Santa, and the opening of Reese's Toyland was a great success that year. He encouraged many children to ask for musical instruments as Christmas gifts by telling them they had the perfect mouth shape for a clarinet, or a trumpet, or even a tuba.

1931

Orville arranged his annual New Year's party for the Junior Band in January. The boys played music a bit first, then they received small gifts and played games after a lunch. Orville had found his mixture of work and play attracted youngsters to the band, which, he believed, kept them engaged and out of mischief.

The Annual Municipal Band meeting was the next day. Officers were elected and Orville laid out his plans for the year's band activities. But since the existence of the band depended on the outcome of the band tax vote in the spring, all plans were contingent on that. The board spent most of the meeting proposing ideas for strengthening support for the Band Tax Bill. They all felt this would be the last time they would try. If it failed to pass, the daunting task of fundraising again was not appealing in these days of austerity. But the third time's the charm, they reassured each other. The Senior Band continued rehearsing regularly, taking IOUs for their services.

Ski Jumpers But No Snow

© *Winona Republican Herald* - February 20, 1931, p. 11

George Graham convinced other Winona skiers in the Sugar Loaf ski club to erect a ski jump in West Burns Valley where they could practice. Unfortunately for them, the weather that year was unseasonably mild, so they weren't able to do much ski jumping. They did arrange to attend one meet in Tamarack, Wisconsin, where they had to truck in snow to cover the run. George did not win, but Freda was there to console him, as usual.

Soon after the meet, Betty called Freda. "I think we need to talk. Will you and Walter be home this evening?"

Freda answered, "I don't have plans, and I think Walter will be here. Why, may I ask?"

"I'd rather talk to you in person, and I'd like to meet at your apartment if you don't mind." Walter and Freda had also sold their 4th Street house and were renting an apartment on 3rd Street not far from Babette and Orville. "Orville is speaking at a meeting tonight," explained Betty.

Freda said, "This all sounds so dramatic and serious, but you're welcome to drop by around seven. Walter should be home by then."

At seven, Betty walked down the street and up the stairs to Walter and Freda's and knocked.

Walter opened the door and smiled knowingly. "Freda told me you were coming by." He led her into the stylishly furnished parlor.

Of course, both families had the first choice of new furniture that came into the store, and they could purchase things at cost. Betty sat on the mohair couch by Walter, and Freda settled into the matching chair.

Betty began, "We need to address a situation that we all know is very real."

"What do you mean by that?" asked Freda.

"I think you know," said Betty. "It's pretty clear that you and George Graham are more than just friends."

Freda looked down and then at Walter. "Oh, Walter, I'm sorry. I do like George a lot, and he likes me too. We have a great deal of fun together. He's introduced me to a whole new world. I've learned how to ski and play tennis. He even taught me how to shoot a rifle so I could go hunt with him. I never knew there were so many interesting things to do outside."

"Yes, Freda," Walter said. "I knew you enjoyed being with him. I could tell we were growing apart."

"Walter, I have always loved singing with you. But that's about all we do together anymore. You always seem so tired after work. By the evening I am ready for some excitement," Freda continued.

"I understand, Freda. You love being active, and I enjoy relaxing after a busy day. But I must tell you that while you've been out with George, Betty and I have grown very fond of each other. We have found that we are very much alike, both of us content with music and quiet evenings," Walter said.

Betty said, "We have to face the fact that we were only starstruck teenagers when we married. We thought we knew everything. But we couldn't see how we'd change in the future."

Freda said, "That's very true, Betty. I know that the two of you have been spending a lot of time together. And even though I still work at the store, my usual hours are in the morning since I've been credit manager. You are together later in the day. I know you practice new songs and probably talk a lot. I'm not surprised. But what about Orville?"

Betty sighed. "Orville is so busy with the Municipal Bands and the other bands he directs. It's as if they have all his love and attention. I feel like he has forgotten about me. He has always had such a strong desire to be successful. And now he spends all of his extra time on the band tax election coming up. Walter says he hasn't been coming to the store as often as he used to. I'm not sure he even notices what I do anymore."

"Oh Betty," said Freda. "I knew you weren't together often, but I never realized how bad it has been for you. I'm so sorry. I've been wrapped up in my own dilemma."

"I am very thankful I have had Walter to comfort me. And he has been very good at it." She hesitated, then took Walter's hand.

Walter said, "I don't think any of us want to hurt each other, but Betty is right. We have to face what we feel." He swallowed, patted Betty's hand, then looked into Freda's eyes "Have you talked with George about marriage, Freda?"

Freda stood and looked out the window. "It has come up," she admitted. "He was married before, but his wife left him to return to her wealthy parents. He was very hurt. The judge granted them a divorce."

"I would like to meet George. I think all four of us need to talk about our next step," said Walter.

Betty said, "Orville has evening band meetings that last until 9 p.m. tomorrow. Why don't you ask George if he's free and could meet with us."

Freda turned back from the window, facing her sister and her husband. Two people she wanted to see happy. Two people she cared about more than she could say. "I will see," she said firmly.

George was free and came to Walter and Freda's at seven the next evening. Betty was already there. Walter let him in.

George greeted Walter and Freda and introduced himself to Betty.

Betty said, "Hello, George. Freda has told me about you."

They settled into the comfortable parlor.

"I trust you know what this is about," said Walter.

"Yes, Freda told me. I think she outlined it very well," George answered. "I want to make it clear that I care very much for her and would marry her if she was free. But I don't want to be the cause of a broken marriage."

"I think you are more of a catalyst than a cause," Walter said dryly. "We've grown apart without your help." He took a sip of the tea Freda had set out. "Now, tell us a bit about yourself, George," Walter continued as if George were courting his daughter.

George recounted his story of being in the Navy, training as an engineer, being married, deserted, and divorced. "Now I have been selling insurance quite successfully, so I can do some of the things I love in the daylight, like ski jumping and playing tennis. Being active is a tonic for me."

"Freda has mentioned that. She says she really likes the sports she's learning from you," Betty said.

Walter concluded, "I guess it seems as if we're matched with the wrong people." He nodded to Freda. "Maybe your father was right, and we should have waited until we were older to get married. But then we wouldn't have had our vaudeville experience.

"That's very true," said Freda. "And it was a wonderful time, a memory I treasure. But now what?"

Betty said, "I would like to wait until the band tax question is settled before I say anything to Orville. I think it would be a better time. I really hope it passes, for his sake."

"I will be concerned about him if it doesn't pass." Walter observed. "I know you think he doesn't care about you anymore, but I am sure Orville will be upset when you tell him, Betty. Still, he would have to be blind to not have noticed the distance between you two. And he may not be aware of it, but there is a young lady at the store named Erna, who took over Freda's bookkeeping job when she was promoted. Every time Orville enters the store, she becomes more animated. She seems very impressed by his musical accomplishments although I'm not sure she has any background in music. I don't think Orville has paid much attention to her, yet. Maybe he will now."

Betty exclaimed, "You never told me that!"

"I guess I never thought about it until now," answered Walter.

"It somehow makes me feel a little better about this mess. I will talk to Orville when the election is over," Betty concluded.

The winter months continued without much change in their activities. Freda and George continued skiing when they could. George was busy with the ski club erecting the ski jump in West Burns Valley. But conditions continued to be unseasonably mild, so there wasn't much chance to use it.

Betty and Walter continued seeing each other after the business day was done. Walter held more clearance sales and participated in some game-like promotions with other stores, one a Dollar Days campaign and another a rather complicated bridge game that had customers running from store to store. As the depression wore on, sales were down all over, and merchants had to figure out new ways to market their wares.

On March 19, Walter and Fred Heyer Jr. were just settling into work at the store about 9:30 am when they were surprised by three men running through the front door yelling, "Fire upstairs!" These men had been working at the Oil Station across the street. One of them looked up at Reese's second floor window and saw flames rolling up to the ceiling. They called the alarm into the fire department, then ran over to alert everyone. The five of them hurried upstairs to find fire engulfing a pile of mattresses. They used fire extinguishers until the firefighters arrived with hoses and other equipment to put out the fire.

The shock from the effort exhausted everyone, and they closed the store to assess the damage. The fire seemed to have started with mattresses that were too close to an overheated chimney. Losses were minimal because of their quick reactions, but there was quite a mess to clean up.

Betty and Walter went to inspect her music studio. They found that there was no damage to her piano, saxophone, or piles of music. Her room was in the opposite corner from the fire, and the hose's water had been directed the other way.

She told him, "I am so relieved that it was no worse and you weren't hurt." He hugged her. She shuddered as she had a brief flashback to the horror of the Iroquois Theater fire in Chicago.

That morning Orville was teaching band in Arcadia. When he returned and heard about the fire, he was glad that he had insurance to cover this setback. As soon as it was safe, they started cleaning up. Some mattresses were totally ruined, and others would be sure to show water stains. There hadn't been much smoke, so nothing had a disagreeable odor.

© *Winona Republican Herald* - March 25, 1931

They immediately listed the things they could still sell and marked them down. A week later they advertised a big fire sale. Real bargains were available. That was very good news for the many people who had lost their jobs in the depression. Some of them worked temporarily for the city of Winona. They were paid small amounts from a fund raised by the Association of Commerce to do street repair projects, so they had a little income and something productive to do.

Wrestling matches had resumed, so George decided to get involved again. He agreed to referee a match between two heavyweight wrestlers, Rudy Steinburn and Mike Gettson, at the armory. It turned into quite a brawl which he and Freda later described to Walter and Betty.

George began, "During the match these two wrestlers attacked each other in ways that were definitely against the rules. They were gouging eyes, ears, and mouths, and constantly swinging their fists. As the referee, I sternly cautioned them to stop, but Mike grabbed Rudy, who was heavier, and tossed him through the ropes. The newspaper report described it this way, "He landed like a ton of Irish confetti on the hardwood armory floor." George chuckled at the image.

Betty and Walter looked a little confused.

George asked, "Do you know what Irish confetti is?"

Betty and Walter shook their heads.

"Rocks!" exclaimed George.

Betty gasped. "That sounds painful."

Walter asked, "What happened then?"

Freda continued, "Rudy was furious and a little dazed. He grabbed a chair and went after Mike. Someone pulled the chair away, and George pinned Rudy to the mat. It took three policemen to keep Mike from lunging after Rudy."

"Oh my." Betty said. "That really sounds dangerous."

George said, "It sure could have been. Things seemed to cool down, so I let Rudy up and announced that the match was over. But then another wrestler, Jack Mason, threatened to kill me. I threw Jack out of the ring and two policemen held him. But it wasn't over yet. Rudy and Mike resumed their bout. Rudy had been weakened, and Mike was finally able to pin him."

Walter said, "Boy, that really sounds frightening. I'm glad you are ok, but I'm also glad I wasn't watching. George, you have a lot more moxie than I do."

George took that as a compliment and smiled.

Freda looked at George gravely, and said, "I was appalled at the poor sportsmanship. I hadn't realized how quickly matches could become violent. I'm glad you were there to help, George."

"Such scuffles are pretty unusual," said George.

Betty said, "Thank heavens it wasn't worse. Are you going to continue wrestling?"

"I am already committed to two more matches coming up, but they will be nothing like this. I am not refereeing. I'm wrestling. People don't get mad at the wrestlers as often as they do the referees who make judgment calls," George answered.

Freda attended both of his next bouts and cheered when he won.

The Band Board was busy circulating petitions again to have the band tax added to the ballot in spring. By mid-March they had the required 730 signatures and presented them to the city council. Resolutions to place the band tax, a public-school bond question, and a new street naming system on the spring referendum ballot were unanimously approved by the aldermen.

Everyone did what they could. Board members spoke with citizen groups, explaining the problem, and received endorsements from many of them like the VFW and the League of Women Voters. Letters and ads appealing for support of the tax appeared multiple times in the newspaper. These stressed again and again that failing to mark a ballot counted as a "no" vote. The bands played concerts, led parades, and even got themselves broadcast over the La Crosse radio station. If the measure passed, the band promised to play thirteen summer concerts as opposed to last summer's four.

The April 6 election was another nail biter. Reports, judging from early returns, indicated that the voting was going to be heavy. Orville and the Band Board members waited in the band rooms, on tenterhooks, looking for any reason for optimism. It was sounding hopeful, but the final results would not be announced until the next day.

The April 7 newspaper headlines read, "Voters Spurn School Bond Issue" and "Street Names Will Not Be Changed" but "Winona Will Have a

Band" The Fourth ward had voted heavily against all three questions, but the band tax vote still won by 649 votes.

Orville felt like he could breathe again. He went about his usual day at the store. Everyone congratulated him. The bookkeeper, Erna, brought a cake to celebrate. The eleven years of work he had put in to develop the bands had been worth it after all. He drove out to their La Moille home a little early since he hadn't slept much the night before.

Babette finished teaching her students for the day and hurried to their river home. Orville was napping on the couch. Supper was waiting when he awoke.

When he opened his eyes, Orville saw her in the kitchen and said, "Did you hear the news? The band tax passed!" He was still slightly dazed and euphoric over the election results.

She said, "That is wonderful. You have worked so hard to make this happen. I am happy the people of Winona do want their Municipal Band."

After they ate, Orville made a few phone calls thanking the Band Board. Everyone was relieved and elated. Orville sat down in his favorite chair to look at the newspaper, but Betty cleared her throat and said, "Orville, there is something very important I need to tell you. Can you listen to me now?"

"Of course," said Orville as he continued looking at the paper. He wanted to read the details of the election, but he decided he could listen if this was so important.

Betty took a big breath. "We seem to have grown apart since we have been in Winona. You are gone so much with all of your directing obligations, building support for the band tax question, and your work at the store. I have felt that you are more in love with the bands and the store than you are with me."

"That's not true, Babette. I have done all of this for you!" protested Orville. He folded the newspaper and slapped it against his knee.

Betty went on in a calm but firm voice, "It doesn't seem that way, Orville. You used to be very interested in my playing and my students. Now I don't think you care like you once did. I don't think you even know where I am playing or remember my students' names, unless they are in your band. You never come to my recitals. . ."

Orville interrupted her saying, "That's because I always have conflicts. You know how busy I am."

"I'm not going to argue about that. But have you even noticed how much time I have been spending with Walter? He has comforted me frequently when I have felt lonely and sad," she said.

"Walter? Your sister's husband?" He sharply drew in his breath and bristled. "How does Freda feel about that?"

"Freda has fallen in love with another man, George Graham. She went to some of his wrestling matches and things developed from there. So, Walter and I have supported and listened to each other a lot. We have always liked each other, and we have discovered we share many ideas and beliefs. I hardly know what you think or believe anymore, since we don't have time for conversations. I can't understand how you didn't notice how far apart we have become."

Orville said, "And I can't believe this is happening. It feels like some bizarre version of musical chairs, where I'm the one left standing."

"Not exactly. It's simply the way things have changed. It's been happening for a long time, Orville." Betty took another deep breath. She clasped her hands together to stop the trembling. "The fact is," she began, paused, and then repeated more firmly. "The fact is, I love Walter and he loves me."

Orville put his head in his hands and covered his face. "You're leaving me. Just like that. I suppose I should have been more attentive. . ." He trailed off. "But now what am I supposed to do?" His voice sounded like it would break.

Betty felt sad for him. She said, "Perhaps you'll find someone else. Someone who doesn't need your attention as much as I do. I hear there is someone at the store who is very interested in you."

"What? Oh, I suppose you mean Erna. She is always telling me how wonderful I am and what amazing things I have done. It's flattering, but she overdoes it a bit. And she is younger than you."

"Maybe you should take her more seriously. We both know that age doesn't matter if you love someone. I think you really enjoy her admiration. I'm sorry I haven't been able provide more of that for you. I do admire you, but it doesn't feel like you appreciate me. Sometimes I wonder if you think I'm competing with you. That has never been the case. I understand what you have accomplished in music because I have done it too. We are both very good musicians. But you seem to want your band students to make beautiful music for your own glory. I just want my students to reap all the benefits they can for themselves when they play music well."

Orville sighed. "This is a lot to take in right after our big election success. Did you have to spoil that for me?"

"I know. I'm sorry to ruin the moment for you. But I didn't want to bring it up while you were in the heat of your campaign. And I have been waiting years. I can't wait any longer."

"I suppose I have to thank you for that," said Orville sarcastically.

Ignoring the barb, Betty continued, "Walter and I want to marry. So do Freda and George. We need to figure out how to get divorces."

With that she went to the bedroom and left Orville to his own thoughts.

The next morning Orville said, "We've only been living in our—or should I say, "the"—river house since last fall. We still have some things in Father's apartment. Should I leave the rest of your things there? I know you love it out here as much as I do," said Orville, with a little edge.

"We can sort it out later. For now, just leave things where they are. Freda and I will be gone to Reno for a few weeks at the end of July and most of August, if our plans work out. Maybe you can have my things moved back to the apartment while I'm gone, before I start my lessons this fall. Walter and I have talked about building a home in La Moille. There seems to be enough property to build a house for us here."

"We'll see," said Orville, not convinced it would be the best idea.

The Senior Municipal Band took back the Memorial Day program and other events that the Junior Band had covered the year before. Walter had played saxophone in Orville's Senior Band since they moved to town. He told Orville that he thought it would be best to take a break from band this next summer, under the circumstances of the changing relationships. Orville agreed and said, "I will plan this summer's concerts without you playing or singing." They were both relieved.

The transition of the Winona Municipal Band from private to city management was more complicated than expected. The private Band Board had about $2,000 in debt, mostly in the form of IOU's given to the Senior Band Members when they were short of cash. The board decided to lock up the larger instruments, chairs, stands, music, and uniforms. They would allow the city access to them if they would assume the debt. The Municipal Band would discontinue their activities until the transition was complete.

Orville was furious. He could no longer hold rehearsals without these resources. He angrily responded that, "This equipment belongs to the people who contributed to sustaining the band. They do not want to see the band harmed by being unable to rehearse."

After calming down and explaining to the board the difficulties this would cause, they changed their minds. He was able to write "This discontinuation of activities . . . applies only to the Municipal Band Board and not the Municipal Band itself" which "will continue as before." He said that he would finance the activities himself to avoid interruption in the work which had already been planned.

Babette's students now numbered more than 40. She held her summer recital in two parts on the afternoon of Sunday, June 7. There were many piano pieces, and solos by 16 saxophone students and one clarinet. A violin teacher had been driving from La Crosse to give lessons, so his students were on the program as well. Since he finally had some time free, Orville wanted to attend, but thought better of it.

Freda and Babette knew that obtaining a divorce was difficult. In most states a divorcing person had to prove inhumane treatment or desertion. Neither of those applied to the sisters. And in states that had more liberal divorce laws, there were also residency requirements, usually of about a year before a divorce could be granted. The western states were well known for harboring "divorce mills." Nevada, in particular, had discovered that divorcing people were a great source of income. To compete with other communities like Las Vegas, Reno had recently reduced its residency requirement to six weeks.

Freda had a friend who had received a divorce in Reno and discretely asked her how she had accomplished it. She told them about her experience and gave them the name of the judge who had approved her divorce. She also provided the name and address of the homeowner who had rented her a room and accompanied her to court to swear she had stayed there the full six weeks.

The sisters did not have to worry about money for their train tickets and lodging because the store was doing well enough. There was even enough cash available for them to reserve two sleeper berths for the three-day round trip. They had to leave by mid-July to allow enough time for the required residency. They sent a letter to the family in Reno about renting a room. Since Nevada's hot summer days were not the most popular time to visit, the family had rooms available. Freda and Babette both experienced some trepidation about the uproar their actions would cause in Winona, but they realized how much better their lives would be when all was said and done. They boarded the train.

In Reno they were met by their hosts and taken to their home. Most days during their residency, they relaxed in the shade, reading books, playing cards, drinking lemonade, and hoping for a breeze. Freda went for a walk, but came back soon, drenched in sweat. "It's too hot to do much of anything." she complained.

"Yes, it is," responded Betty. "It seems like we are long way from our problems. And I do miss Walter."

"And I miss George," said Freda. "Well, we'll be back soon enough. And then we have all the gossip to face."

Betty said, "I don't look forward to that."

They had appointments in two different chambers at the courthouse on August 24. They arrived early and Judge Kessler granted Babette a divorce and Judge Morgan finalized Freda's. The sisters thanked their hosts, quickly packed up and boarded the train for the long trip back to Winona.

On the ride, they talked about how fast the word would spread along the gossip grapevine following their rearrangement. They were sure some tongues were already wagging.

Freda said, "People will wonder if Walter and I have been pretending to be in love all these years when we sang together. I guess we have for the last few years."

Betty said, "What do you think they'll say about me 'stealing' your husband and leaving Orville in the dust?"

"I guess we'll find out. I'm sure some of them will be shocked. At least we'll be happier," said Freda.

"I suppose folks will get used to it. I think we just have to keep our chins up and bear with it until they find some other scandal to discuss."

Freda nodded. They both fell quiet, imagining the kerfuffle.

Back in Winona, they had a couple of weeks to take care of some legal and property matters before the news was public knowledge. Orville sold Babette a parcel of land from their property in La Moille for $1. Walter and she built their own home on it.

Their divorce proceedings were published in the paper on September 9. Out in public they were aware of some finger pointing and head turning, but they did their best to ignore it.

When things were settled legally, Betty and Walter planned their wedding for November 13. They decided they might cause less commotion if they didn't have the wedding in Winona, so they contacted an old family friend, Reverend Edward Strecker, who was the pastor of the Methodist Church in

Mrs. Christensen, Mrs. Reese Given Divorces at Reno

Reno, Nevada—Divorces have been granted in Washoe county district court here to Mrs. Freda E. Christensen from Walter W. Christensen of Winona, Minn., and to Mrs. Babette Reese from O. W. Reese, also of Winona, Minn.

Judgment was entered in the Christensen case by Judge Thomas F. Moran and in the Reese case by Judge B. F. Kessler, both on Aug. 24.

© *Winona Republican Herald* - September 9, 1931, p. 3

Crown Point, Indiana. He knew their family personally from South Bend, and while he was sad to hear their earlier marriages had broken down, he agreed to perform their ceremony in the parsonage.

Finally, Walter and Betty were married and could show their affection openly. No more charades. Their first night together was unlike anything either of them had ever known. More mature and tuned to each other, their union was a deeply fulfilling and intimate experience. They complemented

ANNOUNCE MARRIAGE—

Announcement was made today of the marriage of Babette Reese and Walter W. Christensen, both of Winona, at Crown Point, Ind., Friday Nov. 13. The ceremony was performed by the Rev. Edward W. Strecker at the Methodist parsonage.

© *Winona Republican Herald* - November 21, 1931, p. 6

one another like the melody and harmony they performed together. They knew they had made the right decision. They took their time returning to Winona, enjoying each other with no distractions.

But they did have to face reality when they got home. Reese Furniture had been inundated with questions like, "Are you going to stay in business?" and "Is your partnership over?" and "What happened?" Orville had to field queries like "When did you know?" and "Can you and Walter work together now that he married your wife, er-wife?" and so on. Even the employees, who had suspected something was afoot, wondered about their jobs and the store's future. Orville took the questions stoically and answered them with, "Thank you for your concern. We all appreciate each other's contributions and will carry on as usual."

That fall, the Association of Commerce devised a unique campaign to support their struggling members through these difficult days. Each week a business got to tell its history and showcase its products, services, or offerings, in a full-page spread. The headline read "Do You Know (the business name)" and gave each ample space for them to tell their full story surrounded by small ads for other member businesses.

The Reese Furniture story was scheduled for November 23. Their turn happened to occur at a very convenient time for the store with questions swirling around its future. Orville told everyone, "This will be a great opportunity to let people know we aren't going anywhere, and they can still get reliable goods and service from us."

Orville wrote the copy for the "Do You Know Reese Furniture" feature. It included 13 paragraphs about Orville's business, musical and band background, highlighting his accomplishments with the Winona Municipal Band. He listed the many area bands he had directed, including Rollingstone, Minnieska, Alma, Cochrane, Blair, Arcadia, and Independence. There was one paragraph about his partner, Walter Christensen, a three-sentence paragraph about Babette, a brief mention of Freda Christensen, who was now in charge of the music department, and recognition of the roles of Fred L. Heyer, advertising manager and salesman, Edmund Kluzik, sales, and Miss Erna Klaviter, bookkeeper.

Walter and Betty read through the article and looked at each other.

Betty said, "I shouldn't criticize Orville, but this sounds like it's more about getting to know him and his band directing than about Reese Furniture. I understand that he is probably still upset about how things changed . . . " she trailed off.

"I agree," said Walter. "I wish we had been able to give some input into the article, but it probably suits his needs. When we first came to Winona, he wrote that I graduated from Chicago University. That's not true and I told him so. He just shrugged his shoulders and said, 'We need to appear believable to people.' I did take some evening classes when Freda and I lived there. But that's all."

"Orville has always been a promoter, making everything sound fine and almost too good to be true. Now he's just promoting himself, not the *Musical Reeses,*" concluded Betty, sounding resigned.

At the City Council meeting, December 21, setting up an official new board to regulate band affairs was discussed. City Attorney Lamberton gave an opinion that "the council could not legally turn over money from the levy to the old board" to settle their debts. Several council members favored retaining control of the band by appointing a new band master and regulating band expenditures. Sensing that this could complicate matters unduly, Council Member Choate suggested creating an advisory board to discuss decisions about the band.

Orville was upset and discouraged. He was especially bothered by the council's statement about appointing a new band master. What did that mean? Could they be considering someone else as director? Feeling low, he called his old Band Board friend, Oswald Leicht, to get his perspective. He asked, "Do you think they plan to replace me? After all I've done?"

Oswald replied, "They'd be fools if they did. You have a loyal following, and they are very aware of that. But you know, they are starting a band program in the public schools. The need for your beginner's band could be ending."

"I read about that," said Orville. "I would hate to see my instruction program terminated. I spent so much time perfecting it. But I would hate even more to lose my Senior Band directorship. Being a good band director is my main goal in life. It gives me purpose. Especially now."

"I can understand that," Oswald said, thinking of the recent divorce. "But you can never tell with politicians. Putting band matters in their hands could have unforeseen consequences. The band belongs to Winona, now. You know the old saying 'Be careful what you wish for.'"

Somehow, the conversation did not improve Orville's outlook on things.

Freda and George Graham also went to Crown Point to be married by Reverend Strecker on December 17. That night Freda, lover of passion and drama, and muscular George couldn't get enough of each other. They joined themselves energetically with an intensity Freda had never felt. She couldn't get over George's well-toned muscles and felt every inch of him. He reciprocated. They celebrated the holiday season sure they had made the right decision.

ANNOUNCE MARRIAGE—
Announcement was made today of the marriage of Freda E. Heyer and George A. Graham. The ceremony was performed by the Rev. Edward W. Strecker at the Methodist parsonage at Crown Point, Ind., Thursday, Dec. 17. Mr. and Mrs. Graham will make their home at 161½ East Third street.

© *Winona Republican Herald -*
December 24, 1931, p. 4

1932

At the first City Council meeting of the year, the matter of the band was brought up, but no action was taken. The city attorney was asked to call a meeting of aldermen, the old Band Board and anyone interested, before the end of January to hear their views and suggest solutions to the impasse.

It was difficult for Orville to feel optimistic. The Senior Band kept their regular rehearsal schedule, so they didn't lose their musical edge. But they couldn't plan concerts until the band's transfer to the city was complete. Orville tried not to think about being replaced as director.

Now there was no need for the annual January Band Board meeting and the Senior Band players could do without the customary luncheon and smoker. But Orville knew he couldn't disappoint his younger band members who so looked forward to the New Year's Party. For some of them with families struggling to survive, it was the only holiday celebration they would have.

He announced, "This year's New Years' party will be held on January 15. Of course there will be candy and apples for all the children. We will have lots of games to play and prizes will be awarded to winners." Excitement filled the air as a crowd of 450 band members, their families, and friends attended. Parents formed an association to plan winter activities for the Junior Bands and build camaraderie. February's events included a Mardi gras party with bunco and card games.

George Graham had an exciting winter with a series of ski jump meets. The weather was more cooperative, and there was a good amount of snow. He broke some records, performed demonstrations of good jumping technique, and survived a few falls. Freda was always there to cheer him on.

The number of clients he attracted to his insurance business increased, and the Montana Life Insurance Company noticed. They promoted him to district manager with responsibility for their insurance business in Olmstead,

Wabasha, and Houston Counties, as well as Winona. He told Freda, "With this added territory, I can earn a lot more money."

Freda said, "I am very happy for you. You are a terrific salesman, and I'm glad that the company recognizes your accomplishments." She pretended to scold, shaking a finger at him. "Just don't forget all work and no play makes George a dull boy."

George took her in his arms and told her, "I will be fine, Freda. I'm not giving up any of my outdoor sports. Nothing I've ever done compares with the way ski jumping makes me feel." He looked into her eyes and added, "Nothing except being with you."

This Thrill to Be Repeated Here Sunday

George Graham demonstrates ski jumping
© *Winona Republican Herald -*
January 29, 1932, p. 9

Everywhere in the United States, money was tight, and merchants kept feeling the pinch. Reese Furniture reduced their many elaborate display ads since sales were down, and Walter needed to cut back the advertising budget. Reese Furniture emphasized economy with smaller ads, including less expensive classified ads. They coordinated with other Winona furniture stores and placed a series of cooperative ads urging people to "invest" in furniture because prices had never been lower, nor quality better. Consumers were reminded that merchants depended on local trade to survive these critical times. Furniture was the best investment a person could make since it provided comfort, happiness, and satisfaction for years to come.

Orville needed to wait until the March City Council meeting when all city appointments were announced to find out if he would be the Municipal Band Director for the coming year. He was relieved to hear his name announced as city bandmaster.

Orville called Oswald Leicht and said with excitement, "The City Council decided to hire me for my old job!"

"Congratulations. I can't imagine why they'd choose anyone else," said Oswald.

"There is one thing that really bothers me. The appointment is only for a year." Orville's voice rose. "Do I have to go through this every year? It takes a lot of time to organize future events. How can I make any long-term plans if I only am appointed for a year at a time? And I know not everyone on the council likes me. They all have pretty big egos. I think they may just be jealous."

Oswald said, "Calm down, Orville. I'm sure they will see the short-sightedness of that provision."

"I hope so." Orville felt somewhat reassured.

In the spring, the band had enough money for the purchase of new 'natty' white uniforms with black knee boots, black ties and belts and black berets. The Winona Municipal Band's first formal appearance in this new attire was the Memorial Day ceremony followed that evening with a torchlight parade.

photo courtesy of Winona County Historical Society

Senior Municipal Band in Natty New Uniforms

Attired in natty new white uniforms and black knee boots, the Senior Municipal band will make its first formal appearance as an official city organization tonight at 8 o'clock in the 40 and 8 torchlight parade.

The uniforms consist of the knee boots; white knee breeches, white shirts, black berets, black ties and black belts. The second appearance of the Senior band will be in connection with the Memorial day services at the Lake Park band shell Monday morning. In the picture are:

Front row, left to right—Donald Libera, drum major, Edwin Kirwin, Henry Bentz, Everett Uebel, Fred Dabelstein, Gerald Ruppert, W. W. Christiansen, Edward Hostettler, James Lund-

strom, Luke Rowan, Otto Rumstick, George Ross and O. W. Reese, director.

Second row, left to right—Victor Lynne, Earl Nelson, C. G. Smelser, Frank Bunn, Donald Lockwood, Gordon Ostrom, Max Cieminski, Vincent Kling, Arthur Rackow, Lloyd Dielke, Arthur Boll and Robert Ostrom.

Third row, left to right—Walter Aton, LeRoy Kuhlmann, William Streuber, Arthur Rice, Stanley Streuber, Gerald Lowe, C. A. Rohrer, Edward Urness, Paul Kuhlmann and Everett Nelson.

Back row, left to right—Vernon Smelser, Ward Engel, Stewart Schultz, H. A. Doty, Earl Lowe, Fred Heyer, T. Z. Zabrockl, Harry Smith and Carl Lang.

© Winona Republican Herald - May 28, 1932

Walter and the Reese Furniture staff congratulated Orville on his reappointment. Erna Klaviter, the store's bookkeeper, made a special effort to tell him how happy she was for him. She said, "I can see how much directing the band means to you. You are so good at it. Your concerts are always entertaining. I never miss a summer concert."

Orville said, "I didn't know you enjoyed my work. That makes me very happy."

Erna decided to make a bold suggestion, which was unusual considering her reserved nature. "Maybe some time we could have lunch together. I would love to hear about how you achieve such fine musical results."

"That would be nice," replied Orville, mildly surprised at how pleasant that sounded to him. They decided on a time and place. He began feeling better about himself.

Orville and Erna had an enjoyable lunch and continued seeing each other outside of workdays in the furniture store. Erna was very impressed with Orville's successes and listened attentively to his accounts of what he had accomplished. He basked in her attention and approval. He asked her, "Do you play an instrument?"

"No," she answered. "I would have liked to, but there was no opportunity, and my parents couldn't afford it. If only I could have had the same chance you give your beginners, I might have tried something. But now I am content listening to others, like you, make music."

Her honesty and lack of pretense impressed Orville. He knew her to be scrupulously honest in keeping the books for Reese Furniture. She was not beautiful, but she had a wholesome attractiveness that appealed to him. He genuinely enjoyed being with her. Despite the fact that she was in her later 20's, her conversation showed a depth of maturity and knowledge. He also liked that he didn't feel lonely when they were together. One day in early June, he said to her, "I know I am much older than you. But you make me feel young again."

She answered, "Well, Mr. Reese, you must know that I am 26. I rather like a quiet life. But I enjoy your company and learning about all the things you've experienced. You have done so much."

"You certainly can call me Orville, if you are comfortable with that."

Erna blushed a bit and said, "All right, Orville." She gazed directly in his eyes with a twinkle in hers.

Orville didn't say anything for a bit, but finally blurted out, "Would you consider marrying me? I really like being with you. You are always pleasant. But you do know I will be 56 in August?"

Erna thought for a moment before she answered, "I am aware that you are quite a bit older than I am. But I enjoy our time together too. I think I could be a good wife to you. I'll never get tired of your stories. So, my answer is yes."

They planned their wedding for June 24. They drove to Crown Point, Indiana, as had Betty and Walter, and Freda and George for their weddings. That night they stayed at a hotel there. After their cursory coupling, Orville rolled over and promptly fell asleep. Erna lay awake hoping she had made the right decision.

Orville invited all band members and their families to his and Erna's home in La Moille for the annual summer picnic. At rehearsal he announced, "Anyone who needs transportation, please meet at 8 a.m. at Reese Furniture. A truck will be there

> **REESE-KLAVITER—**
> Announcement has been made of the marriage of Miss Erna Klaviter, 166 Kansas street, and O. W. Reese, head of the Reese Furniture company, and director of the Municipal bands. The ceremony took place at Crown Point, Ind., June 24.
>
> © *Winona Republican Herald -*
> *July 13, 1932, p. 5*

to drive you to our La Moille home for the festivities. Please bring your own picnic lunches and we will provide coffee, lemonade, and ice cream. Then a full afternoon awaits with activities like swimming and canoe races, speedboat and surfboard riding, water and canoe polo, and water horse riding. This summer I have added a deep-water spring diving board and an 8-foot water wheel." Band members applauded and whistled.

The summer band series included eleven concerts, most of them at the bandshell and two at different city parks. Walter rejoined the band and was again featured singing at three concerts. But there were no duets with Freda.

The band played for other civic activities too, and both the Senior and Junior Bands marched in the July 4 parade competition in La Crosse, Wisconsin. There the Senior band won first prize and the Junior Band second, in the 16-band competition. The prize was $85.

1933

The Senior Municipal Band elected Stanley Streuber president in January. A longtime member of the trumpet section, Streuber had served as assistant director under Reese and was a dedicated, well-liked bandsman.

Orville prepared a report of all band activities the previous year and submitted it to the City Council in February. He told Erna, "Since my appointment is for only one year, I want to make sure the council members have a record of the bands' contributions and civic involvement." He added, "It is crazy that I am not assured of being the permanent Municipal Band Director."

She answered, "It's obvious that they don't understand the situation."

Orville said, "No, they certainly don't. At least with the old Band Board, I knew I had their approval, even when they couldn't support us financially. But these City Council politicians could choose any of their buddies to replace me."

George Graham had a busy year with many ski meets and wrestling matches, acting as referee and participating in wrestling matches. He even gave wrestling lessons. Freda attended as his loyal supporter and cheered boisterously for each match.

He had to travel quite a bit for his work. When he returned, Freda was there to welcome him home. But one time she noticed he was driving a different car that was not the one he left in. "What happened to our car?" she asked.

"I had quite a harrowing experience on my trip. I was trying to turn around on some railroad tracks because the road ahead was closed. The car somehow conked out while I was turning. It was facing the way the tracks ran. I couldn't get it started. The crossing was on a little rise. I saw a train coming so I jumped out used all my muscles to give it a mighty shove. But the darned car rolled the wrong way and right into the train. It was demolished."

"Oh George, how frightening. I'm so glad you didn't get hurt. What happened then?" Freda asked.

"I guess it's a good thing I understand insurance and have always made sure we have a good car insurance policy. I called an agent, and he took care of everything. He even found me a replacement car."

He then grinned sheepishly and admitted to her, "You know, I have to be honest. I jumped out of the car so fast I forgot that the gear shift was in reverse! So, I guess I know why the car rolled the wrong way."

Freda covered her mouth with her hands but couldn't hide her laugh. He chuckled too, although the joke was on him. Soon they were both laughing so hard, tears came to Freda's eyes.

By April 19, the council said they had received no applications for the bandmaster position, so Orville felt a little better about his reappointment chances. They deferred naming a bandmaster until the next month. Orville said to Erna, "I hope they haven't heard that someone else is going to apply to be bandmaster. I've never been very good at politics. Business and band directing are another matter. I am good at those."

"Yes, dear, it must be terribly frustrating," Erna said. "But certainly, they know and appreciate everything you have accomplished with the band."

"One can only hope," answered Orville.

At the May Council meeting, to Orville's chagrin, it was announced that another musician had applied for the bandmaster position. Mr. Gratke, the current public-school music and mathematics teacher requested that he be given a chance to show his conducting abilities. His application included a long list of qualifications and recommendations. Orville was really worried.

But the City Council had also received strong statements in favor of Orville's re-appointment from his own band members and the recently appointed City Band Committee. After some discussion, the council made the official decision that Orville Reese would be the Winona Bandmaster again. The appointment once more was for one year.

Orville was very relieved. "I will work hard to show them what I can do." he told Erna.

The financial situation had not improved much for anyone, the city included. Tax revenue was down, and the council had to cut expenses. Salaries were reduced across the board. Orville's yearly compensation was cut from $1,200 to $900. Since he had income from the furniture store, Orville was more financially secure than most, so he could accept this.

Orville kept the band busy and visible. They played for many civic events and several area fairs, parades, pageants, and other special events like the opening of the bridge between Pepin and Buffalo. These were in addition to the usual summer concert series.

When a passage in a concert review especially pleased him, Orville made sure to read it aloud to Erna. "Listen to what they wrote about us playing *The Poet and the Peasant Overture*. 'The band was at its best in the execution of this number.' That piece is well known for its demanding passages."

Erna answered, "I had no idea it was so difficult. It was wonderful. Your band made it sound very polished. You prepared them very well."

Orville smiled.

Walter sang and led sing-alongs as well. The audience asked for more of these to be programmed. The Junior Band also made several appearances.

Erna attended all the summer concerts and some of the other events and always told Orville how much she enjoyed the performances. She got accustomed to spending many evenings alone when he was rehearsing his bands and found herself more sympathetic toward Babette.

Betty and Walter built a home on the land near La Moille and moved there. They had two dogs that they loved and pampered and were glad to have more space for them to exercise. Betty had had many dogs in her lifetime, and she loved them dearly. Unfortunately, there were people who were angry about dogs who weren't kept on their owner's property. Betty was incensed when she heard about a friend whose dog had been poisoned.

She told Walter, "It makes me so mad that someone would kill an innocent animal. Most dogs are so trusting and loving. They deserve to be treated kindly. There's just something about dogs . . ."

Walter said, "Why don't you write a letter to the newspaper? It might open some people's eyes."

She asked, "You don't think it would hurt Reese Furniture, do you? Or my piano studio?"

"No," answered Walter. "The type of person who would do such a thing would not likely be our customer nor your student."

She penned a pointed letter to the *Public Pulse* column in the newspaper.

It said, "The most diabolical act anyone can commit is to poison a dog. It takes a human animal to do such an outrageous thing. The more I learn about animals the less I think of the human animal." She signed off as "A lover of dogs" and added her own name. She showed it to Walter.

Walter said, "You make the way you feel very clear. I agree with you. Go ahead and send it."

In June, a new act was passed by the federal government to assist the nation's economic recovery. It established the National Recovery Administration to supervise fair trade codes and guarantee laborers a right to collective bargaining. It encouraged merchants to increase hours to provide more employment.

Walter said to Orville, "I think we should get behind this effort. People need work. We could stay open on Saturdays and expand our weekly hours. Then we could hire a couple more people."

Orville replied, "I guess it would be a good idea. A lot of Winona businesses are participating. But we are having a bit of a struggle ourselves, so we have to be careful."

"I understand that. But I think we could manage it. More hours should mean more sales," said Walter.

Reese Furniture pledged to support the new act. They enrolled in the program and displayed its blue eagle to indicate they were participating. They were able to hire three more people who became some of the best workers they ever had.

One evening as they were finishing a quiet supper, Betty said, "Did you ever want to have children, Walter?"

"Oh yes," he answered without hesitation. "I always wanted a son. I would have named him Walter Jr. I would have enjoyed a daughter, too. But Freda always had a reason that we weren't ready. She would tell me she wanted to wait until we had a house and decent jobs when we lived in Chicago. After we came here, she wanted to wait until we were sure the furniture store could provide a good income. And you know what happened next. What about you, Betty?"

She said, "Orville never wanted to have children because of his busy, ambitious schedule. I soon realized that his students were his family, but I would have loved to have our own children. My childhood memories are so full of wonderful times spent with Mama and Papa. They were very loving parents. Then when my sister and brothers came along, we had so much fun with each other. Most of the time, that is. Sometimes younger siblings can be annoying, but Mama always had a way of helping resolve our quarrels."

"I was only three when my father was killed, so I don't have much memory of him. But Mother always encouraged my brother and me to try new things and keep learning. She loved to hear us sing. Other than Tillie complaining about work, we got along well. We had money problems like most people, but I always felt happy," said Walter.

"Oh, I wish we had married when I was younger." Betty sighed, then stood to clear the dishes. "I just kept hoping that Orville would change."

Walter stood and put his arms around her, "You have always loved your students like a mother."

"Yes, I suppose they have been my substitute family. And many of them stay in touch long after they've grown up. That is gratifying, but it's not quite the same as having my own children," she said.

Walter said, "Maybe that's why we have our dogs. They need us and love us as much as we need and love them. But they aren't children. I was reading that there are many youngsters in the orphanages now. Mostly their parents have lost jobs and have no way of feeding or caring for them." He paused then looked out the window at the beautiful land surrounding their home. He turned back to Betty and whispered. "We have so much. Would you consider adopting a child?"

Betty said quickly, "Yes, I think that would be wonderful."

They called to set up an appointment at the orphanage in a nearby town, to see what the requirements and procedures would be.

A few days later, they drove their car to the location, parked, and walked to the front door of the big, old house that served as the orphanage. The place was clean, but shabby. The yard was bare, with the grass trampled from the children's play. A tire swing hung from an old oak, and a single rusty bicycle leaned against the porch. They knocked at the door and were let into the large living room that served as a reception area. This room was also clean, but the furniture was worn, and the carpet frayed at the edges. Dark curtains hung at the window. Voices of children playing upstairs wafted down the stairway. A lady seated at the desk consulted the list in front of her and said, "Are you Mr. and Mrs. Christensen? I'm sorry about all the noise. The children are just changing to go outside for playtime before lunch."

"Yes," answered Walter. "We've come to see about adopting a child."

The lady opened a folder of papers and said, "Here are some forms we ask prospective parents to fill out. You can sit over there while you complete them." She gestured to a table and some chairs.

They dutifully filled in all the blanks. One question asked why they wanted to adopt a child. They answered truthfully that they understood the responsibilities of raising a child and felt they could provide a loving home for a youngster who had been orphaned or abandoned. They were hoping to adopt a school aged boy.

When they were done, they returned the forms to the woman who quickly checked to see that they were fully completed. She told them, "Everything seems in order. Someone will contact you soon about the next step. We will want to do a home visit to get to know you a little better."

"Our home is on the river, south of La Moille, Minnesota. I will write down the directions," said Walter as he scribbled them on a paper. The noise had stopped now that the children were outside.

Betty said to Walter as they left, "What a dreary place, so dark and overwhelming. It must be frightening for little ones to come here after they've lost their parents."

"Poor tykes. But it did sound like they were managing to have fun," said Walter.

A few evenings later they heard a knock on their door. Betty opened it. A tall, stern woman, holding a clipboard, stood in front of her. "I'm from the orphanage," the woman said.

Betty invited her in and asked her to have a seat. Walter put down the paper, stood up, and greeted her.

When they all sat down, the lady asked them again why they wanted to adopt a child. They answered as they had before. She followed up with more detailed questions about their ability to support a child, their goals for the child, and how they felt it would change their lives. Did they know raising a child could be challenging? After a tour of the house and grounds, the woman left, promising they would hear back soon.

Their answers must have been adequate because they got a call in a few days. A voice on the other end of the line said, "If you can stop by tomorrow evening, we would like you to meet a young man who seems ideal for your situation."

They smiled at each other and hugged happily. "How wonderful," said Betty. Walter couldn't stop beaming.

They approached the orphanage again and entered the door. They were shown to a cozier room with big, overstuffed chairs and a few toys here and there. They saw a serious looking young boy with big eyes sitting on the edge of a chair so his feet could touch the ground. A matronly looking woman was seated nearby. She said, "Mr. and Mrs. Christensen, I would like you to meet Curtis. He is 11 years old."

"Hello, Curtis," said Betty and Walter at the same time. They shook his small hand and sat down.

Curtis responded, "How do you do?" rather stiffly and looked at them with curiosity.

The lady excused herself, saying, "I will give you some time to get to know one another."

They talked for a bit about what games he liked, his favorite foods, and so on.

He asked, "Do you have any other children?"

"No," answered Betty. "But we do have a dog."

His eyes lit up. "A dog, I have always wanted a dog."

"What are your favorite toys?" asked Walter.

"I really like playing with cars." He pointed at some toy cars on the floor. "Like those. Do you have a car?"

Walter answered, "Yes, we do. It's not new but it gets us places."

Curtis seemed impressed. The lady came back into the room and said, "Curtis needs to join the other children for story time now."

"Would you like to see us again?" Betty asked.

"Yes, I think you seem very nice." As he approached the door, he turned to face them. His eyes were serious and his fists clenched. He took a deep breath and blurted out all at once, "I don't want to be adopted without my little sister. She's six and I promised my Ma that I would take care of her!" He dashed out into the hallway and the door closed.

"Well," said Walter, turning to Betty. "What do you think of that?"

Betty said, "I think we should meet his sister, too."

Before the year ended, the Christensen family increased by two. Curtis agreed to have his name changed to Walter Wilhelm Christensen Junior. His sister, Phyllis, liked her new name too, Gloria Babette. She thought it was glorious.

Walter Junior and Gloria made the adjustment to their new home quite easily and loved playing with the dog. They were very happy to have a home and their own parents. Walter enjoyed taking them to the furniture store where they could test all the toys to make sure they worked. Betty invited them to experiment with her piano.

Betty had lost several of her music students whose parents could not afford lessons. She felt bad that they would miss out on the opportunity to play music. One evening she said to Walter, "I wonder if offering group lessons more cheaply would let those students continue?"

"Why don't you try that? You can make up a new ad, and we'll put it in the paper," he said.

She followed Walter's suggestion and created a new ad for group lessons at a reduced fee. Her studio grew again.

Betty's students gave their usual recital upstairs at the Reese Furniture Store. Her saxophone quartet gained popularity and was invited to perform for many civic and social meetings.

One day she got a letter from the La Crosse Radio station. She had written to the station to tell them about several of her exceptional students. She said to Walter, "Some of my best students have been offered a chance to play live on a La Crosse radio station. I am so excited for them."

Walter said, "That's great. Now a lot more people will know what a wonderful teacher you are."

© Winona Republican Herald - December 30, 1933

1934

Orville started his regular winter band rehearsals with the usual parties. Tuesday evenings the Senior Band practiced. Part of their time was devoted to developing feature numbers with different instrument combinations.

On Wednesday evenings all of the younger bands rehearsed. Orville arranged for parties on the first Wednesday of each month when children would receive candy and play games. He told Erna, "So many of these youngsters have families that are really struggling in this depression. I want them to have something to look forward to." Sometimes he slipped a few extra pieces of candy in the pockets of children who had younger siblings.

Erna said to him, "You treat them so well. They're almost like your children. How nice for them."

Orville appreciated her remark.

Orville was happy and relieved when he was reappointed bandmaster without challenge. He said to Erna, "Maybe they recognize that my efforts in building the band program are important."

She smiled and said, "They have to realize what you've accomplished."

There was also money in the budget for new band uniforms. The city called for bids for new jackets and hats of maroon broadcloth with gold trim that wouldn't fade. However, when the bids came in, the council rejected all of them as too costly.

In January George said to Freda, "I don't think our wrestling promoter is doing a very good job. He sets up and is supposed to advertise our wrestling cards. Crowds are down. He just isn't promoting our matches enough. That's what he's supposed to be, a 'promoter.'"

"Do you think it might be time to stop trying to organize these events? Or are you wondering if you could do a better job?" asked Freda.

He answered, "I don't think I'm ready to be done with wrestling. I enjoy it too much. Setting up the schedules for matches and bringing talented wrestlers to Winona would be a lot of work. But the job needs someone with more initiative to plan and advertise the wrestling cards. We really haven't had much good wrestling here in Winona for a couple of years. Maybe I should think about it."

"I would hate to see the end of wrestling in Winona. You know how much I enjoy these events," said Freda. She grabbed his hand and squeezed it. "Do think about it. I know you could do a great job if you want to."

George's fellow wrestler and promoter, Pinkie, gave him the opportunity. Finding himself too busy with organizing meets in Iowa, Pinkie asked George to be his co-promoter in Winona.

When George told Freda about this opportunity, she smiled. "How wonderful. If you really want to do this, George, you should, if it wouldn't be too much with your business. I can hardly wait to see the next meet."

George decided to accept the offer and began actively setting up meets. He would usually be the referee, although he had discovered that could be dangerous. Sometimes he competed himself, if he knew the other wrestler obeyed the rules. The sportswriter of the *Winona Republican Herald* approved, saying that Pinkie made a good choice. "Graham is a reliable and honest young man and interested in the sport."

Freda loyally attended every event and cheered along with the crowd.

A description of a wrestling incident involving George appeared in the newspaper. Betty asked Freda about it. She said, "It was quite a night! The two wrestlers were Ed Meske and a guy they call 'bad, bold' Ed Schuler. George was the referee. Schuler got rough, slamming and kicking Meske and George stepped in. But Schuler just picked George up and tried to toss him out of the ring. Somehow, George got tangled in the ropes and hit his head just a few feet away from where I was sitting. I almost stopped breathing, I was so startled."

Betty gasped, saying, "That must have been frightening."

"I was more angry than frightened. I grabbed a hatpin out of my hat and lunged at Schuler. Luckily the cops came to grab him first, so I sat back down. I do think I would have stabbed him if they hadn't gotten there right away, though."

Betty shook her head and said, "I imagine you might have, Freda, but that sounds so scary. What happened next?"

"George was going to stop the match, but Shuler was already going after Meske. George told the lawmen to let them continue. Meske ended up pinning Schuler to win."

"Serves him right. What a brute," said Betty with feeling. "I'm relieved that neither of you were hurt. Is wrestling worth all this drama?"

Freda shrugged. "Well, the show lost money. There were only about 200 spectators. George told me that if there's no money to be made on these events, it's easy to see why they can't find promoters. But I still love watching. It's exciting."

A few weeks later, when Freda was out of town visiting friends, George had an unpleasant surprise when he came home to their apartment after an evening appointment. He told Freda the story when she returned the following day. "I sat down to read and heard a noise in the kitchen. I knew it couldn't be you, so I went to see what was happening. There was a stranger in there trying to go out the back door. I yelled at him, but he didn't turn around. I put my wrestling ability to use, and body slammed the fellow. I locked his wrist in a wrestling hold, dragged him to the front door and pulled him down the stairs. Halfway down, the guy tried to break loose, but I didn't lose my hold. We tumbled down the rest of the way to the grocery store below. The grocer called the police. They came and put him in jail for the night. I figured the guy was probably drunk and maybe learned his lesson, so I didn't press charges. But you see, my wrestling skill actually can come in handy."

Freda said, "Oh, George, you are so brave and strong. And I am glad you knew how to handle the situation. I'm also relieved he didn't have a weapon."

George was still very involved with the Winona Odd Fellows Lodge. That spring they were hosting a big anniversary celebration. In addition to being an officer, George was on the committee that planned the program and entertainment for the gathering of over 500. He asked Walter and Betty, "Would you be willing to arrange the entertainment for our celebration? We do have some money in our budget to pay you."

They were honored to be asked. Betty said, "I formed a saxophone quartet with three of my best students. I think we would all be happy to entertain your group."

I. O. O. F. Anniversary Celebration Committee

George A. Graham, left, William Sonnenberg, center, and James A. Millar, right, are members of the committee in charge of arrangements for the "cornerstone anniversary" of the Odd Fellows next Thursday. Graham is chairman of the committee while Sonnenberg is one of the members who was present 50 years ago for the cornerstone laying. He joined the organization April 23, 1883.

© *Winona Republican Herald* - April 21, 1934, p. 2

Walter said, "I could sing some songs and Betty could accompany me."

"Thank you. That sounds very nice. We'll plan on it," said George.

Walter and Betty prepared three songs, *Alone on the Range, One Little Thing at a Time*, and *Roll Out of Bed with a Smile*. They had had a great time choosing and rehearsing these selections.

When they performed, Freda was in the audience, half wishing she could join Walter in harmony.

The summer was very hot with many days reaching 100 degrees. Freda said to George, "I am so tired of trying to sleep in this stuffy apartment. Betty and Walter have their place by the river to get some relief from this heat. So do Orville and Erna. Do you think we could take a trip to Northern Minnesota and see some of the lake country? I'm sure it would be cooler there."

George replied, "I don't see why not." They both enjoyed camping, so they planned a ten-day trip to areas around Brainerd and Bemidji to enjoy cool breezes and lake activities. Their summer trips to the lake became a tradition.

Now that Betty and Walter were supporting their new family, they needed more income.

Betty worked very hard to increase her studio of twenty-some students. The group lessons were working well. Her ads were posted regularly in the newspaper. The list of students participating in her June recital included two special new names, Gloria and Walter Christensen Jr.

The piano accordion was becoming very popular. It had a piano style keyboard on its right side and chord buttons on the left. Betty taught herself to play it and put it in her studio ads as one of the instruments she could teach. More students signed up for lessons.

She was asked to play piano for PTA meetings, a Campfire Girl benefit, and other events. Her promising students performed again on the La Crosse radio station, WKBH. She was thrilled to learn that WKBH, operating remotely, would open a studio in Winona at the Hotel Winona. The broadcasts would begin in November running from 6:30 to 10:00 p.m. on Fridays and include local news and entertainment. The new studio was sponsored by 48 local merchants, among them Reese Furniture. They were all excited to have another way to advertise.

Music Instruction
(Class or Private)
- **Piano**
- **Saxophone**
- **Clarinet**
- **Piano-Accordion**

Babette Christensen
—STUDIO—
Dial 2992
(Reese Furniture Bldg.)

© *Winona Republican Herald -
December 22, 1934*

Betty said to Walter, "Having my students perform in town will be so much easier than making the thirty mile drive to the La Crosse studio. I hope we can arrange to do that."

Walter agreed. "It may be an opportunity for us to perform, too, if they find they need local entertainment."

Walter was encouraged that Reese Furniture was doing better. Along with the extended hours and many classified ads, he placed about two fairly large, illustrated display ads per month. They featured detailed drawings and price listings of floor coverings, furniture suites, porch swings, bedding, and more. He became hopeful that their business would survive this depression.

For the summer series, Orville still planned to take requests from a box on the bandshell steps. But sometimes the band was not prepared to play a request they found there. Orville said to the band, "We need to figure out a different way to handle these special requests. It's embarrassing when we're not ready or don't have the music in our folders. And we can't carry around our whole library."

Stanley Streuber spoke up, "Why not ask people to call with their requests a few days before the concert? Then we could distribute the parts and practice them."

The band members agreed.

Orville said, "That sounds like a good plan. I'll announce it prior to the coming season."

In the announcement for the first summer concert program that year, Orville said, "I request that everyone listen attentively and not start or move cars during the concert. If you have a special number, you would like us to play, instead of placing the name in the box on the bandshell steps, please send it to us earlier in the week so the band has time to prepare it."

Along with the usual spring events, the band was hired by a group of local merchants to play a series of 'Novelty Concerts.' These concerts would be held at the bandshell on Tuesday evenings. The usual summer series of Wednesday evening concerts would be moved to Friday. The Senior band was very busy that summer.

Throughout the summer, the band continued to receive positive reviews, which Orville proudly read to Erna. Her usual reply was, "That's wonderful, Orville. Your band does so much for Winona"

Walter sang at many of the concerts and led audience sing-alongs with the band. One concert on June 21 was particularly memorable for him. The band had been swatting at a big swarm of bugs during the performance. When Walter got up to sing his songs they were still buzzing around. He sang two songs and managed to get through several verses of his encore when one bug dove into his open mouth and lodged in his throat. He was forced to stop singing and cough the creature out. The band carried on.

Wally, Gloria, and Babette were in the audience as usual. Gloria turned to Betty and asked in a worried voice, "Is Father choking?"

Betty told her, "I think he just had a bug fly in his mouth, but he coughed it out."

"Too bad for the bug." said Wally. They all chuckled at the idea of a bug landing in Walter's open mouth.

After the concert, Betty said to Walter, "I'm sorry you had to stop singing. Everyone was enjoying it so much. I'm glad you didn't swallow that bug."

"Me too. But it left quite an impression in my mouth. It wasn't very tasty." he replied with a sour look.

His expression amused them all.

Orville was excited when he heard that President Franklin D. Roosevelt would be coming to town by boat. He was even more excited when the Winona Municipal Band was asked to be at the levee to greet him. A parade would follow.

The band won $300 at the La Crosse Harvest Festival contest, so that was another feather in Orville's hat. The mayor of La Crosse made a special effort to congratulate the band and invite them for the following year's event.

The next day Orville read the newspaper editorials and excitedly said to Erna "Listen to what the editor wrote about us; 'The Winona Municipal Band has given a tuneful declaration that Winona is a good community.'" He told Erna, "They are a wonderful bunch of musicians and always make me proud."

1935

I n the 1930's, local radio advertising was still in its infancy. At the beginning of 1935, Walter decided to see how it could help their business. He said to Orville, "WKBH radio is broadcasting shows from Winona. If we advertise on their station, we may attract customers from La Crosse and surrounding areas. I think it would be good for Reese Furniture to sponsor some regular shows."

Orville agreed. "It can't hurt. Everyone seems to be captivated by these radio shows."

When he got home, Walter asked Betty, "What would you think of coming up with a half hour of music for a Reese Furniture ad?"

Betty asked, "With you singing and me accompanying?"

"Exactly," said Walter. "We know so many songs we could fill up a lot of time. We could talk a little about Reese Furniture's specials in between numbers."

She thought it would be a good idea. They dreamed up the name "The Babette and Christy Show." Reese Furniture reserved spots from January through April. They presented their live show on Thursday evenings from 8 to 8:30.

Reese Furniture did see an increase in sales, but Orville decided it was not worth the cost of sponsoring the shows. He asked Walter to put more of their budget into newspaper ads for the rest of the year.

George told Freda "I can't wait to try out our new ski jump scaffold in West Burns Valley."

She replied, "That's exciting." Then she frowned. "Won't Carl Laumb's recent death cause a decline in ski jumping now?"

"I don't think so," George said. "We feel awful about Carl, of course. Did I tell you we are holding a benefit meet for his widow?"

Freda answered, "Yes, and that's very generous of you. I'm sure she will appreciate that."

George and another skier tried out the new Winona jump at the end of January and announced, "This is a great improvement. We'll practice on it this week so it should be in great shape for the upcoming meet."

The Sugar Loaf Ski Club sponsored a big tourney on February 14. With 35 skiers signed up, a crowd of over 2,000 spectators enjoyed the event.

As the ski season wound down George got busy with boxing matches he had organized as part of his franchise. Unfortunately, spectators did not materialize in the numbers he anticipated. The franchise "fee" from the state was $150 per year and franchise owners had to pay the athletes and other costs. They only took in $152 from their biggest match. Since they were losing money, George and Pinkie announced the Winona Boxing Club was done.

The Municipal Band was still working with the City Council on its new uniforms. They asked two of the bidders to send samples. Council members looked at the uniforms in their boxes. One of them said, "How can we tell how these will look when players wear them?"

They asked city engineer E. E. Chadwick to model them. Orville helped him don the Sam Browne style belt and sparkling gold braid over the maroon jacket. Chadwick marched dramatically back and forth wearing each of the two samples, while one of the council members whistled Yankee Doodle. Another council member remarked that Mr. Chadwick maybe should look into a modeling career. That drew laughter from everyone. The council chose one of the vendors and placed their order. The new uniforms would arrive before the summer.

The Municipal Band members looked impressive in their brand-new uniforms when the summer series concerts began. The first few programs included an opportunity for the younger bands to perform. For the rest of the season, Orville planned a variety of playing and singing, and often included special requests that had been phoned in.

The big opportunity for the Winona Municipal Bands was yet to come that year. Both the Senior Band and the Junior Band were invited to participate in the Minnesota State Fair band competition. Orville urged them to practice very hard so that they would clearly be the best band.

A large contingent of Winonans accompanied the band to the Twin Cities to cheer them on. The band performed with precision in marching

1935 Winona Municipal Band
photo courtesy of Winona County Historical Society

and playing. Everyone knew they were the best band there because of the cheers, whistles, and applause they received.

But the judges ranked the Winona band in 2nd place after the Little Falls City Band. Many people grumbled and booed when the decision was announced.

There was a strong consensus that a particular feature of the Little Falls Band's routine played an unfair part in the prize decision. That was the dazzling performance of its drum major, an attractive young lady wearing shorts, who tossed her baton and led her band in intricate maneuvers. It was apparent that Orville was unhappy with the outcome, but he found some consolation that the Junior Band won first place in its division.

Walter was not much of a joiner. George had invited him to join the Odd Fellows. He had declined because he was too busy with the store and his musical engagements. But when it was announced that a Lions Club was being organized in Winona, he began to think that it would be a good idea to socialize with other like-minded Winonans.

He said to Betty, "I have always admired the work the Lions Clubs do. I agree with their purpose, and they sponsor many good projects. It might even be better for the store too if I participate."

"Why don't you join then? You know many of the men who are organizing it. Let them know you're interested," Betty said.

Walter did join and was promptly elected 'Lion Tamer.' He came home to tell his family. "I think being 'Lion Tamer' suits my abilities."

"Do you get to crack a whip, Papa?" asked Gloria.

"That's what the lion tamers do that I've seen in movies." Wally made a whip cracking motion with a piece of string.

Walter shook his head. "Not exactly. But I am in charge of the property and equipment of the club. I suppose I have to order some people around to take care of things."

Betty raised her eyebrows, teasing him. "Oh yes, you are such a commanding type!" Then she said, "Seriously, you really are a good organizer if you're not distracted!"

Walter had a reputation for being slightly absent minded. He often misplaced items, especially his keys. One time he had to place an ad in the newspaper to locate them.

1936

Walter noticed that Orville was taking less interest in the business affairs of Reese Furniture. He mentioned this to Betty, who said, "The band has always been his primary passion, so I guess I'm not too surprised."

The store carried on with Walter managing most of the buying and sales. He advertised the usual items frequently and made offers to purchase used furniture for their bargain basement.

Erna was concerned about Orville. He had put on weight and was having headaches that interfered with his sleep. He spent most of his time tending to Municipal Band matters. She asked him, "Are you putting much effort into the furniture store?"

He responded, "No, Walter seems to be handling that just fine. I do worry about the band program. The Junior Band is so important, and we must find a way to secure support for it from the city. We have an excellent Senior Band and that's because of the training program I have developed. That's how most of our Senior Band members learned to play."

"It seems to me the band is your priority. You have given it so much of yourself for so many years.. Have you ever thought about selling your interest in the store to Walter? It seems that would allow you more time with the bands," Erna said.

Orville thought a moment and answered, "I might consider that. I don't have as much interest in choosing the latest living room and dining room suites to sell anymore. I will talk this over with Walter. I would like to keep a part interest in the store. Maybe I could take over the musical instrument sales."

Orville proposed the change to Walter saying, "You know my work with the Municipal Band is my first priority. I have enjoyed the furniture business, and it has provided a stable source of income for all of us. But I just don't have the energy I used to. Erna suggested that I let you buy out my share of the business. I would like to continue working here in some capacity and keep a smaller share."

Walter wasn't too surprised but answered, "I will talk it over with Betty. I think I would do a good job with the store, and we have great employees to help us."

Walter told Betty what Orville had proposed.

She asked, "Walter, are you sure you want to take on total responsibility for the furniture store? We have to think of our children too."

"Well, you know I have been running the store by myself for a few years already. I don't think much would change. Your brother Fred has worked for Reese Furniture for many years. He knows the business well, and I think I can count on his help." Herbert had joined them a few years before when he lost his job in Chicago, but returned after he was offered another position in the windy city. "Freda does a great job with our credit department, and Erna knows our bookkeeping system inside and out. I hope they will stay with us if we reorganize."

"Well then I say, why not?" Betty concluded.

The Municipal Bands were as busy as ever, playing for openings, dedications, parades, and other important ceremonies. The first summer concert announcement gave a list of the players' names. Walter had moved to the drum section. It included another plea from Orville for quiet in the audience.

"This summer," Orville told his band members, "I am going to have posters placed on the benches to remind people to stop talking when we play. It honestly seems like some people come to our concerts just to gossip with others. And those parents who let their children run around screaming and yelling. It is so annoying."

The players nodded in agreement, some of them hoping their own families weren't part of the problem.

Walter said, "It's very disrespectful to those who want to listen, but some probably do come just to socialize."

Stanley added, "The car noise is also bothersome."

"I have asked to have police present again to stop people from moving their cars around. I hope that takes care of the problem," said Orville.

Playgrounds to Sponsor Lantern Parade, Amateur Contest, Playlets

A total of 4,283 boys and girls attended Winona's five playgrounds last week, Irwin Gerecke, supervisor of playgrounds, announced today. This is an average attendance of more than 700 each day.

Six coming events to be put on under the direction of the playground 'department were announced by Mr. Gerecke.

On Wednesday, July 15, there will be a lantern parade at Lake park in connection with the weekly band concert by the Winona Municipal band. On July 22 the department will sponsor an amateur contest open to both adults and children. This also will be in connection with a concert.

Three one-act plays are scheduled for Friday, July 31. A checker tournament is slated for August 8 and a playground circus for August 12. The circus is another event which will take place in conjunction with a concert by the band.

The boys' kittenball tournament will be held Monday, August 17, and the girls' tournament Tuesday, August 18, Mr. Gerecke said.

Programs included marches, solos, novelty numbers, classical music favorites, and popular tunes. The lantern parade and an amateur night featuring aspiring young performers were sponsored by the Playground Association and drew huge crowds.

Toward the end of summer, the band once more played at many local county fairs. Their appearance at the Interstate Fair in La Crosse provided a bit of drama. A trapeze artist fell from quite a height and was injured. The audience milled about in turmoil worrying about the wounded performer and wondering whether the show would continue. The ringmaster asked the band to play and that helped to restore order. People became quiet and sat down so the medical people could tend to the acrobat.

In August Orville expressed his concern about support for his Junior Band Program in an appeal to the City Council. He told them, "Maintenance of a Junior Band is essential to proper development of a Senior Band. I ask that the city take over the cost of their training. At the moment, parents of the players are paying 25¢ per week, but the fee keeps some children from joining. There would be no increase in the band's funding because the unpaid Junior Band could be substituted for some paid appearances of the Senior Band." He emphasized that 85% of the present Senior Band members began as Junior Band members. His proposal was taken under consideration.

Orville and Walter had spent the summer making plans for the big change of ownership. On August 30, a two-page ad appeared in the newspaper announcing the close out of all Reese Furniture stock. They needed to liquidate all current merchandise so Orville could be paid fairly. Then Walter would re-open as United Furniture with all new merchandise.

They hired a merchandise expert from Ottumwa, Iowa, to oversee the clearance sales and a final auction.

Sunday, September 6, the Winona Municipal Band competed for a second year in the Minnesota State Fair. Orville was having a little difficulty with his balance and turned over the band's marching and drilling to experienced band member Dayton Merriman. At the fair, the band's exhibit of these skills was impressive. The audience applauded and cheered loudly.

Orville took over and directed an excellent concert at the Grandstand which also was enthusiastically received. Despite their snappy appearance and uniforms which were described as the most elaborate of all participating bands, they were only awarded third prize.

Orville was angry and discouraged. He said to everyone within earshot, "The Winona Municipal Band looked great and played their best. I don't understand this decision. This band is the best one I have ever directed." On the drive back to Winona, he was silent, mulling over this affront to his band.

Within a few days, someone sent him an editorial that had been printed in a St. Paul newspaper. The writer was outraged at the 3rd place prize that had been awarded to the Winona Municipal Band.

"Listen to this, Erna." He began reading in a loud voice. "'It would seem that the points to be awarded on uniforms were really awarded on lack of uniforms.'" Orville harumphed. "'This writer thinks there should be women judges who would not make their decisions based on 'good looking females strutting their stuff.' That's an excellent point." The editorialist concluded that the judges had ignored the loud applause that followed Winona's performance and the boos that were heard when their third-place prize was announced.

"I didn't think it was fair," Orville snorted. "It helps to know I'm not alone."

Erna said, "I know. I was there. You should have won. The band's performance was outstanding."

"We won't compete at the State Fair again as long as I'm in charge!" he declared.

The Reese Furniture store was closed at the beginning of October for renovation. On October 15 the Notice of Incorporation for United Furniture appeared in the newspaper. The incorporators were Babette, Freda, and Walter as president. Orville Reese retained an interest in the store and handled musical instrument sales. Walter announced, "The new store will occupy only the west portion of the property. We will lease out the east building."

United Furniture, Winona's Beautiful New Furniture Store, held its grand opening on October 27, 1936. The opening was advertised in distinctive art deco script, with a detailed description of the completely remodeled and redecorated space done in modern style. Gorgeous art deco windows with frosted glass were installed along the south side to catch the afternoon sun. The ad listed the brands of new furniture the store had stocked and promised to provide the people of Winona with quality, reliable merchandise, courteous service, and free delivery. In smaller print the ad contained the words, "successors to Reese Furniture Co."

Between the opening and Christmas that year, Walter placed display ads in the paper for furniture suites, toys, musical instruments, and other specials. Business picked up.

Announcing

The Opening of Winona's Beautiful New Furniture Store

UNITED FURNITURE, Inc.

Successors to Reese Furniture Co.

173 East Third Street   Winona, Minnesota

on

TUESDAY

October 27

WE take a pardonable pride in inviting you to UNITED FURNITURE, Inc. . . . . For here you will find a completely redecorated store, modern in every design.

Each unit of furniture in our stock is new — recently selected from the showrooms of such outstanding nationally known manufacturers of quality furniture as: Levin Bros. (living room suites), King Koil (mattresses), Mersman (tables), and Doernhegher (bedroom suites). Also featured are Gold Seal Congoleums, Floorplan Rugs and Carpets, and C. G. Conn Band Instruments.

To the People of Winona and Vicinity
———— WE PROMISE ————

Distinctive, Reliable Merchandise	• Known Qualities
Unusual Values	• Personal, Courteous Service
Plainly Marked Prices	• Free Delivery

© *Winona Republican Herald* - July 2, 1936

1937

During the previous summer, Freda had complained, "It's so stuffy and hot in this apartment. I love our camping trips, but it's miserable when we come home to this." She gestured around her. "I would love to have more windows and space and maybe a garage so we wouldn't have to park outside in the winter. And a yard would be nice for our dog."

George concurred. "I think we are finally in a financial position to purchase our own house."

George's insurance business was going well, and Freda continued to manage the credit accounts at Reese's. George did some ski jumping, but conditions were unfavorable again that winter. His and others' interest in the sport tapered off. He was also done with wrestling promotion, since the club had not made any money.

They started looking at houses for sale and found a place they liked at 804 West Mark Street. The offer they made was accepted and they become homeowners. There was a yard and a garage. They moved out of the crowded apartment on 3rd Street. George had a fence put up around the yard so their dog could be outside.

The previous year, the city had established a licensing program for dogs. The Grahams made sure their dog got a license – the second one issued by the city. Unfortunately, people who were not responsible let their pets roam free and there were many abandoned canines. This bothered Freda, since so many animals were neglected and ended up injured or dead. Some were shot or poisoned, as Betty had written about a few years earlier. The licensing program was an attempt to address this problem, but still many people did not bother to register their pets.

Freda felt there was a need to educate people about caring for their dogs. In February she gathered a meeting of about 50 like-minded people to form a Dog Lovers' Club. It was open to all dog lovers, and Freda was elected president. The group discussed various goals like protecting dogs from poisoners, dealing with stray dogs, and holding dog shows. About 60 members met later in March to adopt bylaws and appoint standing committees. Walter Christensen was named head of the Humane Service Committee. The Club made plans for a June picnic.

Walter and Betty traded their La Moille home for the home of their friends, the Kisslings, at 358 West Sanborn Street in Winona. Walter felt he should be closer to the business he now ran, and it would be easier for Gloria and Wally to attend school. They were all sad to leave their beautiful home on the river.

Betty continued accompanying many musical events and programs, featuring her students whenever possible. There were now enough accordion players taking lessons in her studio that she was able to organize an accordion band. As they became popular, they received requests to perform for events.

Fred Heyer Jr. had become known around town for playing drums with his own and various other dance bands. He decided he needed more flexibility in his schedule. Early in the year he announced to Walter, "I think it is time for me to branch out on my own. I plan to resign from the furniture store and open a wallpaper and paint store. My jazz band is getting really busy too."

"So, you want to march to the beat of your own drum, huh?" Walter said with a little smile. "Seriously, I'm sorry to lose the benefit of all your experience here, but I know it's important to take an opportunity when it presents itself."

Fred chuckled and said, "Your sense of humor is one thing I know I will miss."

Walter went on, "We're doing moderately well here at the store, but I understand we can't afford to pay you what your experience is worth. I wish you success."

Rumors of the establishment of Winona's own radio station were confirmed in March, when the newspaper announced that the new stations call letters would be KWNO, K for stations west of the Mississippi and WNO for Winona. There were many details yet to be worked out, but it was going to be a reality.

Betty and Walter were excited. She said to him, "Do you think we should talk to them about a slot for the Babette and Christy show?"

"I don't see why not," answered Walter. "We both enjoy performing, and we still know the same songs plus lots of new ones."

"It shouldn't be too much trouble to plan. After all, we've had enough experience," said Betty.

"I should say so," he answered, smiling at her.

The City Council approved Orville's request to subsidize instruction for the members of the younger bands at $25 per month. The band organizations again played for the usual events in the spring.

In June, a Goodwill Tour from Winona businesses was organized to visit surrounding towns. A 23-car caravan of merchants with a small volunteer group from the Municipal Band made stops in Rushford, Peterson, Lanesboro, Preston, Harmony, and Mabel. They handed out balloons and other novelties while the volunteer band paraded in the streets. The last stop was Spring Grove, where they were celebrating the town's 40th anniversary. There they were joined by the full Municipal Band, and together they presented a concert under O. W. Reese's direction.

The summer concert series at the bandshell was exceptionally well attended. Orville read to Erna from one review, "The Senior Band is to be complimented for having a better balance between the woodwind and brass sections." The amateur nights that the Playground Association organized and presented at the summer concerts were so popular that there were three of them.

In early September, the City Council discovered that the band fund was overdrawn. Orville was relieved that this did not cause as much consternation as it had in earlier years. The Council simply made a motion to raise the tax levy to ½ mill, the maximum amount allowed by the voters in the ordinance passed in 1931. The city had only been using part of the amount. The motion needed to be approved at the October meeting so the funds would not be available immediately. But the problem could be resolved.

Mid-September, the Association of Commerce and other civic groups announced there would be a Pancake Days Festival in early October. The planners said, "This is an event to build good will for Winona. There will be free pancakes, a pancake eating contest, rides, entertainment and dancing for people."

The organizers approached the City Council to ask if the Winona Municipal Band could perform during the new Pancake Days Festival. There was no money to pay them, but the council said they would look into it, since it seemed like a great idea for promoting Winona. They consulted with Orville and the band members who agreed to donate their services.

1938

KWNO began its public broadcasting by February of 1938. The Babette and Christy Show was included in the lineup of shows on Thursdays from 10:15 to 10:30 p.m. Betty's accordion band became very popular and was invited to perform for many events. They auditioned for KWNO's talent roundup and secured a time to perform on the air in April.

By April of 1938, George Graham had decided there wasn't much future in ski jumping or wrestling. He joined the Winona Sportsman's Club and honed his skills in trapshooting. He participated in many contests and markedly improved his scores. It became his new passion.

United Furniture placed multiple classified ads in the paper. These ads could be run more frequently and didn't cost as much. Walter said, "From what I see, we get the same results from classified ads as we do from the expensive display ads." About twice a month he ran larger ads.

He said to Betty one day, "I have an idea that might bring more people to the store."

Used to Walter's quirky humor, she asked, "Now what on earth do you have in mind?"

"What if I bought an aquarium to put in the window?" he said.

She answered, "And just why would people come to see an aquarium? Are you planning to stock it with fish? They need a lot of care, you know."

Walter said, "Not the fish I plan to put in there. They will be invisible. And from France."

"Oh, Walter, you can't be serious!" Betty exclaimed.

He smiled with a mischievous twinkle in his eye and said, "Yes, I am serious. I'll put a sign by the aquarium that says, 'Come in and see the invisible fish from France'. I bet a lot of people will fall for it and venture in to see what it's about."

He was right. The invisible fish attracted lots of people to United Furniture. Some of them even stayed to shop.

By June, Walter had had enough of the weekly radio spots. He said to Betty, "I think I am running out of ideas for our radio show."

She asked, "What makes you say that?"

"Well, the summer band series is starting soon, and I know Orville will want me to sing and lead community sing-alongs again. That is a lot of work, and I don't want the store or my family to suffer from my neglect," he said. "Besides, I get the idea that they want us to find someone to sponsor the show and I don't think United Furniture has enough money to do that."

She replied, "Let's ask the manager if we can take a vacation for a while. If you are still feeling like it's too much, I could fill in some of them." Betty did play for a few more of the 15-minute time slots, but it wasn't as much fun without Walter.

Orville began the summer concerts by the lake on June 22 with a serious concert dedicated to the late F. S. Bell, donor of the bandshell structure. After the band performed *America*, a speaker read a dedication noting that F. S. Bell himself never sought to be lauded for his beautiful gift to the city of Winona that placed Winona among the few communities that had a truly first rate bandshell. The speaker urged people to remember and emulate Bell's deep interest and commitment to Winona and its citizens.

A variety of weekly concerts followed with the usual features, novelties, and solos. Youth amateur concerts and Walter's sing-alongs were popular.

When the newly formed United Furniture leased out the west part of their building, there had been only one entrance in the center of the front. That became a problem when new occupants moved in. Walter told Betty, "United Furniture needs a separate entrance. Now that we have people leasing that space, they need their own door. Otherwise, our merchandise is not secure and their valuables aren't either."

She said, "That makes sense, but can we afford it?"

"I don't think we can afford not to," he answered. He arranged for the alteration.

Babette's accordion band was in constant demand and played for PTA events, Kiwanis and Lions Club gatherings, and on the radio. The electric organ now was becoming very popular, so Betty added organ lessons to her instruction offerings.

By the end of July, Orville was again fed up with all the audience noise and wrote an unsigned, sharply worded letter to concert attendees, imploring them to be quiet and not interfere with people who came to listen to the music. He showed the letter to Erna saying, "It probably won't make any difference, but I find myself so distracted by the talking."

Quiet Please!

The size of the crowd which gathers each Wednesday evening at the Lake park band shell to hear the programs presented by the Winona Municipal band shows the appreciation with which these concerts are received by the public.

Too frequently, however, are listeners given reason to complain of noise in and near the crowd while the band is playing, interfering with the pleasure of those who come to enjoy an evening of good music in the natural outdoor beauty of the park.

Loud talking and other noise while the program is under way is bothersome to all within earshot. Whether wilful or the result of thoughtlessness, it has no place at these concerts, which as a regular summer institution bring so much pleasure to the public audiences.

© *Winona Republican Herald* - July 22, 1938, p. 6

Erna tried to calm him by saying, "I think you notice it more than most people do. I wish you wouldn't upset yourself so." Her words had little effect.

Pancake Days had been a hit the prior year and was organized again for the end of September. The Winona Municipal Band played again, and there was a contest among the visiting bands, with Orville judging.

In September Walter placed a classified ad in the paper to locate the owner of a bike left on his property. But that was part of a bigger story. A few days earlier, he came home, drove his car into the garage, and carried some groceries into the house. Betty had lunch ready for him and they began talking. They sat down to eat and were surprised to hear the unmistakable sound of their car's malfunctioning muffler.

Betty said with alarm, "Your car is running!" They looked out the window to see the car being backed down the driveway by someone unknown.

"Oh no!" Walter blurted. "I left the keys in the ignition." He leapt up, ran out the door and caught up with the departing vehicle. He yelled through the window, "Where the hell are you going in my car?"

The driver ignored him and continued out of the drive and into the street, where he shifted gears and roared off.

Stunned, Walter went inside and called the police, then walked out to the garage to see if anything else was missing. There he found a bicycle neatly parked beside Wally and Gloria's bikes. He assumed that the bike, too, had been stolen, and placed the ad to try to find its rightful owner. The police soon located the vehicle, with two damaged tires and no keys. Walter learned to take his keys with him when he went inside the house.

1939

On January 8, Walter hung his U. S. flag out in front of United Furniture. Businesses up and down 3rd Street took note and soon every building had a U. S. flag flying. But nobody knew what holiday they were celebrating.

Finally, one of his merchant friends came into the furniture store and asked, "What is the occasion we are celebrating with our flags, Walter?"

Walter responded with the smile many of them knew and answered, "It's my birthday!"

A week later, Freda asked Walter and Betty, "Would you be interested in doing a radio show educating people about providing proper care for dogs? There is such a need for that, and you have experience with radio. After all," she said, looking at Walter, "you are already a member of the Dog Lovers' Club."

"Well, you know, Freda, KWNO doesn't let people do these shows for free anymore. We would need to have a sponsor," said Betty.

Freda said, "Could United Furniture be the sponsor? I have looked at our financial reports and we seem to be doing well enough."

Walter looked pensive. "I suppose we could. It is so easy for advertising to eat up our profits. But this is a good cause. It should qualify as a business expense."

"That would be wonderful, Walter. Let me know what you find out."

In February KWNO announced a new live show airing Tuesdays and Thursdays at 7:45 a.m. called *Something About Dogs*. Walter remembered Betty saying those words before she wrote her letter to the editor years before. It seemed appropriate. Sponsored by United Furniture, Betty and Walter told stories about dogs and gave helpful ideas for their care. They offered a service where people could call in news of lost or found dogs. They played some music, too.

United Furniture advertised a unique gimmick. The Great Kirma, a reputed mystic and stage star, would hypnotize a young woman in the store window, where she would remain for 24 hours. Then she would be taken to the Winona Theater for awakening. Known for his psychic powers, he would also appear on KWNO and answer questions sent in.

Walter told Babette, "I'll agree to host this show

because we have large windows, and it might attract some shoppers."

Babette raised her eyebrows. "It sounds like hocus pocus to me."

Walter grinned. "Of course it is, but it gets people's attention."

Orville invited the City Council to the Senior Band's annual lunch and cards meeting. It had always been a social event, and he wanted the council to see firsthand the camaraderie that existed among the players. Several council members attended and learned how the band operated as a unit.

The summer bandshell series featured many of the same themes as other years, including marches, serious pieces, novelties, solos, and sing-alongs. New this summer was a loudspeaker system the city had purchased. Names of pieces could now be announced so all could hear. An earlier attempt had been made to announce each number using placards walked across the stage by winsome young ladies. This had been abandoned when more attention was paid to the young ladies than their placards. One of the summer concerts featured baton twirlers spinning battery-lit batons. It was said to be the first performance of its kind in the area.

The Municipal Band played for many fairs and events through the fall, as usual. But one event was very special. It was the dedication of the new City Hall on December 12, 1939. Built with aid from the WPA at a cost of $224,000, it was "modern in every detail" and would serve Winona for many years to come. The Band played and the public was invited to tour the building. The building included space for the Municipal Band to practice and store their instruments. Orville Reese said, "The Winona Municipal Band is proud to play for the opening of its new home."

Radio show with Walter and Babette
from the private collection of Sue Thurman

1940

The Municipal Bands had their usual January gatherings. This year the party for the young bands was held in the community rooms of the new City Hall. Candy and popcorn were distributed to all. The Senior Band again invited City Council members to their gathering. Several members and the mayor attended, all making favorable remarks about the band's many appearances and excellent presentations under the direction of Orville Reese.

Babette and Christy continued presenting their *Something About Dogs* show on KWNO radio. It seemed to have a positive impact on the public's attitude, and complaints about stray animals decreased. Freda no longer felt her Dog Lovers' Club was necessary and dissolved it.

George participated in a couple of ski jumping meets, but the snow and weather were not cooperative. He joined a curling group to give that a try, but when warmer days arrived, he busied himself with the Winona Sportsmen's Club and was voted vice president. He enjoyed participating in their many trapshooting events.

United Furniture advertised more frequently as sales and profits were increasing once again. Walter was relieved. Betty had her many students perform as often as she could arrange it. Her accordion band played for events, and her electric organ students performed on KWNO. Six of her piano students, including her daughter, Gloria, went with her to Minneapolis to be judged in a competition sponsored by the National Guild of Piano Teachers. All students received high marks.

Orville was reappointed bandmaster as he expected. He no longer was worried about challengers and felt secure in the job. But he kept the bands on a busy schedule playing for events like the new ice frolic show, the annual Spring Opening display of store merchandise, and the Memorial Day Ceremony. He spent his usual hours planning and preparing the music and features for the summer bandshell series. There was a proposal to broadcast the band concerts over the new radio station. In addition to the regular series, the band was requested to play for the State Police Convention to be held in Winona in June.

Written reviews had been positive for the June and July concerts. Orville continued reading each one aloud to Erna. She nodded and smiled as she listened. But there was one phrase in the June 27 review that elicited quite a reaction from him. "What on earth does this mean? 'The fortissimos in the basses were ponderously pleasant?' He looked over the paper at Erna and explained, "Things that are ponderous are not usually pleasant!"

Erna said, "Don't you think they were trying to be complimentary? It is an odd way to put it."

"Ponderously pleasant!" Orville fumed, crumpling the paper onto his lap. "Whoever heard of such a thing! What do they think we are? A bunch of elephants? My bass section is not ponderous."

"Comments like that one bother you so much. Maybe that's what gives you the headaches you've been having," Erna warned.

Orville made an attempt to straighten out the paper and finally slapped it on the table. "I can't help reacting to people who don't seem to know what they're talking about."

Erna set it aside and gently massaged his neck. "Pay them no mind, Orville."

Orville closed his eyes and didn't answer.

The band concert on July 17 received a very favorable review. Orville didn't take Erna's advice and read each word. "A highly enjoyable program, considered by a large portion of the large audience as the best this season . . . " He stopped to look at Erna, repeating, "'the BEST this Season.' Now, that's what I like to hear."

Erna smiled. "It was a great concert, Orville."

On Friday, July 19, Orville drove to the furniture store about noon to check on some musical instruments he had ordered. The instrument counter was upstairs along the west wall. Instruments were displayed in a glass case, and some hung on the wall. He went behind the counter to unpack a new saxophone and look it over.

Walter was in the first-floor sales area. Freda was in her office. Erna was at her desk on the balcony, and Betty was in her studio when they all heard an unusually loud thump.

"What happened?" Erna cried as she raced toward the sound.

Walter sprinted up the stairs and Betty and Freda hurried from their rooms.

They found Orville behind the music case, slumped heavily in a chair. He was conscious.

Erna asked anxiously, "Orville, are you all right?"

Shaken, he answered, "I think so."

"What happened?" asked Walter.

"I don't remember," he mumbled. "I was standing here looking at that new saxophone and all of a sudden, I was sitting in this chair. I'm glad it was behind me, or I think I would have landed on the floor."

Erna said, "Oh dear, you don't look well."

"I will be fine. It was just a dizzy spell," Orville said with some effort.

"You need to go to the hospital," Walter said, taking charge.

Orville tried to stand up, but his legs wouldn't support him. "I don't know what's wrong," he said weakly. "I'm sure I'll be fine . . . " he trailed off.

They helped him out of the chair, down the alley-side stairs and into Walter's car, assisting him into the back seat where Erna got in beside him, comforting him. Betty climbed into the passenger seat and sat clenching her fists. Walter covered the short distance to the General Hospital on Wabasha Street as quickly as he dared. Freda called Freddy who was at his new wallpaper store and then left to pick up George. The cashier locked the door and closed the store.

Betty experienced many feelings at once, worry for Orville, some regret for their long-lost relationship, true gratefulness for Walter's cool-headed response, and a tiny bit of jealousy that Orville had turned to Erna for comfort. She was relieved when they arrived at the hospital and Orville was still telling everyone that he would be fine.

Orville was wheeled to a room where a physician came to examine him. Fred Jr., Freda, and George arrived immediately. Some of Orville's closest friends and band members were notified and got there as soon as they could.

The doctor finally said, "I think Mr. Reese suffered a cerebral hemorrhage."

"What does that mean?" Erna asked. "Will he recover?"

"The fact that he is still conscious and talking is a good sign. It's hard to tell with these problems. He will need to take it very easy for a while."

After the doctor delivered that message mid-afternoon, almost everyone went home, feeling positive about Orville's recovery. Freda offered to stop at Walter and Betty's to talk to Gloria and Wally and assure them that Uncle Orville should be fine.

Erna, Walter, and Betty stayed with Orville. He wasn't hungry so he declined the evening meal and dozed in his bed. The three were talking quietly when, around 6:30, Erna glanced over at Orville.

"Oh no!" she cried and rushed over to Orville's bedside. He had stopped breathing. Sobbing, she hugged his still form. "No, no, no!"

Betty went to the bed, touched Orville's face, put her arm around Erna and started crying. Walter, stood close, wiping his eyes.

Erna showed remarkable strength as she made the funeral arrangements. She contacted the Breitlow Funeral Home to arrange for care of Orville's body and set a time for a service. In Orville's desk drawer, she found a carefully folded paper in an envelope on which was printed "Open in the event of my death." Here was written a history of his life, from birth through military service in musical units, a list of

Bandmaster Dies

O. W. Reese, Winona bandmaster and an influence in the development of band music in a wide area, died Friday at Winona General hospital.

© Winona Republican Herald - July 20, 1940, p. 3

bands and musical groups he directed in Indiana, Winona, southeastern Minnesota, and western Wisconsin. He noted that he, Babette Reese, and Freda Christensen had performed in vaudeville for a time. Erna was surprised. She had known about most of his accomplishments, but much of this was new to her even after eight years of marriage. "Oh, Orville", she sighed through her tears. "What a life you lived. Being appreciated was so important to you. I hope you knew how I admired and loved you. Seeing what you wrote makes me wonder; did you know your time was short?" She showed it to Betty and Walter before sending it in to the newspaper for inclusion in his obituary. Betty was touched that she and Freda were included in his remembrance. She also understood why Walter wasn't mentioned, and was sad for Walter, Orville's partner for so many years. Walter would probably understand. He was so compassionate.

The obituary was published on Friday. Orville's body lay in state Sunday afternoon at the City Hall Community Rooms where the band rehearsed. An honorary guard of his closest band members kept watch as hundreds passed by. There were past and present band musicians, Band Board and City Council members, furniture customers, and grateful Winona citizens. Erna sat nearby, thanking people for coming.

Orville's service at the Breitlow Funeral home was packed with family, friends, colleagues, and admirers. Even musician friends from his years in Indiana traveled to Winona to say farewell. Erna had requested that anyone who wanted to speak be accommodated. Council members described Orville's dogged support of the Winona Municipal band. Some recalled his crucial role in passing the 1931 Band Tax measure. The Indiana friends told about Orville's contribution to music and music education there. Winona Municipal Band members testified to his personal support and encouragement in their musical growth. Others talked about everything the Municipal Band had accomplished under Orville's leadership.

After the service Betty and Walter stayed with Erna and her family until the last person was gone. They finally walked out the door only after they knew Erna would be accompanied home by her sister.

As they got close to their car, Betty broke into tears. "I truly did love him," she said to Walter.

He squeezed her hand and hugged her saying, "I know. So did I."

WINONA MUNICIPAL BAND EPILOGUE

After Orville Reese's death, assistant director, Stanley Streuber, a long-time Municipal Band trumpet player and leader, was appointed to be bandmaster through the end of the 1940 season. In November 1940, the City Council selected the bandmaster for the next year. Most band members supported Streuber, but another popular and talented musician, Harold Edstrom, had made a name for himself in Winona, first as an integral member of the very popular Hal Leonard Dance Orchestra, and then leading the Winona Teacher's College and High School Bands. Parents of his High School students lobbied for him to be hired as the new Winona Municipal Band Master. They feared that "a school with more money will hire him and doubted that the school board can pay what he is worth."

Harold Edstrom got the job and Winona would benefit from that decision in more ways than they could envision. Harold realized he had a talent for arranging popular tunes for his school bands because other directors heard them and asked for copies for their own bands. In 1945 Harold resigned from his teaching job. He and his brother Everett established a photo shop and music store in Winona. They also decided there was a market for Harold's band arrangements and founded Hal Leonard Publishing in 1947 with another dance band buddy, Roger Busdicker. By 1949 they had organized the Edstrom School of Music and introduced many unique and popular teaching techniques.

The Winona Municipal Band often had the first chance to test new band arrangements for Hal Leonard Publishing, as it grew to be the largest print music publishing business in the world. Edstrom remained the director of the Municipal Band until his retirement in 1973 after 32 years.

Dr. Richard Lindner moved to Winona in 1967 to direct the Winona State College band. He soon met Harold Edstrom and joined the Winona

Municipal Band trumpet section. In the early 1970's, Edstrom started coming to Lindner's college band concerts and shortly afterward asked Lindner if he was interested in taking over the Municipal Band. Lindner didn't think too long before he said, "Yes." The opportunity to conduct a wide variety of music was very appealing. Dr. Lindner was named Edstrom's successor in 1974 and remained bandmaster until he retired in 2011 after 38 years.

Myron Haug, Winona High School Band Director and Winona Municipal Band tuba player, then assumed the position. He stepped down after four years, in 2015.

Since 2015, the centennial of the Winona Municipal Band's founding, Levi Lundak, Winona State University Music Education graduate and Winona Municipal Band trombone section member, has led the band.

The Winona Municipal Band currently presents a ten-concert series each summer, beginning in the 2nd week of June and concluding in the 2nd week of August.

But none of this would have been possible without the six-year effort of O. W. Reese to find secure funding for the band. Winonans have been grateful ever since.

Winona Bandshell
courtesy of Kay Shaw Photography

BABETTE AND WALTER
EPILOGUE

Babette (Betty) continued teaching piano lessons in her studio at United Furniture through the 1940s and 1950's. According to her former student, the late Mary Lou Abrahamsen Stoltman Baylon, Babette's Studio was upstairs toward back of the furniture building on the east side. It had a high ceiling, and tall, south-facing windows. She remembered it as very sunny. There were bookcases filled with music and, of course, a piano. Babette was active in the National Guild of Piano Teachers and took her students to Minneapolis to play in many piano tournaments and contests at the MacPhail School of Music.

In July of 1941, Babette and Walter took Gloria and Walter Jr. to Seaside, Oregon, where they visited Walter's brother, John Erwin Christensen, who was living in Portland.

Wally graduated from high school in 1942 and enlisted in the Army Air Corps. He trained at Scott Field in Illinois as a radio operator and became an Air Traffic Controller overseas. He was stationed in New Guinea, Australia, and the Philippines and honorably discharged in 1945. Gloria graduated from high school in 1945.

Throughout the 1940's Babette and Walter were active in musical events, Walter singing for civic groups like the Old Settlers and VFW Auxiliary, often accompanied by Betty. At the spring program of the Winona Civic Chorus in 1947, Babette performed piano duets with Mrs. Dee Tingley, a local radio performer.

Betty's younger brother, Fred, died in April 1948 at age 48. He managed the Economy Wallpaper Company after leaving United Furniture but was also active in Winona's musical community, as president of the Winona Musicians' union, former member of the Winona Municipal band and of various dance band groups. He was a member of the Henry Burton Dance

Band at the time of his death. He was survived by his wife, Louise; siblings, Freda, Babette, and Herbert; one son, Fred Junior; one daughter, Jayne Heyer Bernatz; and four grandchildren.

After his military service, Wally moved to Detroit, Michigan, in 1948. Through a friend he met Patricia Cawley. They were married in 1949 in Detroit.

In June 1948 it was announced in Winona that a "new program of sparkling organ melodies has been added to the schedule of KWNO, live organ music on Mondays and Fridays." Well known piano teacher, Babette Christensen, will "present popular tunes played on the Hammond electric organ each Monday and Friday from 11 to 11:15 a.m." She had developed a unique style of organ performance after studying with Eddie Dunstedter, a well-known theater organ artist and composer, who performed at Twin Cities theaters and on WCCO radio and became a national celebrity.

Walter advertised items for United Furniture regularly in the classified section of the Winona newspaper. He added dog supplies to the store's offerings and advocated for humane treatment of lost and abandoned canines. He made charitable donations and participated in fundraising for the Red Cross, the March of Dimes, Goodfellows, and Poppy Days. United Furniture sponsored a candidate for Miss Steamboat Days, Bernita Krause.

When a dike collapsed in April 1951, a serious flood inundated the downtown area including United Furniture, so a great deal of clean up was needed. In the summer of 1951, United Furniture announced it was fully air conditioned.

After a short-lived marriage and the birth of Robert Walter Kulas in 1945, Gloria followed Wally to Michigan, where she met Charles Arthur Thurman while working at Hite Photo. On January 26, 1951, they were married in Detroit, Michigan. Gloria's brother, Wally, and his wife were living in Royal Oak, Michigan, and the wedding reception was held in their home.

Charles Thurman started a business called MPT Drives with three other men. They sold parts like V-belt drives to other companies. The company is still operating. They had two children, Suzanne Babette Thurman in 1951 and Mark Richard Thurman in 1957. In 1972 they moved to Vancouver, Washington.

EPILOGUES

KWNO ran regular schedules of their programming that included Babette's organ playing. Her studio was busy, but she took time off in the summers. In 1952 she hired two teaching assistants, one for piano students and another for accordion, to lighten her obligations, In September, the Babette and Christie show resumed on KWNO. The radio station promoted it, saying, "Mr. Christensen sings and does the commentary while Mrs. Christensen plays the Hammond electric organ. Beautiful, sentimental music is featured on the show which has gained a large audience in the past few years."

From the 1930's on, helping dogs became a calling for Walter and Betty. They always had dogs as pets, and granddaughter, Suzanne (Sue) Thurman, fondly recalls playing with Mickey and Libby, on their visits. They helped find lost dogs and re-home abandoned ones. They placed ads and used their radio show *Something About Dogs* to teach listeners about caring for dogs. The need was so great, they found themselves overwhelmed. Walter used space in United Furniture to house the animals, operating as a type of humane society. People brought them strays and frequently dropped off unwanted dogs at their house or the store. By the early 1950s they estimated they had helped some 500-600 dogs. The cost of feeding and caring for these creatures added up and had eaten into the profits of United Furniture. In late summer of 1954, Walter announced the closing of United Furniture. A large clearance sale was held in November.

Announcement of the birth of Keith Walter to Mr. and Mrs. Walter Christensen Jr, in Royal Oak Michigan, on November 6, 1954, appeared in the Winona newspaper on November 26. Wally and Pat had two more children, Eric Christensen in 1959 and Kari Christensen in 1963.

When the store closed, Babette moved her studio to their current home at 101 Orrin Street. Among her students were the grandchildren of her late brother, Fred. One of them, David Heyer, remembered taking lessons with Babette at her house. He admitted to some lack of interest because he preferred playing the drums. He said that Babette resorted to paying him 35 cents per lesson to continue. Later in his life he said he regretted missing the opportunity to learn from her. Dave inherited musical ability from the Heyers and was a band director in the Winona Public School System from 1970 until his retirement in 2005.

In January of 1955, Walter accepted the position of sales manager at Kelly Furniture. But by September of 1956, he had returned to the United Furniture building and was operating as "Walt Christensen Furniture" taking used furniture for trade. He kept this up until 1958, when he sold the building, and it became an auction house.

Walter's mother died in 1943. His sister, Otilla, who had married and become Otilla White, moved to Winona and lived across the street from Walter and Betty in a mobile home park.

On November 10, 1964, Babette died at age 74 and was laid to rest in Winona's Woodlawn Cemetery to the left of Orville. Walter died on March 26, 1967, also at age 74. He was buried on Babette's left in Woodlawn.

FREDA AND GEORGE EPILOGUE

George and Freda continued living at 804 West Mark Street, Freda working as secretary-treasurer of United Furniture. In 1950 the *Winona Republican Herald* held a contest to name the "Tops In Our Town." Winonans were asked to nominate people they thought were exceptional examples of good citizens and neighbors. Freda was among the forty people on the final list to be voted upon. She volunteered with the hospital auxiliary activities and the Red Cross. She read and spoke about a popular book of the early 1950s called *The White Witch Doctor*, a book about a missionary to Africa.

George managed the Montana Life Insurance Company in the early 1940's but also began working for Citizen's Savings and Loan of La Crosse, Wisconsin, in 1935. In 1945 he was named manager of the Personal Finance Co. in Winona. This personal loan company specialized in lending small amounts, up to $300, to people and was established in 1941 advertising aggressively (multiple times per week). Most of their ads emphasized that you "PICK YOUR OWN PAYMENTS!"

When George became manager of the Personal Finance Co., he pitched himself in a newspaper ad as "the 'Yes' man at Personal Finance Co., that is, I'm the man who likes to say 'Yes' to requests for Personal loans. You see, I'm the manager of our office, the man who's responsible for building up our business. The more times I say 'yes' to requests for loans, the more business we do. And since making Personal Loans of $25 to $250 or more is our ONLY business, that's mighty important to me. Therefore, if you need extra cash at any time, whether a little for a short time or a lot for a long time, you can depend on my doing my best to say, 'yes' to you."

In 1943 George (Spike) joined the Winona Coast Guard Reserve, was promoted to Commander in 1944 and remained active in the group for many years, planning river activities and giving classes in safe boating and boat operation. He and Freda enjoyed the river for recreation and fishing.

George stayed involved with ski jumping and the Winona Ski Club, advocating for improvements to the ski jump in West Burns Valley. He taught, coached, and judged ski meets and occasionally still jumped, winning the senior title in 1948. He didn't wrestle as often but did coach and referee. He bowled on the Elks' team and tried curling again for a while. His love of hunting continued. He kept active in the Winona Sportsman Club and participated in many trapshooting competitions. He attended the national Trapshooting competition in Vandalia, Ohio from 1937 through the 1960's, winning many awards and eventually being named official scorekeeper.

He continued his activities in many civic organizations: the Odd Fellows, where he served in many offices, the Elks, the Rotary Club, the Masons, and he was an organizing member of the Exchange Club.

George Pelowski had operated car dealerships in Winona since the late 1920's and employed George Graham at times. In 1949 the two Georges formed a partnership and built a large Oldsmobile salesroom and garage at 219 West Third Street. They called it Midwest Motors and were proud of its 7500 square feet of display space. They remained in partnership until Pelowski sold Graham his share and retired in 1952. In November 1952, W. H. (Buzz) Feldmann Jr. moved from Minneapolis to join the firm as a partner with Graham.

A big event in Winona winters was the Winter Carnival, usually held in January, which began as a three-day event in the 1930's and expanded every year. By the late 1940's it featured a big parade with floats, bands, and other marching units, dinners, dances, ice fishing and skating contests, and other winter activities. In 1950, the tradition of naming an outstanding individual as Jack Frost, to "rule" over the festivities was started. In 1955 George was selected Jack Frost V. He made the most of his role for a year with special dinners, parades, and celebrations. He and Freda enjoyed the attention.

EPILOGUES

George continued his civic involvement, raising funds for various organizations such as The March of Dimes for polio, the Heart Fund, and others. Many years he organized hunting trips to Montana in November, returning with a trailer load of game, including trout, partridges, pheasants, bear, elk, deer, and antelope. He frequently donated game for fundraising banquets.

In the 1950's, Freda became active in the Winona Women's Republican Club, fundraising, placing ads, and serving as treasurer, president, and county secretary. She attended Minnesota state conventions and the Washington D. C. Conference of Republican Women.

The grandson of Freda and Babette's brother Fred, David Heyer, related how Freda would take him and his siblings to a rented lake cabin up north each summer in the 1950's. They had great times, and Freda would always drive the newest and biggest Oldsmobile available.

Freda died in July of 1962 after a two-week illness. In January of 1965 the Republican Women of Winona gave a table flag in her honor commemorating her years of volunteering and serving as president. She was buried with her parents, Orville Reese, and her brother, Fred, in Winona's Woodlawn Cemetery.

George remarried in 1965. He and his new wife bought and moved to a lake home near Marcell, Minnesota, in Itasca County. He kept in touch with his friends in Winona and returned for Athletic Club Events and funerals of longtime friends. He died in 1997 at age 94 and was buried at Evergreen Knoll Cemetery in Marcell.

MAJOR SOURCES

Andrews, Clarence A. *Chicago in Story, a Literary History*. Midwest Heritage Publishing Company, Iowa City, Iowa, 1982.

Bailey, Beth L. *From Front Porch to Back Seat, Courtship in Twentieth Century America*. Johns Hopkins University Press, 1989.

Cottrell, Stephen. *The Saxophone*. Yale University Press, 2012.

Cutler, Irving. *Chicago, Metropolis of the Mid-Continent*. 4th Ed., Southern Illinois University Press, 2006.

Goldman, Richard Franko. *The Wind Band*. Allyn and Bacon, 1962.

Lawrence, Daryl Richard. *On The Go All The Time*. Daryl Richard Lawrence, 2022.

May, Elaine Tyler. *Great Expectations: Marriage and Divorce in the Post Victorian America*. University of Chicago Press, 1980.

Mayer, Harold M. and Richard C. Wade. *Chicago, Growth of a Metropolis*. University of Chicago Press, 1969.

Miley, Mary. "When Vaudeville Got Tired." Vaudeville, September 29, 2018, https://marymiley.wordpress.com/category/vaudeville/

Mordden, Ethan. *Ziegfeld, the Man who Invented Show Business*. St. Martin's Press, 2008.

Monod, David. *Vaudeville and the Making of Modern Entertainment 1890-1925*. University of North Carolina Press, 2020.

Rothman, Ellen K. *Hands and Hearts, A History of Courtship in America*. Basic Books Inc., 1984.

Sawyers, June Skinner. *Chicago Sketches Urban Tales and Legends from Chicago History*. Gainesville, Florida, Wild Onion Books, 1995.

Segell, Michael. *The Devil's Horn*. Farrar, Straus and Giroux, 2005.

Sewart, D. Travis. *No Applause, Just Throw Money, The Book That Made Vaudeville Famous*. Faber and Faber Inc., 2005.

"Iroquois Theatre Fire." Wikipedia. Accessed March 12, 2024. https://en.wikipedia.org/wiki/Iroquois_Theatre_fire

Note: The Winona Newspaper Database of The Winona Republican Herald. Courtesy of Archives & Special Collections at Winona State University.

ABOUT THE AUTHOR

Ruth Anfinson Bures graduated from Drake University (BME) and St. Mary's University of Minnesota, (ME, EdD). She is a parent, grandparent, poet, writer, and musician. She has taught music at all levels, from preschool through university. A clarinet player in the Winona Municipal Band for many years, she also performs with other local ensembles, for which she has composed and arranged music. The author of *I'm so Glad There's Someone*, a children's book about emotions, she also wrote the lyrics and music for *Here Comes Christmas*, a musical published by Clarus Music Ltd., and created a large collection of songs for young people called *Ruth's Original Songs for Children*.

ACKNOWLEDGEMENTS

I could never have completed this project without the help of the following people:

Terri Karsten, Wagonbridge Publishing, editor and publisher

Heidi Bryant, Design On Call, graphic designer

Readers: Cynthia Scudiero, retired English Teacher: Clifford Black, former English teacher and retired Amtrak official; Bridgit Jordan, Wendy Magnuson, avid readers; Sue Thurman, granddaughter of Walter and Babette Christensen

Heyer Descendents including David Heyer, retired band director, and Kim Thurman, genealogist and wife of Babette and Walter's grandson, Mark Thurman

Former piano student of Babette, Marylou Abrahamsen Stoltman Baylon

Retired Winona Municipal Band director, Dr. Richard Lindner

Son of Harold Edstrom, O.W. Reese's successor, Nick Edstrom

Winona History Center Archivists: Archivists, Walter Bennick and Anna Gaffey; Curator of Collections, Andy Bloedorn

Winona Public Library Adult Services Librarian, Samantha Terbeest Berhow

Vaudeville information specialist, Mary Miley, website *Mary Miley's Roaring Twenties*

Roosevelt University Archivist, Laura Mills MILS

Allison Quam, Coordinator: Archives & Special Collections, Reference Services, Learning Spaces

Chief supporter, cheerleader, and patient listener, husband Frank Bures

Made in United States
Troutdale, OR
05/03/2024

19575872R00169

SELF CARE

A JOURNAL FOR BEING KIND TO YOURSELF

PETER PAUPER PRESS, INC.
RYE BROOK, NEW YORK

PETER PAUPER PRESS
Fine Books and Gifts Since 1928

Our Company

In 1928, at the age of twenty-two, Peter Beilenson began printing books on a small press in the basement of his parents' home in Larchmont, New York. Peter—and later, his wife, Edna—sought to create fine books that sold at "prices even a pauper could afford."

Today, still family owned and operated, Peter Pauper Press continues to honor our founders' legacy—and our customers' expectations—of beauty, quality, and value.

Designed by Margaret Rubiano

Images used under license from Shutterstock.com

Copyright © 2021 Peter Pauper Press, Inc.
3 International Drive
Rye Brook, NY 10573 USA
All rights reserved
ISBN 978-1-4413-3715-3
Printed in China

14 13 12 11 10 9 8

Visit us at www.peterpauper.com

CONTENTS

INTRODUCTION

Y ou can't pour water from an empty pitcher, you can't drive long distances without refilling your vehicle's fuel tank, and you can't give the world your best unless you have it to give. Self care is the practice of ensuring that your needs are met, by turning your attention and compassion inward.

Begin this journal by answering the questions in the **Where You're Starting From** section, and using your answers to identify the self care areas that most need attention in the **Self Care Challenges** section. Ruminate on how you can start addressing your unmet needs in the **Self Care Plans** section. Finally, and most importantly, write each day in the **Daily Self Care Pages**.

The **Daily Self Care Pages** allow you to log essential acts of self care, thoughts, intentions, and information about your well-being. Designed for quick check-ins, each page has a **Morning**, **During the Day**, and **Evening** section. As time passes, read over the log and notice any recurring patterns or themes.

Extend kindness toward yourself in all areas of your life,
and see how it allows you to grow.

WHERE YOU'RE STARTING FROM

To nurture yourself better, begin by figuring out where you need more nourishment. Check off whether you find each of the things on the pages ahead easy, average, or challenging, and whether it affects you not at all, a little, some, or a lot.

THE PHYSICAL STUFF:

Getting enough sleep: ○ easy ○ average ○ challenging
This affects me: ○ not at all ○ a little ○ some ○ a lot

Drinking water regularly: ○ easy ○ average ○ challenging
This affects me: ○ not at all ○ a little ○ some ○ a lot

Eating regular meals: ○ easy ○ average ○ challenging
This affects me: ○ not at all ○ a little ○ some ○ a lot

Getting good nutrition: ○ easy ○ average ○ challenging
This affects me: ○ not at all ○ a little ○ some ○ a lot

Exercising regularly: ○ easy ○ average ○ challenging
This affects me: ○ not at all ○ a little ○ some ○ a lot

Resting when sick: ○ easy ○ average ○ challenging
This affects me: ○ not at all ○ a little ○ some ○ a lot

Getting medical care: ○ easy ○ average ○ challenging
This affects me: ○ not at all ○ a little ○ some ○ a lot

THE MENTAL STUFF:

Doing things that bring joy: ○ easy ○ average ○ challenging

This affects me: ○ not at all ○ a little ○ some ○ a lot

Taking quiet/alone time: ○ easy ○ average ○ challenging

This affects me: ○ not at all ○ a little ○ some ○ a lot

Laughing: ○ easy ○ average ○ challenging

This affects me: ○ not at all ○ a little ○ some ○ a lot

Experiencing nature/ the outdoors: ○ easy ○ average ○ challenging

This affects me: ○ not at all ○ a little ○ some ○ a lot

Less screen time: ○ easy ○ average ○ challenging

This affects me: ○ not at all ○ a little ○ some ○ a lot

Trying new things: ○ easy ○ average ○ challenging

This affects me: ○ not at all ○ a little ○ some ○ a lot

Doing creative things: ○ easy ○ average ○ challenging

This affects me: ○ not at all ○ a little ○ some ○ a lot

Enjoying a book, movie, or other entertainment: ○ easy ○ average ○ challenging

This affects me: ○ not at all ○ a little ○ some ○ a lot

Noticing my feelings: ○ easy ○ average ○ challenging

This affects me: ○ not at all ○ a little ○ some ○ a lot

Stopping negative self-talk *(the mean little voice in your head)*: ○ easy ○ average ○ challenging

This affects me: ○ not at all ○ a little ○ some ○ a lot

THE INTERPERSONAL STUFF:

Asking for help: ◯ easy ◯ average ◯ challenging

This affects me: ◯ not at all ◯ a little ◯ some ◯ a lot

**Staying in touch
with friends/family:** ◯ easy ◯ average ◯ challenging

This affects me: ◯ not at all ◯ a little ◯ some ◯ a lot

**Spending fun or relaxing
time with friends/family:** ◯ easy ◯ average ◯ challenging

This affects me: ◯ not at all ◯ a little ◯ some ◯ a lot

Discussing problems: ◯ easy ◯ average ◯ challenging

This affects me: ◯ not at all ◯ a little ◯ some ◯ a lot

Expressing feelings: ◯ easy ◯ average ◯ challenging

This affects me: ◯ not at all ◯ a little ◯ some ◯ a lot

**Listening to another person
express their feelings:** ◯ easy ◯ average ◯ challenging

This affects me: ◯ not at all ◯ a little ◯ some ◯ a lot

Standing up for myself: ◯ easy ◯ average ◯ challenging

This affects me: ◯ not at all ◯ a little ◯ some ◯ a lot

Compromising: ◯ easy ◯ average ◯ challenging

This affects me: ◯ not at all ◯ a little ◯ some ◯ a lot

Saying "No": ◯ easy ◯ average ◯ challenging

This affects me: ◯ not at all ◯ a little ◯ some ◯ a lot

Saying "Yes": ◯ easy ◯ average ◯ challenging

This affects me: ◯ not at all ◯ a little ◯ some ◯ a lot

SELF CARE CHALLENGES

Take a look at what you circled in the **Where You're Starting From** section, paying particular attention to things that you find challenging or that significantly influence your life. Are you skipping breakfast? Having trouble putting down your phone and going to bed on time, or suffering from anxious insomnia? Getting caught up in endless self-recrimination over mistakes?

Were any questions difficult to answer or surprising? If so, why?

....

....

What things did you mark **challenging**?

....

....

What things affect you **a lot**?

....

....

What things, if any, fall into both categories?

....

....

....

....

What makes these things so hard for you?

How do these things affect you?

How do you think your life might change if these things grew less challenging?

SELF CARE PLANS

Pick one or more of your **Self Care Challenges**, or another area of your life in which you want to better meet your needs:

....

....

....

What are some obstacles to self care in this area? Are any of them in your power to change?

....

....

....

....

....

What are some things you could research or try that might help?

....

....

....

What one thing can you work into your daily practice, starting now, to take better care of you?

....

....

Try it as you chronicle your daily self care in the pages ahead, and notice how you feel. If it's not working for you, switch it up! If it works, and things get easier, move on to another challenge! It's time to be kind to you.

THOUGHTS AND NOTES

....

....

....

....

....

....

....

....

....

....

....

....

....

MORNING

DATE: ....

Woke up at: .... **Slept:** ◯ well ◯ okay ◯ badly

Feeling about the day ahead: 😧 😟 😐 🙂 😃

Self care intention today:

....

....

DURING THE DAY

Ate: ☐ breakfast ☐ lunch ☐ dinner

Drank water: ☐ morning ☐ afternoon ☐ evening

Notes:

....

....

☐ **Exercised?**

What kind: ....

Mood before exercise: 😧 😟 😐 🙂 😃

Mood after exercise: 😧 😟 😐 🙂 😃

Mental self care for the day:

....

Today's challenges:

....

....

....

Enjoyable things today:

....

....

....

EVENING

Thoughts about today:

....

....

....

....

....

....

....

....

....

....

....

....

Bedtime: ....

Mood at the end of the day:

MORNING

DATE: ....

Woke up at: .... **Slept:** ◯ well ◯ okay ◯ badly

Feeling about the day ahead: ☹ ☹ 😐 🙂 😀

Self care intention today:

....

....

DURING THE DAY

Ate: ☐ breakfast ☐ lunch ☐ dinner

Drank water: ☐ morning ☐ afternoon ☐ evening

Notes:

....

....

☐ **Exercised?**

What kind: ....

Mood before exercise: ☹ ☹ 😐 🙂 😀

Mood after exercise: ☹ ☹ 😐 🙂 😀

Mental self care for the day:

....

Today's challenges:

....

....

....

Enjoyable things today:

....

....

....

EVENING

Thoughts about today:

....

....

....

....

....

....

....

....

....

....

....

....

....

....

....

Bedtime: ....

Mood at the end of the day:

MORNING

DATE: ....

Woke up at: .... **Slept:** ◯ well ◯ okay ◯ badly

Feeling about the day ahead: ☹ ☹ 😐 ☺ 😄

Self care intention today:

....

....

DURING THE DAY

Ate: ☐ breakfast ☐ lunch ☐ dinner

Drank water: ☐ morning ☐ afternoon ☐ evening

Notes:

....

....

☐ **Exercised?**

What kind: ....

Mood before exercise: ☹ ☹ 😐 ☺ 😄

Mood after exercise: ☹ ☹ 😐 ☺ 😄

Mental self care for the day:

....

Today's challenges:

....

....

....

Enjoyable things today:

EVENING

Thoughts about today:

Bedtime:

Mood at the end of the day: 😟 🙁 😐 🙂 😀

MORNING

DATE: ....

Woke up at: .... **Slept:** ◯ well ◯ okay ◯ badly

Feeling about the day ahead: ☹ 🙁 😐 🙂 😃

Self care intention today:

....

....

DURING THE DAY

Ate: ☐ breakfast ☐ lunch ☐ dinner

Drank water: ☐ morning ☐ afternoon ☐ evening

Notes:

....

....

☐ **Exercised?**

What kind: ....

Mood before exercise: ☹ 🙁 😐 🙂 😃

Mood after exercise: ☹ 🙁 😐 🙂 😃

Mental self care for the day:

....

Today's challenges:

....

....

....

Enjoyable things today:

EVENING

Thoughts about today:

Bedtime:

Mood at the end of the day:

MORNING

DATE: ....

Woke up at: .... **Slept:** ◯ well ◯ okay ◯ badly

Feeling about the day ahead: ☹️   😦   😐   🙂   😃

Self care intention today:

....

....

DURING THE DAY

Ate: ☐ breakfast ☐ lunch ☐ dinner

Drank water: ☐ morning ☐ afternoon ☐ evening

Notes:

....

....

☐ **Exercised?**

What kind: ....

Mood before exercise: ☹️   😦   😐   🙂   😃

Mood after exercise: ☹️   😦   😐   🙂   😃

Mental self care for the day:

....

Today's challenges:

....

....

....

Enjoyable things today:

EVENING

Thoughts about today:

Bedtime:

Mood at the end of the day:

MORNING

DATE: ....

Woke up at: .... **Slept:** ◯ well ◯ okay ◯ badly

Feeling about the day ahead: 😦 😔 😐 😊 😃

Self care intention today:

....

....

DURING THE DAY

Ate: ☐ breakfast ☐ lunch ☐ dinner

Drank water: ☐ morning ☐ afternoon ☐ evening

Notes:

....

....

☐ **Exercised?**

What kind: ....

Mood before exercise: 😦 😔 😐 😊 😃

Mood after exercise: 😦 😔 😐 😊 😃

Mental self care for the day:

....

Today's challenges:

....

....

....

Enjoyable things today:

EVENING

Thoughts about today:

Bedtime:

Mood at the end of the day: ☹ 🙁 😐 🙂 😃

MORNING

DATE: ....

Woke up at: .... **Slept:** ◯ well ◯ okay ◯ badly

Feeling about the day ahead: 😟 😦 😐 🙂 😃

Self care intention today:

....

....

DURING THE DAY

Ate: ☐ breakfast ☐ lunch ☐ dinner

Drank water: ☐ morning ☐ afternoon ☐ evening

Notes:

....

....

☐ **Exercised?**

What kind: ....

Mood before exercise: 😟 😦 😐 🙂 😃

Mood after exercise: 😟 😦 😐 🙂 😃

Mental self care for the day:

....

Today's challenges:

....

....

....

Enjoyable things today:

EVENING

Thoughts about today:

Bedtime:

Mood at the end of the day: ☹   🙁   😐   🙂   😃

MORNING

DATE: ....

Woke up at: .... Slept: ◯ well ◯ okay ◯ badly

Feeling about the day ahead: ☹ ☹ 😐 🙂 😃

Self care intention today:

....

....

DURING THE DAY

Ate: ☐ breakfast ☐ lunch ☐ dinner

Drank water: ☐ morning ☐ afternoon ☐ evening

Notes:

....

....

☐ **Exercised?**

What kind: ....

Mood before exercise: ☹ ☹ 😐 🙂 😃

Mood after exercise: ☹ ☹ 😐 🙂 😃

Mental self care for the day:

....

Today's challenges:

....

....

....

Enjoyable things today:

....

....

....

EVENING

Thoughts about today:

....

....

....

....

....

....

....

....

....

....

....

....

....

Bedtime: ....

Mood at the end of the day: ☹ ☹ 😐 🙂 😀

MORNING

DATE: ....

Woke up at: .... **Slept:** ◯ well ◯ okay ◯ badly

Feeling about the day ahead: ☹ 🙁 😐 🙂 😃

Self care intention today:

....

....

DURING THE DAY

Ate: ☐ breakfast ☐ lunch ☐ dinner

Drank water: ☐ morning ☐ afternoon ☐ evening

Notes:

....

....

☐ **Exercised?**

What kind: ....

Mood before exercise: ☹ 🙁 😐 🙂 😃

Mood after exercise: ☹ 🙁 😐 🙂 😃

Mental self care for the day:

....

Today's challenges:

....

....

....

Enjoyable things today:

EVENING

Thoughts about today:

Bedtime:

Mood at the end of the day: ☹ ☹ 😐 🙂 😊

MORNING

DATE: ....

Woke up at: .... **Slept:** ◯ well ◯ okay ◯ badly

Feeling about the day ahead: ☹ ☹ 😐 🙂 😃

Self care intention today:

....

....

DURING THE DAY

Ate: ☐ breakfast ☐ lunch ☐ dinner

Drank water: ☐ morning ☐ afternoon ☐ evening

Notes:

....

....

☐ **Exercised?**

What kind: ....

Mood before exercise: ☹ ☹ 😐 🙂 😃

Mood after exercise: ☹ ☹ 😐 🙂 😃

Mental self care for the day:

....

Today's challenges:

....

....

....

Enjoyable things today:

....

....

....

EVENING

Thoughts about today:

....

....

....

....

....

....

....

....

....

....

....

....

Bedtime: ....

Mood at the end of the day: ☹   🙁   😐   🙂   😀

MORNING

DATE: ....

Woke up at: .... **Slept:** ◯ well ◯ okay ◯ badly

Feeling about the day ahead: ☹ ☹ 😐 🙂 😃

Self care intention today:

....

....

DURING THE DAY

Ate: ☐ breakfast ☐ lunch ☐ dinner

Drank water: ☐ morning ☐ afternoon ☐ evening

Notes:

....

....

☐ **Exercised?**

What kind: ....

Mood before exercise: ☹ ☹ 😐 🙂 😃

Mood after exercise: ☹ ☹ 😐 🙂 😃

Mental self care for the day:

....

Today's challenges:

....

....

....

Enjoyable things today:

....

....

....

EVENING

Thoughts about today:

....

....

....

....

....

....

....

....

....

....

....

....

Bedtime: ....

Mood at the end of the day: ☹ 🙁 😐 🙂 😊

MORNING

DATE: ....

Woke up at: .... **Slept:** ◯ well ◯ okay ◯ badly

Feeling about the day ahead: ☹ ☹ 😐 🙂 😄

Self care intention today:

....

....

DURING THE DAY

Ate: ☐ breakfast ☐ lunch ☐ dinner

Drank water: ☐ morning ☐ afternoon ☐ evening

Notes:

....

....

☐ **Exercised?**

What kind: ....

Mood before exercise: ☹ ☹ 😐 🙂 😄

Mood after exercise: ☹ ☹ 😐 🙂 😄

Mental self care for the day:

....

Today's challenges:

....

....

....

Enjoyable things today:

....

....

....

EVENING

Thoughts about today:

....

....

....

....

....

....

....

....

....

....

....

....

Bedtime: ....

Mood at the end of the day: 😞 ☹️ 😐 🙂 😃

MORNING

DATE: ....

Woke up at: .... **Slept:** ◯ well ◯ okay ◯ badly

Feeling about the day ahead: ☹ ☹ 😐 🙂 😃

Self care intention today:

....

....

DURING THE DAY

Ate: ☐ breakfast ☐ lunch ☐ dinner

Drank water: ☐ morning ☐ afternoon ☐ evening

Notes:

....

....

☐ **Exercised?**

What kind: ....

Mood before exercise: ☹ ☹ 😐 🙂 😃

Mood after exercise: ☹ ☹ 😐 🙂 😃

Mental self care for the day:

....

Today's challenges:

....

....

Enjoyable things today:

....

....

....

EVENING

Thoughts about today:

....

....

....

....

....

....

....

....

....

....

....

....

....

Bedtime: ....

Mood at the end of the day: ☹ ☹ 😐 🙂 😊

MORNING

DATE: ....

Woke up at: .... **Slept:** ◯ well ◯ okay ◯ badly

Feeling about the day ahead: ☹ 🙁 😐 🙂 😃

Self care intention today:

....

....

DURING THE DAY

Ate: ☐ breakfast ☐ lunch ☐ dinner

Drank water: ☐ morning ☐ afternoon ☐ evening

Notes:

....

....

☐ **Exercised?**

What kind: ....

Mood before exercise: ☹ 🙁 😐 🙂 😃

Mood after exercise: ☹ 🙁 😐 🙂 😃

Mental self care for the day:

....

Today's challenges:

....

....

....

Enjoyable things today:

EVENING

Thoughts about today:

Bedtime:

Mood at the end of the day:

MORNING

DATE: ....

Woke up at: .... **Slept:** ◯ well ◯ okay ◯ badly

Feeling about the day ahead: ☹️ 🙁 😐 🙂 😀

Self care intention today:

....

....

DURING THE DAY

Ate: ☐ breakfast ☐ lunch ☐ dinner

Drank water: ☐ morning ☐ afternoon ☐ evening

Notes:

....

....

☐ **Exercised?**

What kind: ....

Mood before exercise: ☹️ 🙁 😐 🙂 😀

Mood after exercise: ☹️ 🙁 😐 🙂 😀

Mental self care for the day:

....

Today's challenges:

....

....

Enjoyable things today:

....

....

....

EVENING

Thoughts about today:

....

....

....

....

....

....

....

....

....

....

....

....

Bedtime: ....

Mood at the end of the day: ☹ ☹ 😐 🙂 😊

MORNING

DATE: ....

Woke up at: .... **Slept:** ◯ well ◯ okay ◯ badly

Feeling about the day ahead: ☹ 🙁 😐 🙂 😃

Self care intention today:

....

....

DURING THE DAY

Ate: ☐ breakfast ☐ lunch ☐ dinner

Drank water: ☐ morning ☐ afternoon ☐ evening

Notes:

....

....

☐ **Exercised?**

What kind: ....

Mood before exercise: ☹ 🙁 😐 🙂 😃

Mood after exercise: ☹ 🙁 😐 🙂 😃

Mental self care for the day:

....

Today's challenges:

....

....

42

Enjoyable things today:

....

....

....

EVENING

Thoughts about today:

....

....

....

....

....

....

....

....

....

....

....

....

Bedtime: ....

Mood at the end of the day: ☹ ☹ 😐 🙂 😀

MORNING

Woke up at: .... Slept: ◯ well ◯ okay ◯ badly

Feeling about the day ahead: 😦 😦 😐 🙂 😃

Self care intention today:

....

....

DURING THE DAY

Ate: ☐ breakfast ☐ lunch ☐ dinner

Drank water: ☐ morning ☐ afternoon ☐ evening

Notes:

....

....

☐ **Exercised?**

What kind: ....

Mood before exercise: 😦 😦 😐 🙂 😃

Mood after exercise: 😦 😦 😐 🙂 😃

Mental self care for the day:

....

Today's challenges:

....

....

....

Enjoyable things today:

....

....

....

EVENING

Thoughts about today:

....

....

....

....

....

....

....

....

....

....

....

....

....

Bedtime: ....

Mood at the end of the day: ☹ 🙁 😐 🙂 😃

MORNING

DATE: ....

Woke up at: .... **Slept:** ◯ well ◯ okay ◯ badly

Feeling about the day ahead: ☹ ☹ 😐 🙂 😃

Self care intention today:

....

....

DURING THE DAY

Ate: ☐ breakfast ☐ lunch ☐ dinner

Drank water: ☐ morning ☐ afternoon ☐ evening

Notes:

....

....

☐ **Exercised?**

What kind: ....

Mood before exercise: ☹ ☹ 😐 🙂 😃

Mood after exercise: ☹ ☹ 😐 🙂 😃

Mental self care for the day:

....

Today's challenges:

....

....

....

Enjoyable things today:

....

....

....

EVENING

Thoughts about today:

....

....

....

....

....

....

....

....

....

....

Bedtime: ....

Mood at the end of the day: ☹ ☹ 😐 🙂 😊

MORNING

DATE: ....

Woke up at: .... **Slept:** ◯ well ◯ okay ◯ badly

Feeling about the day ahead: ☹ 😦 😐 🙂 😃

Self care intention today:

....

....

DURING THE DAY

Ate: ☐ breakfast ☐ lunch ☐ dinner

Drank water: ☐ morning ☐ afternoon ☐ evening

Notes:

....

....

☐ **Exercised?**

What kind: ....

Mood before exercise: ☹ 😦 😐 🙂 😃

Mood after exercise: ☹ 😦 😐 🙂 😃

Mental self care for the day:

....

Today's challenges:

....

....

Enjoyable things today:

....

....

....

EVENING

Thoughts about today:

....

....

....

....

....

....

....

....

....

....

....

....

Bedtime: ....

Mood at the end of the day: ☹ ☹ 😐 🙂 😊

MORNING

Woke up at: .... **Slept:** ◯ well ◯ okay ◯ badly

Feeling about the day ahead: ☹ 🙁 😐 🙂 😀

Self care intention today:

....

....

DURING THE DAY

Ate: ☐ breakfast ☐ lunch ☐ dinner

Drank water: ☐ morning ☐ afternoon ☐ evening

Notes:

....

....

☐ **Exercised?**

What kind: ....

Mood before exercise: ☹ 🙁 😐 🙂 😀

Mood after exercise: ☹ 🙁 😐 🙂 😀

Mental self care for the day:

....

Today's challenges:

....

....

....

Enjoyable things today:

....

....

....

EVENING

Thoughts about today:

....

....

....

....

....

....

....

....

....

....

....

Bedtime: ....

Mood at the end of the day: ☹ ☹ 😐 🙂 😊

MORNING

DATE: ....

Woke up at: .... **Slept:** ◯ well ◯ okay ◯ badly

Feeling about the day ahead: ☹ ☹ 😐 🙂 😃

Self care intention today:

....

....

DURING THE DAY

Ate: ☐ breakfast ☐ lunch ☐ dinner

Drank water: ☐ morning ☐ afternoon ☐ evening

Notes:

....

....

☐ **Exercised?**

What kind: ....

Mood before exercise: ☹ ☹ 😐 🙂 😃

Mood after exercise: ☹ ☹ 😐 🙂 😃

Mental self care for the day:

....

Today's challenges:

....

....

....

Enjoyable things today:

....

....

....

EVENING

Thoughts about today:

....

....

....

....

....

....

....

....

....

....

....

....

....

Bedtime: ....

Mood at the end of the day: 😟   😦   😐   🙂   😃

MORNING

Woke up at: .... **Slept:** ◯ well ◯ okay ◯ badly

Feeling about the day ahead: ☹ ☹ 😐 ☺ 😃

Self care intention today:

....

....

DURING THE DAY

Ate: ☐ breakfast ☐ lunch ☐ dinner

Drank water: ☐ morning ☐ afternoon ☐ evening

Notes:

....

....

☐ **Exercised?**

What kind: ....

Mood before exercise: ☹ ☹ 😐 ☺ 😃

Mood after exercise: ☹ ☹ 😐 ☺ 😃

Mental self care for the day:

....

Today's challenges:

....

....

....

Enjoyable things today:

....

....

....

EVENING

Thoughts about today:

....

....

....

....

....

....

....

....

....

....

....

....

Bedtime: ....

Mood at the end of the day: ☹ ☹ 😐 🙂 😊

MORNING

DATE: ....

Woke up at: .... **Slept:** ◯ well ◯ okay ◯ badly

Feeling about the day ahead: ☹ ☹ 😐 🙂 😃

Self care intention today:

....

....

DURING THE DAY

Ate: ☐ breakfast ☐ lunch ☐ dinner

Drank water: ☐ morning ☐ afternoon ☐ evening

Notes:

....

....

☐ **Exercised?**

What kind: ....

Mood before exercise: ☹ ☹ 😐 🙂 😃

Mood after exercise: ☹ ☹ 😐 🙂 😃

Mental self care for the day:

....

Today's challenges:

....

....

Enjoyable things today:

....

....

....

EVENING

Thoughts about today:

....

....

....

....

....

....

....

....

....

....

....

....

Bedtime: ....

Mood at the end of the day: ☹ ☹ 😐 🙂 😊

MORNING

DATE: ....

Woke up at: .... **Slept:** ⭕ well ⭕ okay ⭕ badly

Feeling about the day ahead: 😞 😟 😐 🙂 😃

Self care intention today:

....

....

DURING THE DAY

Ate: ☐ breakfast ☐ lunch ☐ dinner

Drank water: ☐ morning ☐ afternoon ☐ evening

Notes:

....

....

☐ **Exercised?**

What kind: ....

Mood before exercise: 😞 😟 😐 🙂 😃

Mood after exercise: 😞 😟 😐 🙂 😃

Mental self care for the day:

....

Today's challenges:

....

....

Enjoyable things today:

....

....

....

EVENING

Thoughts about today:

....

....

....

....

....

....

....

....

....

....

....

....

....

Bedtime: ....

Mood at the end of the day: ☹ ☹ 😐 🙂 😀

MORNING

DATE: ....

Woke up at: ....   **Slept:** ◯ well   ◯ okay   ◯ badly

Feeling about the day ahead: ☹   ☹   😐   🙂   😀

Self care intention today:

....

....

DURING THE DAY

Ate: ☐ breakfast ☐ lunch ☐ dinner

Drank water: ☐ morning ☐ afternoon ☐ evening

Notes:

....

....

☐ **Exercised?**

What kind: ....

Mood before exercise: ☹   ☹   😐   🙂   😀

Mood after exercise: ☹   ☹   😐   🙂   😀

Mental self care for the day:

....

Today's challenges:

....

....

....

Enjoyable things today:

....

....

....

EVENING

Thoughts about today:

....

....

....

....

....

....

....

....

....

....

....

....

Bedtime: ....

Mood at the end of the day: ☹ ☹ 😐 🙂 😀

MORNING

Woke up at: .... **Slept:** ◯ well ◯ okay ◯ badly

Feeling about the day ahead: ☹ ☹ 😐 ☺ 😀

Self care intention today:

....

....

DURING THE DAY

Ate: ☐ breakfast ☐ lunch ☐ dinner

Drank water: ☐ morning ☐ afternoon ☐ evening

Notes:

....

....

☐ **Exercised?**

What kind: ....

Mood before exercise: ☹ ☹ 😐 ☺ 😀

Mood after exercise: ☹ ☹ 😐 ☺ 😀

Mental self care for the day:

....

Today's challenges:

....

....

....

62

Enjoyable things today:

....

....

....

EVENING

Thoughts about today:

....

....

....

....

....

....

....

....

....

....

....

....

Bedtime: ....

Mood at the end of the day: ☹ 🙁 😐 🙂 😀

MORNING

DATE: ....

Woke up at: .... **Slept:** ◯ well ◯ okay ◯ badly

Feeling about the day ahead: ☹ ☹ 😐 🙂 😃

Self care intention today:

....

....

DURING THE DAY

Ate: ☐ breakfast ☐ lunch ☐ dinner

Drank water: ☐ morning ☐ afternoon ☐ evening

Notes:

....

....

☐ **Exercised?**

What kind: ....

Mood before exercise: ☹ ☹ 😐 🙂 😃

Mood after exercise: ☹ ☹ 😐 🙂 😃

Mental self care for the day:

....

Today's challenges:

....

....

....

Enjoyable things today:

....

....

....

EVENING

Thoughts about today:

....

....

....

....

....

....

....

....

....

....

....

....

Bedtime: ....

Mood at the end of the day: 😟 🙁 😐 🙂 😃

MORNING

DATE: ....

Woke up at: .... **Slept:** ◯ well ◯ okay ◯ badly

Feeling about the day ahead: ☹ ☹ 😐 🙂 😀

Self care intention today:

....

....

DURING THE DAY

Ate: ☐ breakfast ☐ lunch ☐ dinner

Drank water: ☐ morning ☐ afternoon ☐ evening

Notes:

....

....

☐ **Exercised?**

What kind: ....

Mood before exercise: ☹ ☹ 😐 🙂 😀

Mood after exercise: ☹ ☹ 😐 🙂 😀

Mental self care for the day:

....

Today's challenges:

....

....

....

Enjoyable things today:

EVENING

Thoughts about today:

Bedtime:

Mood at the end of the day: 😧 😦 😐 😊 😃

MORNING

DATE: ....

Woke up at: .... **Slept:** ◯ well ◯ okay ◯ badly

Feeling about the day ahead: ☹️ 🙁 😐 🙂 😃

Self care intention today:

....

....

DURING THE DAY

Ate: ☐ breakfast ☐ lunch ☐ dinner

Drank water: ☐ morning ☐ afternoon ☐ evening

Notes:

....

....

☐ **Exercised?**

What kind: ....

Mood before exercise: ☹️ 🙁 😐 🙂 😃

Mood after exercise: ☹️ 🙁 😐 🙂 😃

Mental self care for the day:

....

Today's challenges:

....

....

....

Enjoyable things today:

....

....

....

EVENING

Thoughts about today:

....

....

....

....

....

....

....

....

....

....

....

Bedtime: ....

Mood at the end of the day: ☹ ☹ ☺ ☺ ☺

MORNING

Woke up at: .... **Slept:** ◯ well ◯ okay ◯ badly

Feeling about the day ahead: ☹ ☹ 😐 🙂 😃

Self care intention today:

....

....

DURING THE DAY

Ate: ☐ breakfast ☐ lunch ☐ dinner

Drank water: ☐ morning ☐ afternoon ☐ evening

Notes:

....

....

☐ **Exercised?**

What kind: ....

Mood before exercise: ☹ ☹ 😐 🙂 😃

Mood after exercise: ☹ ☹ 😐 🙂 😃

Mental self care for the day:

....

Today's challenges:

....

....

....

Enjoyable things today:

....

....

....

EVENING

Thoughts about today:

....

....

....

....

....

....

....

....

....

....

....

....

Bedtime: ....

Mood at the end of the day: ☹ ☹ 😐 🙂 😊

MORNING

DATE: ....

Woke up at: .... **Slept:** ◯ well ◯ okay ◯ badly

Feeling about the day ahead: ☹ ☹ 😐 🙂 😀

Self care intention today:

....

....

DURING THE DAY

Ate: ☐ breakfast ☐ lunch ☐ dinner

Drank water: ☐ morning ☐ afternoon ☐ evening

Notes:

....

....

☐ **Exercised?**

What kind: ....

Mood before exercise: ☹ ☹ 😐 🙂 😀

Mood after exercise: ☹ ☹ 😐 🙂 😀

Mental self care for the day:

....

Today's challenges:

....

....

....

Enjoyable things today:

....

....

....

EVENING

Thoughts about today:

....

....

....

....

....

....

....

....

....

....

....

Bedtime: ....

Mood at the end of the day: 😟   🙁   😐   🙂   😊

MORNING

DATE: ....

Woke up at: .... **Slept:** ◯ well ◯ okay ◯ badly

Feeling about the day ahead: ☹️ 😦 😐 🙂 😄

Self care intention today:

....

....

DURING THE DAY

Ate: ☐ breakfast ☐ lunch ☐ dinner

Drank water: ☐ morning ☐ afternoon ☐ evening

Notes:

....

....

☐ **Exercised?**

What kind: ....

Mood before exercise: ☹️ 😦 😐 🙂 😄

Mood after exercise: ☹️ 😦 😐 🙂 😄

Mental self care for the day:

....

Today's challenges:

....

....

....

Enjoyable things today:

....

....

....

EVENING

Thoughts about today:

....

....

....

....

....

....

....

....

....

....

....

....

Bedtime: ....

Mood at the end of the day: ☹ ☹ 😐 🙂 😊

MORNING

DATE: ....

Woke up at: .... **Slept:** ◯ well ◯ okay ◯ badly

Feeling about the day ahead: ☹ ☹ 😐 🙂 😊

Self care intention today:

....

....

DURING THE DAY

Ate: ☐ breakfast ☐ lunch ☐ dinner

Drank water: ☐ morning ☐ afternoon ☐ evening

Notes:

....

....

☐ **Exercised?**

What kind: ....

Mood before exercise: ☹ ☹ 😐 🙂 😊

Mood after exercise: ☹ ☹ 😐 🙂 😊

Mental self care for the day:

....

Today's challenges:

....

....

Enjoyable things today:

....

....

....

EVENING

Thoughts about today:

....

....

....

....

....

....

....

....

....

....

....

Bedtime: ....

Mood at the end of the day: ☹ ☹ 😐 🙂 😊

MORNING

Woke up at: .... **Slept:** ◯ well ◯ okay ◯ badly

Feeling about the day ahead: ☹ ☹ 😐 🙂 😄

Self care intention today:

....

....

DURING THE DAY

Ate: ☐ breakfast ☐ lunch ☐ dinner

Drank water: ☐ morning ☐ afternoon ☐ evening

Notes:

....

....

☐ **Exercised?**

What kind: ....

Mood before exercise: ☹ ☹ 😐 🙂 😄

Mood after exercise: ☹ ☹ 😐 🙂 😄

Mental self care for the day:

....

Today's challenges:

....

....

....

Enjoyable things today:

....

....

....

EVENING

Thoughts about today:

....

....

....

....

....

....

....

....

....

....

....

....

....

Bedtime: ....

Mood at the end of the day: ☹ 😕 😐 🙂 😃

MORNING

DATE: ....

Woke up at: .... **Slept:** ◯ well ◯ okay ◯ badly

Feeling about the day ahead: ☹ 😦 😐 🙂 😄

Self care intention today:

....

....

DURING THE DAY

Ate: ☐ breakfast ☐ lunch ☐ dinner

Drank water: ☐ morning ☐ afternoon ☐ evening

Notes:

....

....

☐ **Exercised?**

What kind: ....

Mood before exercise: ☹ 😦 😐 🙂 😄

Mood after exercise: ☹ 😦 😐 🙂 😄

Mental self care for the day:

....

Today's challenges:

....

....

....

Enjoyable things today:

EVENING

Thoughts about today:

Bedtime:

Mood at the end of the day:

MORNING

DATE: ....

Woke up at: .... **Slept:** ◯ well ◯ okay ◯ badly

Feeling about the day ahead: ☹ ☹ 😐 🙂 😊

Self care intention today:

....

....

DURING THE DAY

Ate: ☐ breakfast ☐ lunch ☐ dinner

Drank water: ☐ morning ☐ afternoon ☐ evening

Notes:

....

....

☐ **Exercised?**

What kind: ....

Mood before exercise: ☹ ☹ 😐 🙂 😊

Mood after exercise: ☹ ☹ 😐 🙂 😊

Mental self care for the day:

....

Today's challenges:

....

....

....

82

Enjoyable things today:

EVENING

Thoughts about today:

Bedtime:

Mood at the end of the day: 🙁 😟 😐 🙂 😃

MORNING

DATE: ....

Woke up at: .... **Slept:** ◯ well ◯ okay ◯ badly

Feeling about the day ahead: ☹ ☹ 😐 ☺ 😃

Self care intention today:

....

....

DURING THE DAY

Ate: ☐ breakfast ☐ lunch ☐ dinner

Drank water: ☐ morning ☐ afternoon ☐ evening

Notes:

....

....

☐ **Exercised?**

What kind: ....

Mood before exercise: ☹ ☹ 😐 ☺ 😃

Mood after exercise: ☹ ☹ 😐 ☺ 😃

Mental self care for the day:

....

Today's challenges:

....

....

....

Enjoyable things today:

EVENING

Thoughts about today:

Bedtime:

Mood at the end of the day: 😞 ☹️ 😐 🙂 😃

MORNING

DATE: ....

Woke up at: .... **Slept:** ◯ well ◯ okay ◯ badly

Feeling about the day ahead: 😟 🙁 😐 🙂 😃

Self care intention today:

....

....

DURING THE DAY

Ate: ☐ breakfast ☐ lunch ☐ dinner

Drank water: ☐ morning ☐ afternoon ☐ evening

Notes:

....

....

☐ **Exercised?**

What kind: ....

Mood before exercise: 😟 🙁 😐 🙂 😃

Mood after exercise: 😟 🙁 😐 🙂 😃

Mental self care for the day:

....

Today's challenges:

....

....

....

86

Enjoyable things today:

....

....

....

EVENING

Thoughts about today:

....

....

....

....

....

....

....

....

....

....

....

....

Bedtime: ....

Mood at the end of the day:

MORNING

Woke up at: .... **Slept:** ◯ well ◯ okay ◯ badly

Feeling about the day ahead: ☹ 🙁 😐 🙂 😀

Self care intention today:

....

....

DURING THE DAY

Ate: ☐ breakfast ☐ lunch ☐ dinner

Drank water: ☐ morning ☐ afternoon ☐ evening

Notes:

....

....

☐ **Exercised?**

What kind: ....

Mood before exercise: ☹ 🙁 😐 🙂 😀

Mood after exercise: ☹ 🙁 😐 🙂 😀

Mental self care for the day:

....

Today's challenges:

....

....

....

Enjoyable things today:

....

....

....

EVENING

Thoughts about today:

....

....

....

....

....

....

....

....

....

....

....

....

....

....

....

Bedtime: ....

Mood at the end of the day:

MORNING

Woke up at: .... **Slept:** ◯ well ◯ okay ◯ badly

Feeling about the day ahead: ☹ ☹ 😐 🙂 😃

Self care intention today:

....

....

DURING THE DAY

Ate: ☐ breakfast ☐ lunch ☐ dinner

Drank water: ☐ morning ☐ afternoon ☐ evening

Notes:

....

....

☐ **Exercised?**

What kind: ....

Mood before exercise: ☹ ☹ 😐 🙂 😃

Mood after exercise: ☹ ☹ 😐 🙂 😃

Mental self care for the day:

....

Today's challenges:

....

....

Enjoyable things today:

....

....

....

EVENING

Thoughts about today:

....

....

....

....

....

....

....

....

....

....

....

....

Bedtime: ....

Mood at the end of the day: ☹ ☹ 😐 ☺ 😊

MORNING

DATE: ....

Woke up at: .... **Slept:** ◯ well ◯ okay ◯ badly

Feeling about the day ahead: ☹ ☹ 😐 🙂 😄

Self care intention today:

....

....

DURING THE DAY

Ate: ☐ breakfast ☐ lunch ☐ dinner

Drank water: ☐ morning ☐ afternoon ☐ evening

Notes:

....

....

☐ **Exercised?**

What kind: ....

Mood before exercise: ☹ ☹ 😐 🙂 😄

Mood after exercise: ☹ ☹ 😐 🙂 😄

Mental self care for the day:

....

Today's challenges:

....

....

....

Enjoyable things today:

....

....

....

EVENING

Thoughts about today:

....

....

....

....

....

....

....

....

....

....

....

....

....

....

Bedtime: ....

Mood at the end of the day: 😟 🙁 😐 🙂 😊

MORNING

DATE: ....

Woke up at: .... **Slept:** ◯ well ◯ okay ◯ badly

Feeling about the day ahead: ☹ ☹ 😐 🙂 😃

Self care intention today:

....

....

DURING THE DAY

Ate: ☐ breakfast ☐ lunch ☐ dinner

Drank water: ☐ morning ☐ afternoon ☐ evening

Notes:

....

....

☐ **Exercised?**

What kind: ....

Mood before exercise: ☹ ☹ 😐 🙂 😃

Mood after exercise: ☹ ☹ 😐 🙂 😃

Mental self care for the day:

....

Today's challenges:

....

....

....

Enjoyable things today:

....

....

....

EVENING

Thoughts about today:

....

....

....

....

....

....

....

....

....

....

....

....

Bedtime: ....

Mood at the end of the day: ☹   ☹   😐   🙂   😃

MORNING

DATE: ....

Woke up at: .... **Slept:** ◯ well ◯ okay ◯ badly

Feeling about the day ahead: ☹ ☹ 😐 🙂 😀

Self care intention today:

....

....

DURING THE DAY

Ate: ☐ breakfast ☐ lunch ☐ dinner

Drank water: ☐ morning ☐ afternoon ☐ evening

Notes:

....

....

☐ **Exercised?**

What kind: ....

Mood before exercise: ☹ ☹ 😐 🙂 😀

Mood after exercise: ☹ ☹ 😐 🙂 😀

Mental self care for the day:

....

Today's challenges:

....

....

Enjoyable things today:

....

....

....

EVENING

Thoughts about today:

....

....

....

....

....

....

....

....

....

....

....

....

Bedtime: ....

Mood at the end of the day: 😧   😟   😐   🙂   😀

MORNING

DATE: ....

Woke up at: .... **Slept:** ◯ well ◯ okay ◯ badly

Feeling about the day ahead: ☹ ☹ 😐 🙂 😊

Self care intention today:

....

....

DURING THE DAY

Ate: ☐ breakfast ☐ lunch ☐ dinner

Drank water: ☐ morning ☐ afternoon ☐ evening

Notes:

....

....

☐ **Exercised?**

What kind: ....

Mood before exercise: ☹ ☹ 😐 🙂 😊

Mood after exercise: ☹ ☹ 😐 🙂 😊

Mental self care for the day:

....

....

Today's challenges:

....

....

....

Enjoyable things today:

....

....

....

EVENING

Thoughts about today:

....

....

....

....

....

....

....

....

....

....

....

....

Bedtime: ....

Mood at the end of the day: ☹ 🙁 😐 🙂 😄

MORNING

Woke up at: .... **Slept:** ◯ well ◯ okay ◯ badly

Feeling about the day ahead: ☹ ☹ 😐 🙂 😃

Self care intention today:

....

....

DURING THE DAY

Ate: ☐ breakfast ☐ lunch ☐ dinner

Drank water: ☐ morning ☐ afternoon ☐ evening

Notes:

....

....

☐ **Exercised?**

What kind: ....

Mood before exercise: ☹ ☹ 😐 🙂 😃

Mood after exercise: ☹ ☹ 😐 🙂 😃

Mental self care for the day:

....

Today's challenges:

....

....

....

Enjoyable things today:

EVENING

Thoughts about today:

Bedtime:

Mood at the end of the day: 😟 😦 😐 🙂 😄

MORNING

DATE: ....

Woke up at: .... **Slept:** ◯ well ◯ okay ◯ badly

Feeling about the day ahead: ☹ 🙁 😐 🙂 😃

Self care intention today:

....

....

DURING THE DAY

Ate: ☐ breakfast ☐ lunch ☐ dinner

Drank water: ☐ morning ☐ afternoon ☐ evening

Notes:

....

....

☐ **Exercised?**

What kind: ....

Mood before exercise: ☹ 🙁 😐 🙂 😃

Mood after exercise: ☹ 🙁 😐 🙂 😃

Mental self care for the day:

....

Today's challenges:

....

....

....

Enjoyable things today:

....

....

....

EVENING

Thoughts about today:

....

....

....

....

....

....

....

....

....

....

....

Bedtime: ....

Mood at the end of the day: ☹ ☹ 😐 🙂 😃

MORNING

DATE: ....

Woke up at: .... **Slept:** ◯ well ◯ okay ◯ badly

Feeling about the day ahead: ☹ ☹ 😐 🙂 😃

Self care intention today:

....

....

DURING THE DAY

Ate: ☐ breakfast ☐ lunch ☐ dinner

Drank water: ☐ morning ☐ afternoon ☐ evening

Notes:

....

....

☐ **Exercised?**

What kind: ....

Mood before exercise: ☹ ☹ 😐 🙂 😃

Mood after exercise: ☹ ☹ 😐 🙂 😃

Mental self care for the day:

....

Today's challenges:

....

....

....

Enjoyable things today:

....

....

....

EVENING

Thoughts about today:

....

....

....

....

....

....

....

....

....

....

....

....

Bedtime: ....

Mood at the end of the day:

MORNING

DATE: ....

Woke up at: .... **Slept:** ◯ well ◯ okay ◯ badly

Feeling about the day ahead: 😦 🙁 😐 🙂 😃

Self care intention today:

....

....

DURING THE DAY

Ate: ☐ breakfast ☐ lunch ☐ dinner

Drank water: ☐ morning ☐ afternoon ☐ evening

Notes:

....

....

☐ **Exercised?**

What kind: ....

Mood before exercise: 😦 🙁 😐 🙂 😃

Mood after exercise: 😦 🙁 😐 🙂 😃

Mental self care for the day:

....

Today's challenges:

....

....

....

Enjoyable things today:

....

....

....

EVENING

Thoughts about today:

....

....

....

....

....

....

....

....

....

....

....

....

Bedtime: ....

Mood at the end of the day:

MORNING

DATE: ....

Woke up at: .... Slept: ◯ well ◯ okay ◯ badly

Feeling about the day ahead: 😣 😔 😐 🙂 😃

Self care intention today:

....

....

DURING THE DAY

Ate: ☐ breakfast ☐ lunch ☐ dinner

Drank water: ☐ morning ☐ afternoon ☐ evening

Notes:

....

....

☐ **Exercised?**

What kind: ....

Mood before exercise: 😣 😔 😐 🙂 😃

Mood after exercise: 😣 😔 😐 🙂 😃

Mental self care for the day:

....

Today's challenges:

....

....

....

Enjoyable things today:

....

....

....

EVENING

Thoughts about today:

....

....

....

....

....

....

....

....

....

....

....

....

....

Bedtime: ....

Mood at the end of the day:

MORNING

DATE: ....

Woke up at: .... Slept: ◯ well ◯ okay ◯ badly

Feeling about the day ahead: ☹ 🙁 😐 🙂 😃

Self care intention today:

....

....

DURING THE DAY

Ate: ☐ breakfast ☐ lunch ☐ dinner

Drank water: ☐ morning ☐ afternoon ☐ evening

Notes:

....

....

☐ **Exercised?**

What kind: ....

Mood before exercise: ☹ 🙁 😐 🙂 😃

Mood after exercise: ☹ 🙁 😐 🙂 😃

Mental self care for the day:

....

Today's challenges:

....

....

....

Enjoyable things today:

....

....

....

EVENING

Thoughts about today:

....

....

....

....

....

....

....

....

....

....

....

Bedtime: ....

Mood at the end of the day: 😟 😦 😐 🙂 😃

MORNING

DATE: ....

Woke up at: .... **Slept:** ⚪ well ⚪ okay ⚪ badly

Feeling about the day ahead: ☹ ☹ 😐 🙂 😃

Self care intention today:

....

....

DURING THE DAY

Ate: ☐ breakfast ☐ lunch ☐ dinner

Drank water: ☐ morning ☐ afternoon ☐ evening

Notes:

....

....

☐ **Exercised?**

What kind: ....

Mood before exercise: ☹ ☹ 😐 🙂 😃

Mood after exercise: ☹ ☹ 😐 🙂 😃

Mental self care for the day:

....

Today's challenges:

....

....

....

Enjoyable things today:

....

....

....

EVENING

Thoughts about today:

....

....

....

....

....

....

....

....

....

....

....

....

....

....

Bedtime: ....

Mood at the end of the day:

MORNING

DATE: ....

Woke up at: .... **Slept:** ⚪ well ⚪ okay ⚪ badly

Feeling about the day ahead: ☹️ 🙁 😐 🙂 😀

Self care intention today:

....

....

DURING THE DAY

Ate: ☐ breakfast ☐ lunch ☐ dinner

Drank water: ☐ morning ☐ afternoon ☐ evening

Notes:

....

....

☐ **Exercised?**

What kind: ....

Mood before exercise: ☹️ 🙁 😐 🙂 😀

Mood after exercise: ☹️ 🙁 😐 🙂 😀

Mental self care for the day:

....

Today's challenges:

....

....

....

Enjoyable things today:

EVENING

Thoughts about today:

Bedtime:

Mood at the end of the day: 😧   🙁   😐   🙂   😃

MORNING

DATE: ....

Woke up at: .... **Slept:** ◯ well ◯ okay ◯ badly

Feeling about the day ahead: ☹ ☹ 😐 ☺ 😃

Self care intention today:

....

....

DURING THE DAY

Ate: ☐ breakfast ☐ lunch ☐ dinner

Drank water: ☐ morning ☐ afternoon ☐ evening

Notes:

....

....

☐ **Exercised?**

What kind: ....

Mood before exercise: ☹ ☹ 😐 ☺ 😃

Mood after exercise: ☹ ☹ 😐 ☺ 😃

Mental self care for the day:

....

Today's challenges:

....

....

....

Enjoyable things today:

....

....

....

EVENING

Thoughts about today:

....

....

....

....

....

....

....

....

....

....

....

Bedtime: ....

Mood at the end of the day: ☹ ☹ 😐 ☺ 😊

MORNING

DATE: ....

Woke up at: .... **Slept:** ◯ well ◯ okay ◯ badly

Feeling about the day ahead: ☹ 🙁 😐 🙂 😀

Self care intention today:

....

....

DURING THE DAY

Ate: ☐ breakfast ☐ lunch ☐ dinner

Drank water: ☐ morning ☐ afternoon ☐ evening

Notes:

....

....

☐ **Exercised?**

What kind: ....

Mood before exercise: ☹ 🙁 😐 🙂 😀

Mood after exercise: ☹ 🙁 😐 🙂 😀

Mental self care for the day:

....

Today's challenges:

....

....

....

Enjoyable things today:

....

....

EVENING

Thoughts about today:

....

....

....

....

....

....

....

....

....

....

....

....

Bedtime: ....

Mood at the end of the day: ☹ 🙁 😐 🙂 😃

MORNING

DATE: ....

Woke up at: .... **Slept:** ◯ well ◯ okay ◯ badly

Feeling about the day ahead: ☹ ☹ 😐 🙂 😃

Self care intention today:

....

....

DURING THE DAY

Ate: ☐ breakfast ☐ lunch ☐ dinner

Drank water: ☐ morning ☐ afternoon ☐ evening

Notes:

....

....

☐ **Exercised?**

What kind: ....

Mood before exercise: ☹ ☹ 😐 🙂 😃

Mood after exercise: ☹ ☹ 😐 🙂 😃

Mental self care for the day:

....

Today's challenges:

....

....

....

Enjoyable things today:

....

....

....

EVENING

Thoughts about today:

....

....

....

....

....

....

....

....

....

....

Bedtime: ....

Mood at the end of the day: ☹ 🙁 😐 🙂 😃

MORNING

DATE: ....

Woke up at: .... **Slept:** ◯ well ◯ okay ◯ badly

Feeling about the day ahead: ☹ ☹ 😐 🙂 😄

Self care intention today:

....

....

DURING THE DAY

Ate: ☐ breakfast ☐ lunch ☐ dinner

Drank water: ☐ morning ☐ afternoon ☐ evening

Notes:

....

....

☐ **Exercised?**

What kind: ....

Mood before exercise: ☹ ☹ 😐 🙂 😄

Mood after exercise: ☹ ☹ 😐 🙂 😄

Mental self care for the day:

....

Today's challenges:

....

....

Enjoyable things today:

....

....

....

EVENING

Thoughts about today:

....

....

....

....

....

....

....

....

....

....

....

....

Bedtime: ....

Mood at the end of the day:

MORNING

DATE: ....

Woke up at: .... **Slept:** ◯ well ◯ okay ◯ badly

Feeling about the day ahead: ☹ ☹ 😐 🙂 😊

Self care intention today:

....

....

DURING THE DAY

Ate: ☐ breakfast ☐ lunch ☐ dinner

Drank water: ☐ morning ☐ afternoon ☐ evening

Notes:

....

....

☐ **Exercised?**

What kind: ....

Mood before exercise: ☹ ☹ 😐 🙂 😊

Mood after exercise: ☹ ☹ 😐 🙂 😊

Mental self care for the day:

....

Today's challenges:

....

....

....

Enjoyable things today:

....

....

....

EVENING

Thoughts about today:

....

....

....

....

....

....

....

....

....

....

Bedtime: ....

Mood at the end of the day: ☹ ☹ 😐 🙂 😊

MORNING

DATE: ....

Woke up at: .... Slept: ◯ well ◯ okay ◯ badly

Feeling about the day ahead: ☹ ☹ 😐 🙂 😀

Self care intention today:

....

....

DURING THE DAY

Ate: ☐ breakfast ☐ lunch ☐ dinner

Drank water: ☐ morning ☐ afternoon ☐ evening

Notes:

....

....

☐ **Exercised?**

What kind: ....

Mood before exercise: ☹ ☹ 😐 🙂 😀

Mood after exercise: ☹ ☹ 😐 🙂 😀

Mental self care for the day:

....

Today's challenges:

....

....

....

Enjoyable things today:

....

....

....

EVENING

Thoughts about today:

....

....

....

....

....

....

....

....

....

....

....

....

Bedtime: ....

Mood at the end of the day:

MORNING

DATE: ....

Woke up at: .... **Slept:** ○ well ○ okay ○ badly

Feeling about the day ahead: ☹ ☹ 😐 🙂 😃

Self care intention today:

....

....

DURING THE DAY

Ate: ☐ breakfast ☐ lunch ☐ dinner

Drank water: ☐ morning ☐ afternoon ☐ evening

Notes:

....

....

☐ **Exercised?**

What kind: ....

Mood before exercise: ☹ ☹ 😐 🙂 😃

Mood after exercise: ☹ ☹ 😐 🙂 😃

Mental self care for the day:

....

Today's challenges:

....

....

....

Enjoyable things today:

....

....

....

EVENING

Thoughts about today:

....

....

....

....

....

....

....

....

....

....

....

....

....

....

....

Bedtime: ....

Mood at the end of the day:

MORNING

DATE: ....

Woke up at: .... **Slept:** ◯ well ◯ okay ◯ badly

Feeling about the day ahead: ☹ ☹ 😐 🙂 😄

Self care intention today:

....

....

DURING THE DAY

Ate: ☐ breakfast ☐ lunch ☐ dinner

Drank water: ☐ morning ☐ afternoon ☐ evening

Notes:

....

....

☐ **Exercised?**

What kind: ....

Mood before exercise: ☹ ☹ 😐 🙂 😄

Mood after exercise: ☹ ☹ 😐 🙂 😄

Mental self care for the day:

....

....

Today's challenges:

....

....

....

Enjoyable things today:

....

....

....

EVENING

Thoughts about today:

....

....

....

....

....

....

....

....

....

....

....

....

....

Bedtime: ....

Mood at the end of the day: ☹ ☹ 😐 🙂 😊

MORNING

DATE: ....

Woke up at: .... **Slept:** ◯ well ◯ okay ◯ badly

Feeling about the day ahead: ☹ ☹ 😐 🙂 😃

Self care intention today:

....

....

DURING THE DAY

Ate: ☐ breakfast ☐ lunch ☐ dinner

Drank water: ☐ morning ☐ afternoon ☐ evening

Notes:

....

....

☐ **Exercised?**

What kind: ....

Mood before exercise: ☹ ☹ 😐 🙂 😃

Mood after exercise: ☹ ☹ 😐 🙂 😃

Mental self care for the day:

....

Today's challenges:

....

....

....

Enjoyable things today:

....

....

....

EVENING

Thoughts about today:

....

....

....

....

....

....

....

....

....

....

....

Bedtime: ....

Mood at the end of the day: 😟   🙁   😐   🙂   😃

MORNING

DATE: ....

Woke up at: .... **Slept:** ◯ well ◯ okay ◯ badly

Feeling about the day ahead: ☹ ☹ 😐 🙂 😃

Self care intention today:

....

....

DURING THE DAY

Ate: ☐ breakfast ☐ lunch ☐ dinner

Drank water: ☐ morning ☐ afternoon ☐ evening

Notes:

....

....

☐ **Exercised?**

What kind: ....

Mood before exercise: ☹ ☹ 😐 🙂 😃

Mood after exercise: ☹ ☹ 😐 🙂 😃

Mental self care for the day:

....

Today's challenges:

....

....

Enjoyable things today:

....

....

....

EVENING

Thoughts about today:

....

....

....

....

....

....

....

....

....

....

....

Bedtime: ....

Mood at the end of the day:

MORNING

DATE: ....

Woke up at: .... **Slept:** ◯ well ◯ okay ◯ badly

Feeling about the day ahead: ☹ ☹ 😐 🙂 😊

Self care intention today:

....

....

DURING THE DAY

Ate: ☐ breakfast ☐ lunch ☐ dinner

Drank water: ☐ morning ☐ afternoon ☐ evening

Notes:

....

....

☐ **Exercised?**

What kind: ....

Mood before exercise: ☹ ☹ 😐 🙂 😊

Mood after exercise: ☹ ☹ 😐 🙂 😊

Mental self care for the day:

....

....

Today's challenges:

....

....

....

Enjoyable things today:

....

....

....

EVENING

Thoughts about today:

....

....

....

....

....

....

....

....

....

....

....

....

Bedtime: ....

Mood at the end of the day: ☹ ☹ 😐 🙂 😊

137

MORNING

DATE: ....

Woke up at: .... **Slept:** ◯ well ◯ okay ◯ badly

Feeling about the day ahead: ☹ 🙁 😐 🙂 😃

Self care intention today:

....

....

DURING THE DAY

Ate: ☐ breakfast ☐ lunch ☐ dinner

Drank water: ☐ morning ☐ afternoon ☐ evening

Notes:

....

....

☐ **Exercised?**

What kind: ....

Mood before exercise: ☹ 🙁 😐 🙂 😃

Mood after exercise: ☹ 🙁 😐 🙂 😃

Mental self care for the day:

....

Today's challenges:

....

....

....

Enjoyable things today:

....

....

....

EVENING

Thoughts about today:

....

....

....

....

....

....

....

....

....

....

....

Bedtime: ....

Mood at the end of the day: ☹ ☹ 😐 🙂 😃

MORNING

DATE: ....

Woke up at: .... **Slept:** ◯ well ◯ okay ◯ badly

Feeling about the day ahead: 😟 😟 😐 🙂 😃

Self care intention today:

....

....

DURING THE DAY

Ate: ☐ breakfast ☐ lunch ☐ dinner

Drank water: ☐ morning ☐ afternoon ☐ evening

Notes:

....

....

☐ **Exercised?**

What kind: ....

Mood before exercise: 😟 😟 😐 🙂 😃

Mood after exercise: 😟 😟 😐 🙂 😃

Mental self care for the day:

....

Today's challenges:

....

....

....

140

Enjoyable things today:

....

....

....

EVENING

Thoughts about today:

....

....

....

....

....

....

....

....

....

....

....

....

Bedtime: ....

Mood at the end of the day:

MORNING

Woke up at: .... **Slept:** ◯ well ◯ okay ◯ badly

Feeling about the day ahead: ☹️ 🙁 😐 🙂 😀

Self care intention today:

....

....

DURING THE DAY

Ate: ☐ breakfast ☐ lunch ☐ dinner

Drank water: ☐ morning ☐ afternoon ☐ evening

Notes:

....

....

☐ **Exercised?**

What kind: ....

Mood before exercise: ☹️ 🙁 😐 🙂 😀

Mood after exercise: ☹️ 🙁 😐 🙂 😀

Mental self care for the day:

....

Today's challenges:

....

....

....

Enjoyable things today:

....

....

....

EVENING

Thoughts about today:

....

....

....

....

....

....

....

....

....

....

....

....

....

....

Bedtime: ....

Mood at the end of the day: ☹   🙁   😐   🙂   😃

MORNING

DATE: ....

Woke up at: .... **Slept:** ◯ well ◯ okay ◯ badly

Feeling about the day ahead: ☹ ☹ 😐 🙂 😃

Self care intention today:

....

....

DURING THE DAY

Ate: ☐ breakfast ☐ lunch ☐ dinner

Drank water: ☐ morning ☐ afternoon ☐ evening

Notes:

....

....

☐ **Exercised?**

What kind: ....

Mood before exercise: ☹ ☹ 😐 🙂 😃

Mood after exercise: ☹ ☹ 😐 🙂 😃

Mental self care for the day:

....

Today's challenges:

....

....

Enjoyable things today:

....

....

....

EVENING

Thoughts about today:

....

....

....

....

....

....

....

....

....

....

....

....

....

Bedtime: ....

Mood at the end of the day: ☹ ☹ 😐 🙂 😊

MORNING

DATE: ....

Woke up at: .... **Slept:** ⭘ well ⭘ okay ⭘ badly

Feeling about the day ahead: 😟 🙁 😐 🙂 😊

Self care intention today:

....

....

DURING THE DAY

Ate: ☐ breakfast ☐ lunch ☐ dinner

Drank water: ☐ morning ☐ afternoon ☐ evening

Notes:

....

....

☐ **Exercised?**

What kind: ....

Mood before exercise: 😟 🙁 😐 🙂 😊

Mood after exercise: 😟 🙁 😐 🙂 😊

Mental self care for the day:

....

Today's challenges:

....

....

....

Enjoyable things today:

....

....

....

EVENING

Thoughts about today:

....

....

....

....

....

....

....

....

....

....

....

....

Bedtime: ....

Mood at the end of the day:

MORNING

DATE: ....

Woke up at: .... **Slept:** ◯ well ◯ okay ◯ badly

Feeling about the day ahead: ☹ 😕 😐 🙂 😃

Self care intention today:

....

....

DURING THE DAY

Ate: ☐ breakfast ☐ lunch ☐ dinner

Drank water: ☐ morning ☐ afternoon ☐ evening

Notes:

....

....

☐ **Exercised?**

What kind: ....

Mood before exercise: ☹ 😕 😐 🙂 😃

Mood after exercise: ☹ 😕 😐 🙂 😃

Mental self care for the day:

....

Today's challenges:

....

....

....

Enjoyable things today:

....

....

....

EVENING

Thoughts about today:

....

....

....

....

....

....

....

....

....

....

....

....

Bedtime: ....

Mood at the end of the day: 😞 🙁 😐 🙂 😃

149

MORNING

DATE: ....

Woke up at: .... **Slept:** ◯ well ◯ okay ◯ badly

Feeling about the day ahead: ☹ ☹ 😐 🙂 😃

Self care intention today:

....

....

DURING THE DAY

Ate: ☐ breakfast ☐ lunch ☐ dinner

Drank water: ☐ morning ☐ afternoon ☐ evening

Notes:

....

....

☐ **Exercised?**

What kind: ....

Mood before exercise: ☹ ☹ 😐 🙂 😃

Mood after exercise: ☹ ☹ 😐 🙂 😃

Mental self care for the day:

....

Today's challenges:

....

....

....

Enjoyable things today:

EVENING

Thoughts about today:

Bedtime:

Mood at the end of the day: 😞 😟 😐 😊 😃

MORNING

DATE: ....

Woke up at: .... **Slept:** ◯ well ◯ okay ◯ badly

Feeling about the day ahead: 😦 🙁 😐 🙂 😃

Self care intention today:

....

....

DURING THE DAY

Ate: ☐ breakfast ☐ lunch ☐ dinner

Drank water: ☐ morning ☐ afternoon ☐ evening

Notes:

....

....

☐ **Exercised?**

What kind: ....

Mood before exercise: 😦 🙁 😐 🙂 😃

Mood after exercise: 😦 🙁 😐 🙂 😃

Mental self care for the day:

....

Today's challenges:

....

....

Enjoyable things today:

....

....

....

EVENING

Thoughts about today:

....

....

....

....

....

....

....

....

....

....

....

Bedtime: ....

Mood at the end of the day:

MORNING

DATE: ....

Woke up at: .... **Slept:** ◯ well ◯ okay ◯ badly

Feeling about the day ahead: ☹ ☹ 😐 🙂 😄

Self care intention today:

....

....

DURING THE DAY

Ate: ☐ breakfast ☐ lunch ☐ dinner

Drank water: ☐ morning ☐ afternoon ☐ evening

Notes:

....

....

☐ **Exercised?**

What kind: ....

Mood before exercise: ☹ ☹ 😐 🙂 😄

Mood after exercise: ☹ ☹ 😐 🙂 😄

Mental self care for the day:

....

Today's challenges:

....

....

....

Enjoyable things today:

....

....

....

EVENING

Thoughts about today:

....

....

....

....

....

....

....

....

....

....

....

....

....

Bedtime: ....

Mood at the end of the day:

MORNING

DATE: ....

Woke up at: .... **Slept:** ◯ well ◯ okay ◯ badly

Feeling about the day ahead: ☹ ☹ ☺ ☺ ☺

Self care intention today:

....

....

DURING THE DAY

Ate: ☐ breakfast ☐ lunch ☐ dinner

Drank water: ☐ morning ☐ afternoon ☐ evening

Notes:

....

....

☐ **Exercised?**

What kind: ....

Mood before exercise: ☹ ☹ ☺ ☺ ☺

Mood after exercise: ☹ ☹ ☺ ☺ ☺

Mental self care for the day:

....

Today's challenges:

....

....

....

Enjoyable things today:

....

....

....

EVENING

Thoughts about today:

....

....

....

....

....

....

....

....

....

....

....

....

Bedtime: ....

Mood at the end of the day:

MORNING

DATE: ....

Woke up at: .... **Slept:** ◯ well ◯ okay ◯ badly

Feeling about the day ahead: ☹ 🙁 😐 🙂 😃

Self care intention today:

....

....

DURING THE DAY

Ate: ☐ breakfast ☐ lunch ☐ dinner

Drank water: ☐ morning ☐ afternoon ☐ evening

Notes:

....

....

☐ **Exercised?**

What kind: ....

Mood before exercise: ☹ 🙁 😐 🙂 😃

Mood after exercise: ☹ 🙁 😐 🙂 😃

Mental self care for the day:

....

Today's challenges:

....

....

....

Enjoyable things today:

....

....

....

EVENING

Thoughts about today:

....

....

....

....

....

....

....

....

....

....

....

....

Bedtime: ....

Mood at the end of the day:

SELF CARE IS HOW YOU TAKE YOUR POWER BACK.

—LALAH DELIA